INSIDE

LANGUAGE • LITERACY • CONTENT

NATIONAL GEOGRAPHIC LEARNING | CENGAGE Learning

Acknowledgments

Grateful acknowledgment is given to the authors, artists, photographers, museums, publishers, and agents for permission to reprint copyrighted material. Every effort has been made to secure the appropriate permission. If any omissions have been made or if corrections are required, please contact the Publisher. **Counterpoint Press:** Excerpt from *The Selected Letters of Wallace Stegner* by Wallace Stegner, edited by Page Stegner. Copyright © 2007 by Page Stegner. Reprinted by permission of Counterpoint. **Hyperion:** Excerpt from *The Words We Live By: Your Annotated Guide to the Constitution* by Linda R. Monk. Copyright © 2003 by Linda R. Monk and Stonesong Press, Inc. Used by permission of Hyperion. All rights reserved. **National Geographic Society:** "Mireya Mayor: Ultimate Explorer" is adapted from "Mireya Mayor: Primatologist/Conservationist" from NationalGeographic.com. Used by permission of National Geographic Society. All rights reserved. **New York Times:** Excerpt from "Math Lessons for Locavores" by Stephen Budiansky from the *New York Times,* August 20, 2010. Copyright © the New York Times. Reprinted by permission of the New York Times. **Penguin Group (USA) Inc.:** Excerpt from *The Omnivores Dilemma: Young Readers Edition* by Michael Pollan. Copyright © 2009 by Michael Pollan. Used by permission of Dial Books for Young Readers, a division of Penguin Group (USA) Inc. **W. W. Norton & Company and David Higham Associates:** Excerpt from "So You're Going to Mars" by Arthur C. Clarke from *The Snows of Olympus: A Garden on Mars.* Copyright © 1994 by Arthur C. Clarke. Used by permission of W. W. Norton & Company, Inc. and David Higham Associates.

Photography

Cover ©JH Pete Carmichael/Riser/Getty Images. **Back cover** ©Loeiza JACQ/Gamma-Rapho via Getty Images. **7** ©Sylvain Grandadam/The Image Bank/Getty Images. **8** ©Milk Photographie/Corbis. **14** ©WorldFoto/Alamy Images. **15** ©Peter McBride/Aurora photos. **21** ©Peter Titmuss/Alamy Images. **28–29** ©Peter Steiner/Alamy. **40** ©Dennis Johnson/Papilio/Corbis. **41** ©Stuart Westmorland/Corbis. **47** ©Images.com/Corbis. **48** ©David Diaz. **54** ©Blue Lantern Studio/Corbis. **72** ©Bettman/Corbis. **79** ©Bettmann/Corbis. **80** ©Time & Life Pictures/Getty Images. **86** ©Dana White/PhotoEdit. **87** ©David Young-Wolff/PhotoEdit. **92–93** (bkgd) ©Tom Grill/Corbis. **92** (t) ©Vladislav Gurfinkel/Shutterstock. **92** (c) ©Rolls Press/Popperfoto/Getty Images. **93** (b) ©Bettmann/Corbis. **94–95** (bkgd) ©Tom Grill/Corbis. **94** (t) Courtesy William J. Clinton Presidential Library. **94** (b) ©AP Photo/Will Counts. **107** ©Tim Kiusalaas/Corbis. **108** ©Myron Jay Dorf/Corbis. **114** ©Michael Lewis/Corbis. **115** ©Rex Stucky/National Geographic Image Collection. **121** ©image100/Corbis. **143** ©DLILLC/Corbis. **144** ©Tom Brakefield/Photodisc/Getty Images. **150** ©Joe McDonald/Corbis. **157** ©Steve Kaufman/Corbis. **158** ©Alissa Everett/Alamy Images. **165** ©Peter Carroll/Getty Images. **176** ©SW Productions/Photodisc/Getty Images. **177** © blickwinkel/Alamy. **183** ©AP Photo/HO, Randy Rodriguez, AIN. **190** ©AP Photo/The Roanoke Times, Eric Brady. **197** ©R Heyes Design/Alamy. **208** ©PNC/Photodisc/Getty Images. **215** ©Kenneth Garrett/National Geographic Image Collection. **216** ©Martin Ruegner/Getty Images. **222** ©Leland Bobbe/Corbis. **223** Vince Bucci/AFP/Getty Images. **228–229** (bkgd) ©Chris Collins/Corbis. **228** (b) ©Dennis Brack/Newscom. **229** (t,l) ©FPG/Taxi/Getty Images. **229** (t,c) ©PhotoQuest/Archive Photos/Getty Images. **229** (t,r) Courtesy of Steve Petteway, Collection of the Supreme Court of the United States. **240** ©David R. Frazier/Photolibrary, Inc./Alamy Images. **241** ©Stocksearch/Alamy Images. **247** ©Emilio Ereza/Alamy Images. **248** ©IMAGE13/Getty Images. **254** ©Stewart Cohen/Blend Images/Getty Images. **260–261** (t) ©Gib Martinez/Alamy. **260** (inset) ©sash77/Shutterstock. **262** (insets) ©Nicholas Eveleigh/Alamy. **263** (t) ©Jochen Tack/Alamy. **263** (inset) ©Kapreski/Shutterstock.

Illustration

128–131 Marc Kohn. **145** flower diagram, Dartmouth Publishing. **152** map of Antarctica, Mapping Specialists. **159** Brazillian Amazon map, Mapping Specialists.

Fine Art

160 Tom Sawyer ' "Well, I don't see why I oughtn't to like it." ' (*Tom Sawyer Whitewashing the Fence* by Norman Rockwell) The Adventures of Tom Sawyer; Twain, Mark; 1936.

INSIDE

LANGUAGE • LITERACY • CONTENT

Contents: Reading

Contents: Reading, continued

Contents: Reading, continued

Contents: Reading, continued

Contents: Grammar

Contents: Grammar, continued

Unit 5

Unit 6

Unit 7

Unit 8

Proofreader's Marks

Mark	Meaning	Example
≡	Capitalize.	I love new york city.
/	Do not capitalize.	I'm going shopping at my favorite Store.
⊙	Add a period.	Mr⊙Lopez is our neighbor.
?	Add a question mark.	Where is my black pen?
↓	Add an exclamation point.	Look out↓
⌄ ⌄	Add quotation marks.	"You are late," said the teacher.
∧	Add a comma.	Amy∧how are you feeling today?
⩗	Add a semicolon.	This shirt is nice∧however, that one brings out the color of your eyes.
◇	Add a colon.	He wakes up at 6◇30 a.m.
⊼	Add a dash.	Barney⊼he's my pet dog⊼has run away.
{ }	Add parentheses.	I want to work for the Federal Bureau of Investigation {FBI}.
=	Add a hyphen.	You were born in mid=September, right?
⌄	Add an apostrophe.	I⌄m the oldest of five children.
#	Add a space.	She likes him #alot.
⌒	Close up a space.	How much home⌒work do you have?
∧	Add text.	My keys are ^on the table.
ℰ	Delete.	I am going too my friend's house.
⌒ℰ	Change text.	We have to much garbage.
∩	Transpose words, letters.	Did you see thier new car?
sp	Spell out.	Today he is turning 16. sp
⊬	Begin a new paragraph.	"I win!" I shouted.⊬"No you don't," he said.
ⓘtal	Add italics.	The Spanish word for table is mesa. ital
u/s	Add underlining.	Little Women is one of my favorite books.

Name _____

Mind Map

Think about a **decision** you or someone else has made. Use the mind map to write some reasons for and against **deciding** to do something. Write the final **decision** in the mind map.

Answers will vary.

Choice Should I do this, or not?
How will it affect how I feel about myself?

| **Pros** I should do it because _____ _____ _____. | **Cons** I should not do it because _____ _____ _____. |

Decision I am/am not going to _____ _____.

Academic Vocabulary

Think about some **decisions** you make every day. What are some things that affect your **decisions**? Use the word **decisions** in your answer.

Answers will vary.

_____

_____

_____

_____

Name _____

Reading Strategies: Plan, Monitor, Ask Questions

A. You use the strategy **Plan** before you read the whole text. Answer the questions.

1. What will you look at to preview the passage?

   I will look at the title and the first sentence.

2. What is your purpose for reading this passage?

   I will read to find out about the life of Helen Keller and what made her special.

3. Read the first paragraph. What do you predict you will learn in the second paragraph?

   Possible response: I think I will learn about how Helen Keller received help.

> **The Life of Helen Keller**
> Helen Keller was born in 1880. She was a happy and healthy baby, but then she got very sick. When she got well again, Helen could not see or hear. She was scared and unhappy.
> When Helen was seven, she had a teacher who spelled words in Helen's hand. Helen was angry and she did not behave at first. Then Helen learned to understand words. This made her happy because she could talk with her hands.

4. Now read the second paragraph. Was your prediction correct? Explain.

   Possible response: My prediction was correct. Helen Keller had a teacher who helped Helen communicate.

B. You can use the strategies **Monitor** and **Ask Questions** as you read. Read the passage and answer the questions.

> **Peter Pan and Never Land**
> My name is Peter Pan. I live in Never Land and I use magic to fly. I lost my shadow at the Darling family house. When I went back to find it, Wendy Darling sewed my shadow back on. I asked Wendy and her brothers to come to Never Land with me. I taught them to fly, then we flew away to my island.

5. If you knew nothing about Peter Pan, you might be confused when you read that he can fly. What monitoring strategy would you use and why?

   Possible response: I'd read on to find out more about him—and learn he is not a real person.

6. What is a question you might ask about Peter Pan's shadow?

   Possible response: Did it hurt to have his shadow sewed on?

Focus on Reading

Reading Strategies: Visualize, Make Inferences, Determine Importance

A. Read the passage below. Use the reading strategy **Visualize** to answer the question. Which sense do you use most when reading this passage?

I use the sense of taste.

> **How's It Taste?**
>
> If you were asked to name the four basic tastes of food, what would you answer? Most people say that foods taste sweet or bitter, salty or sour. However, there is a fifth taste that scientists have identified. Its name is *umami*, a Japanese word that means "yummy."
>
> You might respond that your favorite food is yummy and that it tastes sweet or bitter, salty or sour. However, certain foods that people find absolutely delicious do not exactly have any of these four tastes. These foods... they're *umami!* Examples include tomatoes, soy sauce, and cheese. You love the taste, but you have never quite been able to describe it. Now you can!
>
> Who discovered *umami?* The secret began with two chefs in the 1800s. One was from France. One was from Japan. Both of them tried to explain the delicious taste of certain dishes they created. None of the usual words fit. People thought these chefs were just trying to be special. However, nearly 100 years later, scientists decided to investigate. When they studied the sense of taste, they found that a fifth type of taste was indeed possible.

B. Reread the passage. Use the strategies **Make Inferences** and **Determine Importance** to answer the questions.

1. What do you know that helps you make an inference about why people didn't believe the chefs?

   Possible response: I know that people often doubt new ideas when they hear them. I also know people who want to be

   famous can make things up. So, I could make the inference that people thought the chefs were just bragging to get diners

   interested in their food.

2. Draw a box around the main idea of the third paragraph. Underline the ideas that are the most important. Use the main idea and the most important details to summarize the third paragraph with a partner.

Academic Vocabulary

If you were asked to **identify** a food with *umami*, which food would it be?

Responses will vary.

Focus on Reading

Reading Strategies: Synthesize, Make Connections

A. Read the passage below. As you read, think about how you can use the strategies **Synthesize** and **Make Connections**.

> **A Kind Teacher**
>
> Claudia came from Germany in the early 1900s. She did not speak any English. Claudia was told that she would have to learn English with the first-grade students. This scared Claudia because in Germany she was in the eighth grade. Claudia was afraid to go to the lower grade. She was afraid she would never learn English. She was afraid everyone would make fun of her.
>
> But then the teacher smiled at Claudia and spoke to her in German. She told Claudia not to be afraid. Claudia would not have to go to the first grade. She would study after school with the teacher. Soon she would be speaking English and making new friends.
>
> A couple of months later, Claudia realized that the teacher was right. Claudia did learn to speak English, and she made many new friends. But more importantly, Claudia got good grades in all her classes.

B. Answer the questions about the passage.

1. What conclusion can you draw about Claudia's teacher?

   I conclude that Claudia's teacher wanted to help students who did not speak English well.

   _____

2. The author mentions learning English many times. Form a generalization to answer this question: Why do people new to the United States want to learn English?

   People want to learn English so that they will make American friends and succeed.

   _____

3. How can you connect to this text?

   Possible response: Once a teacher helped me understand a new idea, so I know how Claudia feels.

   _____

Focus on Vocabulary

Use Word Parts

Suffix	Meaning
-ful	"full of"
-able, -ible	"can be" or "having"
-ion, -tion	"act of"
-less	"without"

▶ Follow the directions below. Write the meaning of each underlined word.

1. Look closely at the word to see if you know any of the parts.
2. If the word has a suffix, cover it up. Think about the meaning of the base word.
3. Uncover the suffix and determine its meaning.
4. Put the meanings of the word parts together to define the whole word.
   Be sure the meaning makes sense in the passage.

A. Follow the directions above. Read the passage. Write the meaning of each underlined word.

> Your heart is the strongest muscle in your body. It may also be the most underline{valuable} muscle. It pumps blood from your head to your toes and back again. Even when you are underline{motionless}, it still pumps blood through your body. Your heart is in your chest behind your rib cage. The ribs provide underline{protection} for your heart in case you are hit in the chest.

valuable _having value_

motionless _without movement, not moving_

protection _the act of protecting_

B. Follow the directions above. Read the passage. Write the meaning of each underlined word.

> Monroe High School girl's basketball tryouts were in one week. Carolina thought it was underline{useless} to try out for the team since she was only a freshman. Her older brother was the most underline{successful} basketball player on the boy's team. When she got home from school that day, her brother offered to help her practice for the tryouts. Carolina felt underline{hopeful} that she could become a star player, too!

useless _not useful, without use_

successful _full of success_

hopeful _full of hope_

Academic Vocabulary

I **analyzed** the flower in the garden and saw _Possible responses: that it had many parts; there were petals, a_ stem, and seeds _____ .

Build Background

Critical Viewing Guide

▶ Take Notes

A. View the video. Take notes on at least three things that you learned.

Answers will vary.

_____

_____

_____

_____

_____

_____

_____

▶ Analyze the Video

B. Review your notes to help answer these questions.

1. Write two sentences to explain what was in the video.

Answers will vary.

_____

_____

2. What was the most interesting thing you learned?

Answers will vary.

_____

_____

3. How could your name **affect** your life?

Answers will vary.

_____

_____

_____

_____

Learn Key Vocabulary

American Names: Key Vocabulary

A. Study each word. Circle a number to rate how well you know it. Then complete the chart.

Rating Scale	**1** I have never seen this word before.	**2** I am not sure of the word's meaning.	**3** I know this word and can teach the word's meaning to someone else.

▲ This man feels no **doubt** about how to ride a bike. Riding a bike is a common activity in his **culture**.

Key Words	Check Understanding	Deepen Understanding
❶ culture (**kul**-chur) *noun* Rating: 1 2 3	You might find different foods in a different **culture**. (Yes) No	How can you share your culture with others? _____ *Possible response:* I can share food, music, and stories that are popular in my culture.
❷ disfavor (dis-**fā**-vor) *noun* Rating: 1 2 3	A smile is one way to show **disfavor**. Yes (No)	How would you feel if a friend showed disfavor toward you? *Possible response:* I would feel sad, angry, or confused if my friend showed me disfavor.
❸ doubt (dowt) *noun* Rating: 1 2 3	You feel **doubt** when you feel sure about something. Yes (No)	Why might a person feel doubt before they take a test? *Possible response:* He or she might not feel prepared to take the test.
❹ erase (e-**rās**) *verb* Rating: 1 2 3	When you **erase** a drawing, you remove it from the page. (Yes) No	What can you use to erase a drawing on a chalkboard? *Possible responses:* You could use a chalkboard eraser; you could use your hand; you could use a wet sponge.

Name _____

The brothers make a **pact**. They will **erase** the worst score during their game. ▶

Key Words	Check Understanding	Deepen Understanding
❺ excessive (ik-**ses**-iv) *adjective* Rating: 1 2 3	An **excessive** amount is too much. (Yes) No	Would you like to have an excessive amount of homework? Tell why or why not. _____ *Possible response:* No. An excessive amount of homework would be too much homework. _____
❻ pact (pakt) *noun* Rating: 1 2 3	A **pact** is a promise between people. (Yes) No	Why is it important to make a pact with someone you trust? _*Possible response:* If you trust someone, you know they will keep a promise. _____
❼ scrape (skrāp) *verb* Rating: 1 2 3	It hurts to **scrape** your knee. (Yes) No	What could you use to scrape gum off the bottom of your shoe? _*Possible response:* I could use a stick, a pen, or a toothpick. _____
❽ shame (shām) *noun* Rating: 1 2 3	A person who feels **shame** also feels proud. Yes (No)	If you teased someone, would you feel shame? Tell why or why not. _*Possible response:* Yes, I would feel shame because teasing someone can hurt his or her feelings. _____

B. Use at least two of the Key Vocabulary words. Write about a time when you had to make an important decision.

Answers will vary. _____

_____

_____

Name _____

American Names: Reading Strategies Log

Complete at least one row of the Strategies Log for each section of "American Names."

Text I read	Strategy I used	How I used the strategy
Page: 18 **Text:** Our family came… to L.A.	☑ Plan ☐ Monitor ☐ Ask Questions ☐ ___	To plan, I predicted that the story will be about L.A. This helped me plan my reading.
Page: 22 **Text:** Though the pull at school is pretty strong…	☐ Plan ☑ Monitor ☐ Ask Questions ☐ ___	Possible Response: I reread in order to understand what "the pull" is.
Page: 26 **Text:** I buy a little cactus, prickly to touch and with one red bloom.	☐ Plan ☐ Monitor ☑ Ask Questions ☐ ___	Possible Response: I asked myself why Arturo would buy this particular plant. Asking questions helps me better understand what is happening.

American Names

A. Read the paragraph.
Write a Key Vocabulary word in each blank.
Reread the paragraph to make sure the words make sense.

When Arturo's new teacher called him Arthur, he didn't correct her. He was afraid it might cause ___disfavor___ . When Arturo's grandmother found out, she was very unhappy. She was very proud of their Mexican ___culture___ . She didn't want anyone to ___erase___ the family's proud history. She didn't want anyone to ___scrape___ away their Mexican names, beliefs, and traditions. Arturo felt ___shame___ because he knew his grandmother was right. He had no ___doubt___ about what to do next. He made a ___pact___ with his Mexican friends. They decided to always use their real names, even if other people thought their concerns were ___excessive___ .

B. Write complete sentences to answer these questions about "American Names."

1. What could Miss Pringle do to be more sensitive to students from other **cultures** ?

   Possible response: Miss Pringle could ask kids what they want to be called and make an effort to learn to pronounce

   everyone's given name.

   _____

   _____

   _____

   _____

2. Friends and family members often call each other by special names. What names are you called? Which name fits you the best?

   Answers will vary. _____

   _____

   _____

   _____

   _____

   _____

Vocabulary Study

Use Compound Words

▶ Follow the steps below to figure out the meaning of each compound word.

1. Find the base words.
2. Figure out the meaning of the base words.
3. Put the meanings of the base words together to figure out what the word means. Then complete the sentence.

1. **tabletop** the top of a table

My grandmother _Possible response: put a pretty vase of flowers_ on her tabletop.

2. **wheelchair** a chair with wheels

Her sister used a wheelchair after _Possible response: she broke her leg_ .

3. **classroom** a room where classes are held

We came back to our classroom after we _Possible responses: finished recess; went to lunch_ .

4. **fishbowl** a bowl that holds fish

Bryan used his fishbowl to _Possible response: hold his pet fish_ .

5. **walkway** a path used for walking

My neighbor needed a new walkway because _Possible response: he needed a path to his garden_ .

6. **gumball** a piece of gum in the shape of a ball

I bought a gumball because _Possible response: I wanted to chew something sweet_ .

7. **ballpark** a park where people play ball

Josephina enjoys going to the ballpark because _Possible response: she likes to watch the game_ .

8. **earache** an ache in the ear

Chris had an earache, so _Possible responses: his mother gave him some medicine_ .

Academic Vocabulary

American Names: Academic Vocabulary Review

Academic Vocabulary

analyze   decision

compound identify

A. Use your own words to tell what each Academic Vocabulary word means.

Word	My Definition
1. **analyze**	*Possible response:* to separate into parts and study
2. **compound**	*Possible response:* something that is made up of two or more parts
3. **decision**	*Possible response:* a choice
4. **identify**	*Possible response:* to tell what something is

B. Rewrite each sentence. Replace the underlined words with an Academic Vocabulary word.

1. Table salt is a chemical <u>mixture</u> made from two elements.

    Table salt is a chemical compound made from two elements. _____

    _____

2. Buying a pet is a difficult <u>choice</u> to make.

    Buying a pet is a difficult decision to make. _____

    _____

3. The detective will <u>carefully study</u> each piece of evidence.

    The detective will analyze each piece of evidence. _____

4. Ben can look at almost any flag and <u>name</u> the country it represents.

    Ben can look at almost any flag and identify the country it represents. _____

    _____

Build Background

Critical Viewing Guide

▶ Take Notes

A. View the video. Take notes on at least three things that you learned.

Answers will vary.

_____

_____

_____

_____

_____

_____

_____

▶ Analyze the Video

B. Review your notes to help answer these questions.

1. Write two sentences to explain what was in the video.

   Answers will vary.

   _____

   _____

   _____

2. What was the most interesting thing you learned?

   Answers will vary.

   _____

   _____

   _____

3. What are some ways that one person's decision can **affect** others?

   Answers will vary.

   _____

   _____

   _____

   _____

   _____

Learn Key Vocabulary

A Lion Hunt: Key Vocabulary

A. Study each word. Circle a number to rate how well you know it. Then complete the chart.

Rating Scale	**1** I have never seen this word before.	**2** I am not sure of the word's meaning.	**3** I know this word and can teach the word's meaning to someone else.

▲ A lion can be a **symbol** of **bravery**.

Key Words	Check Understanding	Deepen Understanding
❶ **bravery** (**brā**-vu-rē) *noun* **Rating:** 1 2 3	**Bravery** is another word for ⟨courage⟩ cowardice	I show bravery whenever I _____ *Possible response:* sing in front of a large crowd for school recitals _____.
❷ **brotherhood** (**bruth**-ur-hood) *noun* **Rating:** 1 2 3	**Brotherhood** is another word for homeland ⟨group⟩	A baseball team can be a brotherhood because ____ *Possible response:* the players form a close group and work towards a common goal _____.
❸ **decision** (dē-**si**-zhun) *noun* **Rating:** 1 2 3	**Decision** is another word for award ⟨choice⟩	The first decision I make in the morning is _____ *Possible response:* what clothes to wear for school _____.
❹ **defend** (dē-**fend**) *verb* **Rating:** 1 2 3	**Defend** is another word for ⟨protect⟩ attack	One way to defend skin from a sunburn is to _____ *Possible response:* wear sunblock _____.

Key Vocabulary, continued

Name _____

A **warrior** shows he can **defend** his people. ▶

Key Words	Check Understanding	Deepen Understanding
⑤ pride (prīd) *noun* Rating: 1 2 3	**Pride** is another word for shame (self-respect)	I feel pride when I _Possible response: score a goal for_ my soccer team _____ _____ _____ _____ .
⑥ society (so-sī-i-tē) *noun* Rating: 1 2 3	**Society** is another word for (community) communication	The United States is an example of a big society because _Possible response: it has a large group of_ people who share some common beliefs and goals _____ _____ _____ .
⑦ symbol (sim-bul) *noun* Rating: 1 2 3	**Symbol** is another word for (sign) instrument	Birds make a good symbol for freedom because _____ _Possible response: they are free to fly wherever they_ like _____ _____ _____ .
⑧ warrior (wor-ē-yur) *noun* Rating: 1 2 3	**Warrior** is another word for teacher (fighter)	A warrior should be _Possible response: strong,_ brave, and loyal to his/her people _____ _____ _____ _____ .

B. Use at least two of the Key Vocabulary words. Write about a time when you had to prove yourself.

Answers will vary.

_____

_____

_____

A Lion Hunt: Reading Strategies Log

Complete at least one row of the Reading Strategies Log for each section of "A Lion Hunt."

Text I read	Strategy I used	How I used the strategy
Page: 40 **Text:** What's the big deal about a lion?	☒ Make Inferences ☐ Determine Importance ☐ Synthesize ☐ _____	Making an inference about the author's attitude helps me understand the selection better.
Page: 43 **Text:** So there were only three experienced warriors who could fight a lion...	☐ Make Inferences ☒ Determine Importance ☐ Synthesize ☐ _____	*Possible Response:* I think this detail is an important one because it helps me understand the author's situation.
Page: 45 **Text:** "No way," I said. "Are you kidding me? I'm a warrior. I'm just as brave as you..."	☐ Make Inferences ☐ Determine Importance ☒ Synthesize ☐ _____	*Possible Response:* Synthesizing helped me think of a new idea: It's very difficult to back down once you've announced to everyone that you will do something considered brave.

A Lion Hunt

Key Vocabulary

bravery	pride
brotherhood	society
decision	symbol
defend	warrior

A. Read the paragraph.
Write a Key Vocabulary word in each blank.
Reread the paragraph to make sure the words make sense.

When Lekuton was young, he wanted to be a great ____warrior____ . He wanted to join the ____brotherhood____

of brave men who fight lions. In Kenya, the lion is a ____symbol____ of ____bravery____ . The first time

Lekuton came face-to-face with a lion, things did not go so well. He made the ____decision____ to run away.

Instead of feeling ____pride____ , he felt embarrassed. Everyone in his ____society____ knew that he had

run away. Lekuton had to work to show everyone that he could ____defend____ their cattle.

B. Write complete sentences to answer these questions about "A Lion Hunt."

1. What does Lekuton learn from his experience on the lion hunt?

   Possible response: Lekuton learns that nothing can make up for experience no matter how brave you think you are.

   _____

   _____

   _____

   _____

   _____

2. What do you think will happen the next time Lekuton meets a lion?

   Answers will vary.

   _____

   _____

   _____

   _____

   _____

   _____

   _____

Vocabulary Study

Use Suffixes

Suffix	Meaning
-ful	"full of"
-ness	"quality or state of"
-ous	"full of"
-ly	"in the manner of"

▶ Follow the steps below to figure out the meaning of each underlined word. Then complete each sentence.

1. Look closely at the word to see if you know any of the parts. If you see two base words, analyze the meaning of each one.
2. Do you see a suffix? If yes, cover it.
3. Think about the meaning of the base word. Uncover the suffix, and put the meanings of the word parts together. Write the definition.

1. **sadness** state of being sad

    Lyle felt sadness when *Possible response: his dog ran away from home* .

2. **curiously** in the manner of being curious

    She curiously opened the box and found *Possible response: some old costumes* .

3. **thunderous** full of thunder

    The sound of applause was thunderous when *Possible response: the speaker finished his speech* .

4. **wishful** full of wishes

    I was wishful that *Possible response: I would get a new videogame for my birthday* .

5. **emptiness** state of being empty

    The emptiness of the field was different from *Possible response: the crowded shopping mall* .

6. **certainly** in the manner of being certain

    Mr. Lexington certainly broke his leg when *Possible response: he slipped on the ice* .

7. **boldness** state of being bold

    My younger brother is full of such boldness that he often *Possible response: thinks he can do anything* .

8. **glamorous** full of glamour

    Neyla thought the movie stars were glamorous because *Possible response: of their fancy dresses* .

A Lion Hunt: Academic Vocabulary Review

A. Read each statement. Circle **Yes** or **No** to answer.

1. A **decision** is a choice or a resolution.   (Yes)   No

2. When you **analyze** something, you examine its parts carefully.   (Yes)   No

3. If you **identify** someone, you can tell who that person is.   (Yes)   No

B. Use each Academic Vocabulary word in a sentence.

1. **analyze** _Answers will vary._ _____

_____

_____

2. **decision** _Answers will vary._ _____

_____

_____

3. **identify** _Answers will vary._ _____

_____

_____

Critical Viewing Guide

▶ **Take Notes**

A. View the images. Take notes on at least three things that you learned.

Answers will vary.

_____

_____

_____

_____

_____

_____

_____

▶ **Analyze the Images**

B. Review your notes to help answer these questions.

1. Write two sentences to explain what was in the images.

   Answers will vary.

   _____

   _____

   _____

   _____

2. What was the most interesting thing you learned?

   Answers will vary.

   _____

   _____

   _____

   _____

3. How can a dream affect your life?

   Answers will vary.

   _____

   _____

   _____

from The House on Mango Street:
Key Vocabulary

A. Study each word. Circle a number to rate how well you know it. Then complete the chart.

Two travelers take a **temporary** break to **appreciate** a good book. ▶

Rating Scale	**1** I have never seen this word before.	**2** I am not sure of the word's meaning.	**3** I know this word and can teach the word's meaning to someone else.

Key Words	Check Understanding	Deepen Understanding
❶ appreciate (u-**prē**-shē-āt) *verb* Rating: 1 2 3	☐ to give someone a compliment ☒ to understand the value of something	List 3 things that you appreciate: _____ *Possible response:* my family, a funny movie, and a warm jacket _____ _____
❷ despite (di-**spīt**) *preposition* Rating: 1 2 3	☒ even though ☐ in addition to	List 3 reasons why you should study hard despite the time it takes: *Possible response:* to get good grades, to feel a sense of accomplishment, and to move on to the next level _____
❸ disgusted (di-**skus**-tid) *adjective* Rating: 1 2 3	☐ feeling jealous ☒ feeling sickened	List 3 things that make you feel disgusted: _____ *Possible response:* curdled milk, slugs, and bad smells _____ _____
❹ expectation (eks-pek-**tā**-shun) *noun* Rating: 1 2 3	☐ a judgment about the past ☒ a belief about the future	List 3 expectations that you have for yourself: _____ *Possible response:* to learn how to make tortilla soup, to make first chair in band, and to go to college _____

Name _____

Key Words	Check Understanding	Deepen Understanding
❺ **landlord** (**land**-lawrd) *noun* **Rating:** 1 2 3	☐ a person who protects the laws of the land ☒ a person who rents a room or building to someone	List 3 things a landlord might do: _____ *Possible response:* advertise an open apartment, check on his or her tenants, and collect rent _____ _____
❻ **rent** (rent) *noun* **Rating:** 1 2 3	☒ money paid to the owner of a property ☐ proof of ownership for a house or building	List 3 reasons to pay rent: _____ *Possible response:* to stay living in a place, to avoid buying a place to live, and to keep the landlord happy _____ _____
❼ **strength** (strength) *noun* **Rating:** 1 2 3	☐ having support from friends ☒ having power	List 3 of your personal strengths: _____ *Possible response:* courage, hard worker, and sense of humor _____ _____
❽ **temporary** (**tem**-pa-rair-ē) *adjective* **Rating:** 1 2 3	☒ a short period of time ☐ a steady climate	List 3 things that are temporary: _____ *Possible response:* a rainstorm, a cold, and a bus ride _____ _____

B. Use at least two of the Key Vocabulary words. Write about an experience you hope to have in the future. Write about your expectations.

Answers will vary. _____

_____

_____

The House on Mango Street: Reading Strategies Log

Complete at least one row of the Reading Strategies Log for each section of "The House on Mango Street."

Text I read	Strategy I used	How I used the strategy
Page: 62 **Text:** We don't have to... share the yard with the people downstairs, or be careful not to make too much noise...	**☒ Make Connections** **☐ Visualize** **☐ _____**	Making connections to houses I know about helps me understand how the character and her family live.
Page: 67 **Text:** Today while cooking oatmeal she is Madame Butterfly... I was a smart cookie then.	**☐ Make Connections** **☒ Visualize** **☐ _____**	*Possible Response:* Visualizing this scene of the narrator's mother cooking and talking helps me understand the narrator's mother and how the narrator lives.
Page: 68 **Text:** Not a flat... clean as paper before the poem.	**☒ Make Connections** **☐ Visualize** **☐ _____**	*Possible Response:* Making connections to my own experiences and feelings about spaces of my own help me understand how the narrator feels.

from **The House on Mango Street**

Key Vocabulary

appreciate	landlord
despite	rent
disgust	strength
expectations	temporary

A. Read the paragraph.
Write a Key Vocabulary word in each blank.
Reread the paragraph to make sure the words make sense.

> Esperanza and her family used to live in an apartment on Loomis Street. It was a ____temporary____
>
> home, until they could buy their own house. They had to pay ____rent____ to a ____landlord____. It was
>
> not very nice. A nun from school once looked at their building with ____disgust____. Later, they bought a
>
> house on Mango Street. ____Despite____ this improvement, Esperanza did not ____appreciate____ the house
>
> on Mango Street. It was small and falling apart. She had high ____expectations____ for the future. She dreamed
>
> of living in a beautiful house. Her dreams gave her ____strength____.

B. Write complete sentences to answer these questions about "The House on Mango Street."

1. How does the nun make Esperanza see her home in a different way?

   Possible response: The nun's surprise at Esperanza's home makes her realize how shabby and run down it is.

   _____

   _____

   _____

   _____

   _____

2. What has Esperanza learned from all of the moving she has done?

   Possible response: Esperanza knows what her dream house looks like.

   _____

   _____

   _____

   _____

   _____

   _____

Vocabulary Study

Use Word Parts

Suffix	Meaning
-ful	"full of"
-ion	"condition or action"

▶ Follow the steps below to figure out the meaning of each word.
Then complete each sentence.

1. Look closely at the word to see if you know any of the parts.
2. Do you see a suffix? If yes, cover it. Think about the meaning of the base word. Uncover the suffix, and think about its meaning.
3. Do you see a compound word? If yes, find the connection between the base words and the meaning of the whole word.
4. Put the meanings of the word parts together to understand the whole word. Write the definition.

1. **boastful** full of boasting

   He was boastful when he won the prize and *Possible response:* I thought he was bragging .

2. **erosion** the action of eroding

   The beach erosion was so bad that *Possible response:* one of the houses fell into the water .

3. **rainstorm** a storm accompanied by rain

   The rainstorm lasted for so long that *Possible response:* the street became flooded .

4. **sunglasses** glasses that protect eyes from the sun

   I wore sunglasses while I was *Possible response:* driving my car down the street .

5. **forceful** full of force

   The storm was so forceful that *Possible responses:* the tree in my uncle's yard fell over .

6. **acceleration** the action of accelerating

   The race car had such great acceleration that it *Possible response:* was faster than all the other cars in the race

7. **overcoat** coat worn over clothing

   My aunt wore a beautiful overcoat when she *Possible response:* went to a fancy restaurant .

8. **painful** full of pain

   It was painful when Robert *Possible response:* fell down and skinned his knee .

Name _____

from **The House on Mango Street:**
Academic Vocabulary Review

A. Write the Academic Vocabulary word under its definition.

1. to name or tell what something is

   identify _____

2. to separate something into parts and examine it

   analyze _____

3. a choice

   decision _____

4. something that makes two things go together

   connection _____

B. Circle the word that best fits in each sentence.

1. Ana and Simon share a (**connection**/ **decision**) because they both play the guitar.

2. Can you (**identify**/ **analyze**) which desk is yours?

3. Raul made a (**decision**/ **connection**) to go to bed early before the basketball tournament.

4. If you (**analyze**/ **identify**) the fabric, you will see that it is woven together tightly.

C. Use at least two Academic Vocabulary words. Write about a place where you can go to think or relax.

Answers will vary. _____

_____

_____

_____

The Road Not Taken

by Robert Frost

Two roads **diverged** in a yellow wood,
And sorry I could not travel both
And be one traveler, long I stood
And looked down one as far as I could
5   To where it bent in the undergrowth;

Then took the other, as just as fair,
And having perhaps the better **claim**
Because it was grassy and wanted wear,
Though as for that the passing there
10   Had worn them really about the same,

And both that morning equally lay
In leaves no step had trodden black.
Oh, I marked the first for another day!
Yet knowing how way leads on to way
_{E.2}
15   I doubted if I should ever come back.

I shall be telling this with a sigh
Somewhere ages and ages **hence**:
Two roads diverged in a wood, and I,
I took the one less traveled by,
_{F.2}
20   And that has made all the difference.

In Other Words
diverged split
claim look
hence in the future

▶ Read for Understanding

A. What kind of text is this? How do you know?

Possible response: poem; I can tell by the rhyme, meter, and stanzas.

B. Write a sentence that tells the topic of the poem.

Possible response: This poem is mostly about a traveler who had to choose between roads and how he chose the road less

traveled by.

▶ Reread and Summarize

C. On **Practice Book** page 28, circle the 3–5 most important words in each section. Make notes about why you chose each word. Why is the word important in the section?

1. Section 1: (stanzas 1–2; lines 1–10)

Answers will vary.

2. Section 2: (stanzas 3–4; lines 11–20)

Answers will vary.

D. Use your topic sentence from above and your notes to write a summary of the selection.

Possible response: A traveler saw two roads in the woods and had to choose between them. He thinks about how this choice will

affect his life.

▶ Reread and Analyze

E. Make connections to the poem.

1. Reread the fourth stanza on **Practice Book** page 28. Think of a time when you made a difficult choice. How does this experience help you understand the poem?

   Possible response: I remember when others in my class were being rude to someone. I decided to say that it was wrong

   because that's how I felt. I think this was the "road less traveled by" because my choice was different from what others did.

2. Underline words or sentences on **Practice Book** page 28 that tell about the choice the poet made. Continue to make connections to your own choice.

   Answers will vary. Possible response: I underlined "I doubted if I should ever come back." After I said something about my

   classmates' rudeness, we couldn't go back in time and ignore it. I think the poet is saying actions cannot be reversed.

F. Make inferences about the poem.

1. Reread the fourth stanza on **Practice Book** page 28. Make an inference about how the poet feels about the choice he made.

   Possible response: I think the poet is proud of his choice. He realizes that his choices can lead to big differences in his

   life, and he accepts responsibility for making them.

2. On **Practice Book** page 28, underline parts of the poem that support your inference. Tell what personal knowledge helped you make this inference.

   Answers will vary. Possible response: I underlined *that has made all the difference.* Like the poet, I know that my decisions

   have affected my life very much.

▶ Discuss and Write

G. Synthesize your ideas about making connections and inferences.

1. With the class, discuss how your connections and inferences added to your understanding of the poem. How did linking your experiences and things you know with the poem help you figure it out?

Answers will vary. Possible response: The poem reminds me of my experience being the only one to speak out against my

classmates' rudeness. It helped me understand the meaning of "the one less traveled by" and "I doubted if I should ever

come back." I also know that my choices affect what happens in my life, that my choices make "all the difference."

_____

_____

2. Write a paragraph about how your connections or inferences added to your understanding. Choose one connection or inference.

   · What connection or inference did you make?

   · How did your connection or inference help you understand the poem?

Answers will vary.

_____

_____

_____

▶ Connect with 🗨 GUIDING QUESTION

H. Discuss the Guiding Question: How do decisions affect your identity?

1. Based on the decisions the poet made, what kind of person do you think he is?

Answers will vary.

_____

_____

2. What choice have you made that has affected your identity?

Answers will vary.

_____

_____

Academic Vocabulary Review

Academic Vocabulary

analyze	decision
compound	identify
connection	

A. Read the paragraph. Replace each bold word or phrase with the correct Academic Vocabulary word.

Mark's class is learning about ancient Egypt. Mark's teacher asked each student to report on a topic related to life in the ancient civilization. Mark couldn't decide whether to report on mummies or the pyramids. Mark decided to _____ *analyze* _____ both topics. He learned that the **look closely at**

_____ *connection* _____ between mummies and pyramids was so strong that it made sense to **common traits**

study both.

B. Write the word or phrase that means the same as the Academic Vocabulary word.

Word	Choose from these words:			Synonym
1. **analyze**	tell	study	try	study
2. **compound**	mixture	structure	same	mixture
3. **decision**	want	need	choice	choice
4. **identify**	see	name	face	name

C. Have you ever had to make a difficult **decision**? What was your **decision** and how did you choose?

Answers will vary.

_____

_____

_____

_____

Key Vocabulary Review

A. Read each sentence. Circle the Key Vocabulary word that best fits into each sentence.

1. A frown is a sign of (**disfavor** / **despite**).

2. Police officers enforce the laws of a (**pact** / **society**).

3. A good (**landlord** / **warrior**) takes care of his or her building.

4. It is best to (**scrape** / **rent**) mud off boots.

5. A passing breeze is (**excessive** / **temporary**).

6. Language is an important part of any (**expectation** / **culture**).

7. A fan helps you stay cool (**despite** / **defend**) hot weather.

8. It is easier to (**shame** / **erase**) mistakes if you write in pencil.

B. Use your own words to write what each Key Vocabulary word means.
Then write an example for each definition.

Word	My Definition	Example
1. **bravery**	*Possible response:* not feeling afraid	*Possible response:* diving off the high board at a pool
2. **brotherhood**	*Possible response:* a close group	*Possible response:* a soccer team
3. **decision**	*Possible response:* a choice	*Possible response:* choosing what to have for dinner
4. **excessive**	*Possible response:* too much	*Possible response:* having ten cats
5. **pact**	*Possible response:* an agreement people make	*Possible response:* a peace treaty between countries
6. **shame**	*Possible response:* a bad feeling about something you do	*Possible response:* how you feel if you steal
7. **symbol**	*Possible response:* a sign that stands for something else	*Possible response:* the @ symbol in e-mail
8. **warrior**	*Possible response:* a fighter	*Possible response:* a soldier

---

Unit 1 Key Vocabulary

appreciate	decision	disgusted	expectation	rent	strength
bravery	defend	doubt	landlord	scrape	symbol
brotherhood	despite	erase	pact	shame	temporary
culture	disfavor	excessive	pride	society	warrior

C. Answer the questions in complete sentences.

1. What qualities do you **appreciate** most in others?

    Possible response: I appreciate kindness, humor, bravery, and enthusiasm in others.

    _____

2. How would you **defend** yourself against a bully?

    Possible response: I would try to stay calm and speak in a confident tone.

    _____

3. Describe a time when you felt **disgusted** .

    Possible response: I felt disgusted when I had to clean out the garage and found a dead rat.

    _____

4. Do you have any **doubts** ? Explain.

    Possible response: Yes, I doubt I will be as tall as my brother because he is already very tall.

    _____

5. What is an **expectation** you have?

    Possible response: I expect to learn how to drive when I am older.

    _____

6. Describe a time when you felt **pride** .

    Possible response: I felt pride when I blocked all the goals from the other team during my last soccer match.

    _____

7. Do you think it is fair for a **landlord** to charge **rent** ? Explain.

    Possible response: Yes, a landlord should get money if he or she allows people to live in his or her building.

    _____

8. What are some ways to improve your physical **strength** ?

    Possible response: You can exercise regularly and eat a good diet.

    _____

Mind Map

Use the mind map to show ways that people and animals **survive** and the dangers they face. Add more ideas to the map as you read the selections in this unit.

Answers will vary.

How People
Survive

How
Animals
Survive

Stand

Fall

Dangers
People
Face

Dangers Animals
Face

Academic Vocabulary

Think about how explorers **survive** in harsh places. What do you think you might need to **survive** near the North Pole? Use the word **survive** in your answer.

Answers will vary.

_____

_____

_____

_____

Elements of Fiction: Plot, Character, Setting

Read the passage. Then answer the questions.

> Jonathan looked for his puppy. It was not in the backyard. The puppy had escaped through a hole in the fence. Jonathan and his mother searched the whole neighborhood. They called out over and over, "Ruffles! Come home!"
>
> Then Jonathan sat on the front steps. He clutched the dog's empty leash. His mother hugged him and said, "Ruffles will come home soon."
>
> Jonathan did not think so. He sat and thought about the past week. He and Ruffles had walked to the park together every day. Ruffles loved to play in the water fountain.
>
> Then Jonathan had an idea. He asked his mom to drive him to the park. The sun was setting when they arrived. There was Ruffles. He lay by the fountain. He was wet and tired from playing all afternoon.

1. What is the setting?

   Possible response: The setting is Jonathan's home and the park nearby.

2. Who are the characters, and what are they like?

   Possible response: The characters are Jonathan, his mom, and Ruffles. Jonathan is caring and concerned about

   Ruffles. His mom is helpful and understanding. Ruffles is a puppy that likes to have fun.

3. What is the conflict?

   Possible response: The conflict is that Jonathan's puppy is missing.

Academic Vocabulary

What is your favorite story? Write what **elements** you like the most in that story. Write how **characterization** makes the story more interesting.

Answers will vary.

Focus on Vocabulary

Relate Words

▶ Read the passages. Follow these steps.

1. Put words into groups, or categories, to see how they relate to one another. This will help you understand their specific definitions.
2. Use a Synonym Scale to rank synonyms from weakest to strongest.

A. Follow the directions above. Make a Synonym Scale for the underlined words.

> My two friends, Mark and Aaron, came to my house for a sleepover. By midnight we started to feel tired. Later, Aaron was so sleepy that he lay down on the floor. Finally, we were all so exhausted that we had to go to sleep. I know we will be weary tomorrow.

Synonym Scale

| tired | sleepy | weary | exhausted |

How does the Synonym Scale help you understand how tired the boys are?

Possible response: It shows how each synonym for *tired* has a slightly different meaning. *Exhausted* is a stronger word than *sleepy*.

B. Follow the directions above. Make a Synonym Scale for the underlined words.

> My brother and I hike in the park near our house. One day we discovered a stream. The water trickled along the trail. We followed the stream. As the hill got steeper, the water surged faster. It rushed down the hill. When it reached the bottom of the hill, the water flowed calmly again.

Synonym Scale

| trickled | flowed | surged | rushed |

How does the Synonym Scale help you understand how the water moves?

Possible response: It helps me understand that the water moved the slowest when it trickled and the fastest when it rushed.

Academic Vocabulary

I can **relate** a dog to a cat because *Possible response:* they both can be pets in a home

_____ .

Name _____

Critical Viewing Guide

▶ Take Notes

A. View the video. Take notes on at least three things that you learned.

Answers will vary.

_____

_____

_____

_____

_____

_____

_____

▶ Analyze the Video

B. Review your notes to help answer these questions.

1. Write two sentences to explain what was in the video.

Answers will vary.

_____

_____

_____

2. What was the most interesting thing you learned?

Answers will vary.

_____

_____

_____

3. What did the video tell about different ways animals **survive**? Explain.

Answers will vary.

_____

_____

_____

_____

Learn Key Vocabulary

Name _____

On the Menu: Key Vocabulary

A. Study each word. Circle a number to rate how well you know it. Then complete the chart.

Rating Scale	**1** I have never seen this word before.	**2** I am not sure of the word's meaning.	**3** I know this word and can teach the word's meaning to someone else.

▲ A grasshopper uses **camouflage** to **survive**.

Key Words	Check Understanding	Deepen Understanding
❶ adaptation (a-dap-**tā**-shun) *noun* Rating: 1 2 3	When you make **adaptations**, you make _____ . promises (changes)	Share one example of an adaptation you have made. *Possible response:* I learned how to ride a bus in a new city.
❷ advantage (ad-**van**-tij) *noun* Rating: 1 2 3	It is an **advantage** to be ____ . (stronger) weaker	What advantages can help a person win a race? ____ *Possible responses:* speed; persistence; strength; confidence
❸ camouflage (**kam**-a-flazh) *noun* Rating: 1 2 3	**Camouflage** helps people or animals _____ . run (hide)	Why is camouflage hard to see? _____ *Possible response:* The color or pattern of camouflage matches the surroundings.
❹ disguise (dis-**gīz**) *noun* Rating: 1 2 3	A good **disguise** might be a _____ . necklace (mask)	What kind of disguise would you like to wear? _____ *Possible response:* I would like to wear a fake beard, thick glasses, a heavy coat, and a wig.

Name _____

An octopus can squirt ink to escape the **threat** of **predators**.

Key Words	Check Understanding	Deepen Understanding
⑤ predator (**pre**-du-tur) *noun* **Rating:** 1 2 3	A **predator** eats _____. plants (animals)	How are people sometimes predators? _____ *Possible response:* They hunt and eat other animals, such as fish and deer.
⑥ prey (prā) *noun* **Rating:** 1 2 3	Fish are **prey** for _____. (sharks) worms	Would you like to be prey for another animal? Tell why or why not. ___ *Possible response:* No, because I don't want another animal to hunt or eat me.
⑦ survive (sur-vīv) *verb* **Rating:** 1 2 3	People need _____ to **survive**. (water) cars	What other things can help people to survive? _____ *Possible responses:* food; shelter; clothing; heat
⑧ threat (thret) *noun* **Rating:** 1 2 3	The **threat** of fire makes most people _____ . (nervous) hopeful	How is a snake a threat to a mouse? _____ *Possible response:* A snake can eat a mouse.

B. Use at least two of the Key Vocabulary words. Write about a time you adapted to a new environment.

Answers will vary. _____

_____

_____

Name _____

Relate Cause and Effect

Read "On the Menu" and complete the Cause-and-Effect Chart.

Cause-and-Effect Chart

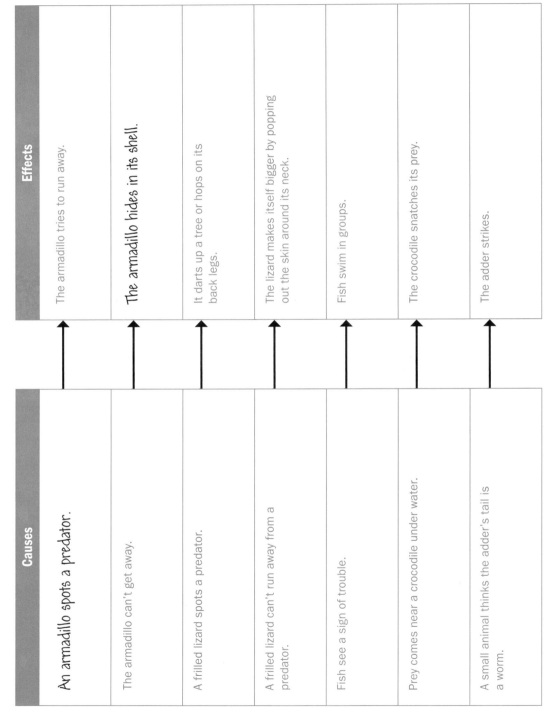

Causes	Effects
An armadillo spots a predator.	The armadillo tries to run away.
The armadillo can't get away.	The armadillo hides in its shell.
A frilled lizard spots a predator.	It darts up a tree or hops on its back legs.
A frilled lizard can't run away from a predator.	The lizard makes itself bigger by popping out the skin around its neck.
Fish see a sign of trouble.	Fish swim in groups.
Prey comes near a crocodile under water.	The crocodile snatches its prey.
A small animal thinks the adder's tail is a worm.	The adder strikes.

On the Menu

A. Read the paragraph.
Write a Key Vocabulary word in each blank.
Reread the paragraph to make sure the words make sense.

Many animals develop useful traits called ___adaptations___ that help them ___survive___ the dangers of the wild. Every day, ___predators___ on the hunt are a ___threat___ to other animals. They are looking for easy ___prey___ to catch and eat. A ___disguise___ such as ___camouflage___ can keep an animal from being eaten. It can give an animal the ___advantage___ it needs to stay alive.

B. Write complete sentences to answer these questions about "On the Menu."

1. Why is it important for animals in the wild to have **camouflage**?

Possible response: Camouflage acts as a disguise and protects the animals from predators.

_____

_____

_____

_____

_____

_____

2. How do **adaptations** attract **prey** and trick **predators**?

Possible response: Some adaptations, such as stripes and spots, make prey curious. Some adaptations, such as coloring or shape. make predators stay away.

_____

_____

_____

_____

_____

_____

Vocabulary Study

Relate Words: Synonyms

▶ Follow the steps below to complete the activity.

1. Read each sentence. Use a thesaurus to find synonyms for the underlined word.
2. Think about the shades of meaning for the synonyms.
3. Rewrite the sentence by replacing the underlined word with a more specific synonym.

1. I hope we eat dinner soon because I am <u>hungry</u>.

   Possible response: I hope we eat dinner soon because I am famished. _____

2. The music at the concert was <u>loud</u>.

   Possible response: The music at the concert was deafening. _____

3. Nate was <u>angry</u> when his brother broke his new skates.

   Possible response: Nate was furious when his brother broke his new skates. _____

4. Please <u>take</u> the pencil from the baby immediately.

   Possible response: Please seize the pencil from the baby immediately. _____

5. Everyone likes Rob because he is so <u>kind</u>.

   Possible response: Everyone likes Rob because he is so considerate. _____

6. He <u>held</u> the handlebars tightly as the bike wobbled.

   Possible response: He grasped the handlebars tightly as the bike wobbled. _____

7. My sister was <u>sad</u> when we had to leave so soon.

   Possible response: My sister was disappointed when we had to leave so soon. _____

8. When Max saw the presents, he was <u>surprised</u>.

   Possible response: When Max saw the presents, he was astonished. _____

Academic Vocabulary

On the Menu: Academic Vocabulary Review

Academic Vocabulary	
element	structure
relate	survive

A. Circle the Academic Vocabulary word that matches each definition.

1. to show how things are connected (**survive** / **relate**)

2. an important part of something (**structure** / **element**)

3. to remain alive (**relate** / **survive**)

4. how parts are arranged or organized (**element** / **structure**)

B. Use each Academic Vocabulary word in a sentence.

1. **element** _Answers will vary._ _____

_____

2. **relate** _Answers will vary._ _____

_____

3. **structure** _Answers will vary._ _____

_____

4. **survive** _Answers will vary._ _____

_____

Build Background

Critical Viewing Guide

▶ Take Notes

A. View the images. Take notes on at least three things that you learned.

Answers will vary.

_____

_____

_____

_____

_____

_____

_____

_____

▶ Analyze the Images

B. Review your notes to help answer these questions.

1. Write two sentences to explain what was in the images.

Answers will vary.

_____

_____

_____

2. What was the most interesting thing you learned?

Answers will vary.

_____

_____

_____

3. Why do some stories, like "The Three Little Pigs," **survive**? Explain.

Answers will vary.

_____

_____

_____

Learn Key Vocabulary

The Three Chicharrones: Key Vocabulary

A. Study each word. Circle a number to rate how well you know it. Then complete the chart.

Each pig in the story chooses a different **property**. Which pig has the best **fortune**? ▶

Rating Scale	**1** I have never seen this word before.	**2** I am not sure of the word's meaning.	**3** I know this word and can teach the word's meaning to someone else.

Key Words	Check Understanding	Deepen Understanding
❶ advice (ad-**vīs**) *noun* **Rating:** 1 2 3	Friends try to give good **advice**. (Yes) No	Some good advice I gave was _____ *Possible response:* when I told my friend to study for a test _____ _____ .
❷ business (**biz**-nis) *noun* **Rating:** 1 2 3	A successful **business** makes more money than it spends. (Yes) No	I would like to run my own business because _____ *Possible response:* I would like to be my own boss _____ _____ _____ .
❸ cheat (chēt) *verb* **Rating:** 1 2 3	The best teachers help their students **cheat**. Yes (No)	If I saw someone cheat on a test, I would _____ *Possible responses:* quietly ask the person to stop; notify the teacher _____ _____ .
❹ deal (dēl) *noun* **Rating:** 1 2 3	Two quarters for one dollar is a good **deal**. Yes (No)	One good deal I made was _____ *Possible response:* when I traded with my friend for a good baseball card _____ _____ .

Key Vocabulary, continued

Name _____

Animals in folk tales and fairy tales often make **deals** and give **advice.** ▶

Key Words	Check Understanding	Deepen Understanding
❺ **deserve** (di-**zurv**) *verb* **Rating:** 1 2 3	You **deserve** an allowance if you do no chores. **Yes** **(No)**	One reward I really deserved was _____ *Possible response:* my new basketball shoes that I earned by mowing the lawn _____ _____ .
❻ **fortune** (**for**-chun) *noun* **Rating:** 1 2 3	Most people would feel lucky to find a **fortune**. **(Yes)** **No**	My ideal fortune would include _____ *Possible responses:* lots of money; expensive electronic equipment; rare baseball cards _____ _____ .
❼ **fustration** (frus-**trā**-shun) *noun* **Rating:** 1 2 3	A big **frustration** could lead to big headaches. **(Yes)** **No**	One way to deal with frustration is to _____ *Possible response:* take deep breaths to calm down _____ _____ _____ .
❽ **property** (**prop**-er-tē) *noun* **Rating:** 1 2 3	A person can buy and sell **property**. **(Yes)** **No**	If I could have property anywhere, I would choose ____ *Possible response:* to live in the mountains _____ _____ _____ .

B. Write about a frustrating experience you have had. Use two of the Key Vocabulary words. Write how you dealt with the frustration.

Answers will vary.

_____

_____

_____

48   Unit 2 Stand or Fall

© National Geographic Learning, a part of Cengage Learning, Inc.

Name _____

Analyze Modern Fiction

Use the Venn Diagram to compare the two stories.

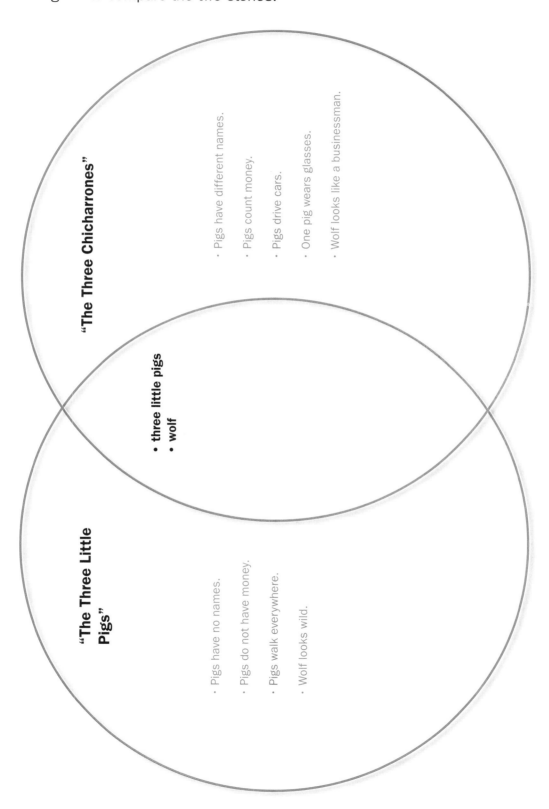

Venn Diagram

"The Three Chicharrones"
- Pigs have different names.
- Pigs count money.
- Pigs drive cars.
- One pig wears glasses.
- Wolf looks like a businessman.

- three little pigs
- wolf

"The Three Little Pigs"
- Pigs have no names.
- Pigs do not have money.
- Pigs walk everywhere.
- Wolf looks wild.

Name _____

The Three Chicharrones

A. Read the paragraph.
Write a Key Vocabulary word in each blank.
Reread the paragraph to make sure the words make sense.

Papá Chicharrón sent his three sons away from home to earn a _____fortune_____ . He gave Pereza,

Gordo, and Astuto some wise _____advice_____ . He told them to watch for the wolf at the door. Each son

bought _____property_____ to live on. Of the three brothers, Astuto was the smartest at managing his

_____business_____ . Soon, a wolf named Dinero Martínez visited all three brothers, offering each one a

_____deal_____ to buy their homes. Dinero tried to _____cheat_____ all of them. Much to Dinero's

_____frustration_____ , Astuto was the only brother who did not fall for his scheme. Finally, the brothers

arranged for the sheriff to catch Dinero and give him the punishment he _____deserved_____ .

B. Write complete sentences to answer these questions about "The Three Chicharrones."

1. Do you think Gordo and Pereza will keep their promise to Astuto? Why?

Answers will vary.

_____

_____

_____

_____

2. What would have happened if Gordo and Pereza had not learned their lesson?

Possible response: Gordo and Pereza would have been poor and homeless.

_____

_____

_____

_____

Vocabulary Study

Relate Words: Cognates

Spanish	English
banco	bank
falso	false
famoso	famous
mapa	map
pausa	pause
rancho	ranch
talento	talent
tren	train

▶ Follow the steps below to complete the activity.

1. Write the English word for each Spanish cognate.
2. Then write a sentence to show what each English word means.
3. Use the chart to help you.

1. **tren** _train_
   _____
   Possible response: I rode a train across the country to visit my family.
   _____

2. **pausa** _pause_
   _____
   Possible response: The traffic paused for the girl as she crossed the street.
   _____

3. **talento** _talent_
   _____
   Possible response: Leo's talent was juggling.
   _____

4. **famoso** _famous_
   _____
   Possible response: There is a famous scientist who grew up in my town.
   _____

5. **banco** _bank_
   _____
   Possible response: I went with my parents to the bank to open a savings account.
   _____

6. **falso** _false_
   _____
   Possible response: My teacher gave us a true or false test.
   _____

7. **rancho** _ranch_
   _____
   Possible response: Cows, pigs, and horses lived on the ranch.
   _____

8. **mapa** _map_
   _____
   Possible response: I studied the map so I could win our geography contest at school.
   _____

Academic Vocabulary

Name _____

affect   relate
definition   survive
element

The Three Chicharrones: Academic Vocabulary Review

A. Rewrite each sentence. Replace the underlined words with an Academic Vocabulary word.

1. Where can you find the <u>meaning</u> of a word?

   Where can you find the definition of a word?

2. If you don't get enough rest, it can <u>change</u> your performance.

   If you don't get enough rest, it can affect your performance.

3. When I learn about a new subject, I can <u>connect</u> it to what I already know.

   When I learn about a new subject, I can relate it to what I already know.

4. Animals need good defenses to <u>stay alive</u> in the wild.

   Animals need good defenses to survive in the wild.

5. Research is one <u>part</u> of writing a paper.

   Research is one element of writing a paper.

B. Write a definition for each word. Use your own words.

1. **affect** _Possible response:_ to change in some way

2. **definition** _Possible response:_ the meaning of a word

3. **element** _Possible response:_ one part of a whole

4. **relate** _Possible response:_ to connect things together

5. **survive** _Possible response:_ to stay alive

52 Unit 2 Stand or Fall

© National Geographic Learning, a part of Cengage Learning, Inc.

Name _____

Critical Viewing Guide

▶ **Take Notes**

A. View the video. Take notes on at least three things that you learned.

Answers will vary.

_____

_____

_____

_____

_____

_____

_____

_____

▶ **Analyze the Video**

B. Review your notes to help answer these questions.

1. Write two sentences to explain what was in the video.

Answers will vary.

_____

_____

_____

_____

2. What was the most interesting thing you learned?

Answers will vary.

_____

_____

_____

3. What skills help characters **survive** dragon attacks in fairy tales?

Answers will vary.

_____

_____

_____

Learn Key Vocabulary

Name _____

Dragon, Dragon: Key Vocabulary

A. Study each word. Circle a number to rate how well you know it. Then complete the chart.

Many fairy tales tell the story of a knight on a **quest** to slay a dragon. The knight must be **decent** and brave to succeed. ▶

	Rating Scale	**1** I have never seen this word before.	**2** I am not sure of the word's meaning.	**3** I know this word and can teach the word's meaning to someone else.

Key Words	Check Understanding	Deepen Understanding
❶ bargain (bär-gen) *noun* **Rating:** 1 2 3	A **bargain** is a good deal. (Yes) No	The best bargain I ever got was _____ *Possible response: the time I found the bike I wanted* on sale _____ _____ _____ .
❷ decent (dē-sent) *adjective* **Rating:** 1 2 3	It is **decent** to help someone in need. (Yes) No	A decent person is _____ *Possible responses: kind; honest; hard-working;* fair _____ _____ _____ .
❸ kingdom (king-dum) *noun* **Rating:** 1 2 3	A **kingdom** is usually smaller than a baseball field. Yes (No)	If I ruled a kingdom, I would _____ *Possible response: be kind to its people* _____ _____ _____ .
❹ nervous (ner-vus) *adjective* **Rating:** 1 2 3	Tests make some people **nervous**. (Yes) No	Something that always makes me nervous is _____ *Possible response: speaking in front of the class* _____ _____ _____ .

Name _____

Did You Know?

Martin Luther King, Jr. once said, "There is an almost universal **quest** for easy answers and half-baked solutions. Nothing pains some people more than having to think."

Key Words	Check Understanding	Deepen Understanding
❺ opinion (u-**pin**-yun) *noun* Rating: 1 2 3	An **opinion** is the same as a fact. Yes (No)	In my opinion, people should try _____ _Possible response:_ to treat one another with respect _____ _____ _____ .
❻ plague (plāg) *verb* Rating: 1 2 3	When something **plagues** you, it worries you. (Yes) No	It plagues me to think about _____ _Possible response:_ finding a job after school _____ _____ _____ .
❼ quest (kwest) *noun* Rating: 1 2 3	A **quest** is a very easy trip. Yes (No)	I would like to go on a quest to _____ _Possible response:_ save a town from a giant _____ _____ _____ .
❽ recite (ri-sīt) *verb* Rating: 1 2 3	To **recite** well, you must speak clearly. (Yes) No	In school, a student might recite_____ _Possible responses:_ a poem; the names of the states; the answers to a quiz _____ _____ .

B. Use at least two of the Key Vocabulary words to tell about an adventure you have had.

Answers will vary.
_____

_____

_____

Name _____

Analyze Plot

Read "Dragon, Dragon" and complete the Plot Diagram.

Plot Diagram

Dragon, Dragon

Climax: Because of the youngest son's poem, the dragon laughs himself to death.

Complication: The eldest and middle sons of the cobbler cannot kill the dragon.

Complication: The king offers a reward for slaying the dragon.

Complication: The king, the knights, and the wizard cannot get rid of the dragon.

Conflict: A dragon plagues the kingdom.

Resolution: The youngest son wins treasure and the hand of the princess.

Dragon, Dragon

A. Read the paragraph.
Write a Key Vocabulary word in each blank.
Reread the paragraph to make sure the words make sense.

The dragon that used to ____plague____ the entire ____kingdom____ is dead. This is because the cobbler's

sons made a ____bargain____ with the king. One of them would marry the princess if his

____quest____ to slay the dragon succeeded. Two of the sons did not succeed. Their father told them

to ____recite____ a poem at the dragon's cave, and they ignored the advice. It was their ____opinion____

that they could slay the dragon without their father's help. The youngest son was scared and

____nervous____ but he was ____decent____ enough to take his father's advice. The youngest son

successfully defeated the dragon and rescued his brothers!

B. Write complete sentences to answer these questions about "Dragon, Dragon."

1. What was the cobbler's **opinion** of the king?

   Possible response: The cobbler was not impressed by the king.

   _____

   _____

   _____

   _____

   _____

2. Why did the cobbler's two older sons ignore their father's advice?

   Possible response: The sons thought they were smarter than their father.

   _____

   _____

   _____

   _____

   _____

Name _____

Relate Words: Use Synonyms and Antonyms

▶ Follow the steps below to show how words relate to each other.

1. Read the word in each Synonym-Antonym Scale.
2. Write a synonym and an antonym for each word.
3. Then write the synonym or antonym in a sentence.

1. ◀——————————————————————▶

_____   _____   _____
small   large   gigantic

Sentence: _Answers will vary._ _____

2. ◀——————————————————————▶

_____   _____   _____
correct   wrong   false

Sentence: _Answers will vary._ _____

3. ◀——————————————————————▶

_____   _____   _____
frown   smile   grin

Sentence: _Answers will vary._ _____

4. ◀——————————————————————▶

_____   _____   _____
suggest   tell   lecture

Sentence: _Answers will vary._ _____

5. ◀——————————————————————▶

_____   _____   _____
bottom   center   top

Sentence: _Answers will vary._ _____

6. ◀——————————————————————▶

_____   _____   _____
dim   light   bright

Sentence: _Answers will vary._ _____

Dragon, Dragon: Academic Vocabulary Review

A. Choose the best synonym for each Academic Vocabulary word.

Word	Choose from these words			Synonym
1. **affect**	name	change	how	change
2. **element**	part	some	mix	part
3. **relate**	disconnect	leave	connect	connect
4. **structure**	arrangement	place	department	arrangement

B. Read each sentence. Circle the word that best fits into each sentence.

1. When you (**survive** / **affect**), you stay alive or exist.

2. When you (**affect** / **structure**) someone or something, you make a change.

3. The way parts are put together or arranged is called a (**structure** / **relate**).

4. A (**scale** / **survive**) is a chart that shows how a series of items are related.

C. Rewrite each sentence. Replace each underlined word with an Academic Vocabulary word.

1. A visual aid is just one <u>part</u> of Tori's presentation.

   A visual aid is just one element of Tori's presentation. _____

2. I can <u>connect</u> the grades I receive to the effort I put into my school work.

   I can relate the grades I receive to the effort I put into my school work. _____

from the Adventures of
TOM SAWYER

BY MARK TWAIN

Tom Sawyer ' "Well, I don't see why I oughtn't to like it." ' (Tom Sawyer Whitewashing the Fence by Norman Rockwell) *The Adventures of Tom Sawyer;* Twain, Mark; 1936

1   Tom began to think of the fun he had planned for this day, and his sorrows multiplied. Soon the free boys would come tripping along on all sorts of delicious expeditions, and they would make a world of fun of him for having to work—the very thought of it burnt him like fire. He got out his worldly wealth and examined it—bits of toys, marbles, and trash; enough to buy an exchange of work, maybe, but not half enough to buy so much as half an hour of pure freedom. So he returned his **straitened means** to his pocket, and gave up the idea of trying to buy the boys. At this dark and hopeless moment an inspiration burst upon him! Nothing less than a great, magnificent inspiration.

2   He took up his brush and went tranquilly to work. Ben Rogers hove in sight presently—the very boy, of all boys, whose ridicule he had been dreading. Ben's gait was the hop-skip-and-jump—proof enough that his heart was light and his anticipations high. He was eating an apple, and giving a long, melodious whoop, at intervals, followed by a deep-toned ding-dong-dong, ding-dong-dong, for he was personating a steamboat. As he drew near, he slackened speed, took the middle of the street, leaned far over to starboard and rounded to ponderously and with laborious pomp and circumstance—for he was personating the Big Missouri, and considered himself to be drawing nine feet of water.

3   Tom went on whitewashing—paid no attention to the steamboat. Ben stared a moment and then said:

4   "Hi-*yi! You're* **up a stump, ain't you**?"

5   No answer. Tom surveyed his last touch with the eye of an artist, then he gave his brush another gentle sweep and surveyed the result, as before. Ben ranged up alongside of him. Tom's mouth watered for the apple, but he stuck to his work. Ben said:

6   "Hello, old chap, you got to work, hey?"

7   Tom wheeled suddenly and said:

8   "Why, it's you, Ben! **I warn't noticing**."

In Other Words
straitened means tiny amount of treasure
up a stump, ain't you in trouble, aren't you
I warn't noticing I didn't see you.

9   "Say—I'm going in a-swimming, I am. Don't you wish you could? But of course you'd **druther** *work*—wouldn't you? Course you would!"

10   Tom contemplated the boy a bit, and said:

11   "What do you call work?"

12   "Why, ain't *that* work?"

13   Tom resumed his whitewashing, and answered carelessly:

14   "Well, maybe it is, and maybe it ain't. All I know, is, it suits Tom Sawyer."

15   "Oh come, now, you don't mean to let on that you like it?"

16   The brush continued to move.

17   "Like it? Well, I don't see why I oughtn't to like it. Does a boy get a chance to whitewash a fence every day?"

18   **That put the thing in a new light**. Ben stopped nibbling his apple. Tom swept his brush daintily back and forth—stepped back to note the effect—added a touch here and there—criticized the effect again—Ben watching every move and getting more and more interested, more and more absorbed. Presently he said:

19   "Say, Tom, let me whitewash a little."

20   Tom considered, was about to consent; but he altered his mind:

21   "No—no—I reckon it wouldn't hardly do, Ben. You see, Aunt Polly's awful particular about this fence—right here on the street, you know—but if it was the back fence I wouldn't

"What do you call work?"

E.1
mind and she wouldn't. Yes, she's awful particular about this fence; it's got to be done very careful; I reckon there ain't one boy in a thousand, maybe two thousand, that can do it the way it's got to be done."

22   "Oh, shucks, I'll be just as careful. Now lemme try. Say—I'll give you the core of my apple."

23   "Well, here—No, Ben, now don't. I'm afeard—"

24   "I'll give you *all* of it!"

F.1
25   Tom gave up the brush with reluctance in his face, but **alacrity** in his heart. And while the late steamer Big Missouri worked and sweated in the sun, the retired artist sat on a barrel in the shade close by, dangled his legs, munched his apple, and planned the slaughter of more innocents. There was no lack of material; boys happened along every little while; they came to jeer, but remained to whitewash. And when the middle of the afternoon came, from being a poor poverty-stricken boy in the morning, Tom was literally rolling in wealth.

26   Tom said to himself that it was not such a hollow world, after all. He had discovered a great law of human action, without knowing it—namely, that in order to make a man or a boy covet a thing, it is only necessary to make the thing difficult to attain.

In Other Words
druther prefer to
That put the thing in a new light.
   That changed how Ben saw it.
alacrity eagerness

▶ Read for Understanding

A. From what kind of text is this passage taken? How do you know?

Possible response: a novel or short story; I can tell because it has characters, setting, and a beginning, middle, and end.

B. Write a sentence that tells the topic of the selection.

Possible response: This text is mostly about Tom and how he tricks his friends to paint the fence.

▶ Reread and Summarize

C. On **Practice Book** pages 60–61, circle the 3–5 most important words in each section. Make notes about why you chose the word. Why is each word important?

1. Section 1: (paragraphs 1–8)

   Answers will vary.

2. Section 2: (paragraphs 9–24)

   Answers will vary.

3. Section 3: (paragraphs 25–26)

   Answers will vary.

D. Use your topic sentence from above and your notes to write a summary of the selection.

Possible response: When Tom has to paint a fence, he tricks his friends to do the work for him by convincing them that it is

a fun job.

▶ Reread and Analyze

E. Analyze how the author uses dialogue to characterize Tom.

1. Reread paragraph 21 on **Practice Book** page 61. What does the writer show you about Tom through this dialogue? Underline words and phrases to support your answers. Explain how the text evidence supports your answer.

   Answers will vary. Possible response: Tom is dishonest. The writer shows this when Tom refuses Ben's help by lying about

   how "awful particular" Aunt Polly is about how the fence is painted. The writer also shows this when Tom makes Ben

   believe that painting the fence is specialized work by saying "there ain't one boy in a thousand, maybe two thousand, that

   can do it the way it's got to be done."

2. Underline another line of dialogue on **Practice Book** pages 60–61 that shows what Tom is like. Explain what it shows about Tom.

   Answers will vary.

F. Analyze how the author uses actions to characterize Tom.

1. Read the first sentence in paragraph 25 on **Practice Book** page 61. What does the writer show you about Tom through this action? Underline the words and phrases that support your answer. Explain how the text evidence supports your answer.

   Answers will vary. Possible response: The writer shows that Tom is insincere. The words "reluctance in his face, but

   alacrity in his heart" show that Tom pretends as if he doesn't want to give up the paintbrush, but he's really joyful

   about it.

2. In the **Practice Book**, underline other words about Tom's actions that show what he is like. Explain what it shows about Tom.

   Answers will vary.

▶ Discuss and Write

G. Synthesize your ideas about how the author characterized Tom.

1. With the class, discuss how the writer showed Tom's characteristics. List the characteristics that you discuss.

Possible response: _____ _____

clever, tricky, wily _____ _____

_____ _____ _____

2. Choose one of the characteristics that you listed. Write a paragraph about how the writer showed the characteristic. Use the questions below to organize your thoughts.

   · What characteristic did the writer show?

   · What dialogue supports this characteristic? Give 2 examples.

   · What actions support this characteristic? Give 2 examples.

   · Was the writer's characterization convincing? Why?

   Answers will vary. _____

   _____

   _____

   _____

   _____

▶ Connect with (GUIDING QUESTION)

H. Discuss the Guiding Question: What happens when people come face-to-face with a rival?

1. Who are Tom's rivals in this text?

   Possible response: Ben, painting the fence, Aunt Polly, neighborhood boys

2. How does he respond to the rivals?

   Possible response: Tom outsmarts his rivals.

3. What is the writer's message about rivals?

   Possible response: The writer believes that one way to deal with rivals is to make them envious of you.

Name _____

Academic Vocabulary Review

Academic Vocabulary		
affect	relate	structure
definition	scale	survive
elements	similar	

A. Use the Academic Vocabulary words to finish the paragraph. Clues are provided for you.

If you were lost in the wilderness, would you know how to _____survive_____? One
stay alive

survival skill is to know how to build a fire. Fire provides warmth, light, and a way to cook food. Food

and water are also important _____elements_____ of survival. You should take along extra
parts of the whole

food and water when you are planning a trip. Finding shelter is also important to survival. Perhaps one

of the most important survival skills is to stay calm. The way you react can _____affect_____
change in some way

your chances for survival.

B. Read each statement. Circle **Yes** or **No** to answer.

1. A **scale** shows how a series of items are **related**. (Yes)   No

2. A **structure** is how parts are arranged or organized. (Yes)   No

3. A **definition** tells the meaning of a word. (Yes)   No

4. When you **relate** things, you tell how they are different. Yes   (No)

5. Things that are **similar** are different. Yes   (No)

6. When you **affect** something, you change it in some way. (Yes)   No

7. An **element** is made of many parts. Yes   (No)

Key Vocabulary Review

A. Use these words to complete the paragraph.

advice	cheat	deserve	frustration
business	deal	fortune	property

Do you want to start your own ____business____ ? Follow this helpful ____advice____ . First, find a

piece of ____property____ in a busy location. Try to get a good ____deal____ on it. Stay away from

anyone who might want to ____cheat____ you. This will save you ____frustration____ along the way.

Remember, it takes time and effort to earn a ____fortune____ . However, if you work hard you will surely

____deserve____ to do well.

B. Use your own words to write the meaning of each Key Vocabulary word.
Then write examples for each word.

Word	My Definition	Examples
1. **adaptation**	*Possible response:* a change an animal makes to help it survive	*Possible response:* the snowshoe hare's white fur
2. **bargain**	*Possible response:* a good deal	*Possible response:* a jacket that is on sale
3. **disguise**	*Possible response:* something that helps a person look different	*Possible response:* a mask
4. **opinion**	*Possible response:* a belief about something	*Possible response:* Pizza is my favorite food.
5. **plague**	*Possible response:* to bother	*Possible response:* worrying about doing my chores
6. **predator**	*Possible response:* an animal that hunts other animals	*Possible response:* a lion
7. **prey**	*Possible response:* an animal that is hunted by other animals	*Possible response:* a mouse
8. **threat**	*Possible response:* a danger	*Possible response:* a storm in the distance

---

Unit 2 Key Vocabulary

adaptation	business	decent	frustration	plague	quest
advantage	camouflage	deserve	kingdom	predator	recite
advice	cheat	disguise	nervous	prey	survive
bargain	deal	fortune	opinion	property	threat

C. Complete the sentences.

1. An **advantage** you would want in a race is   *Possible response:* speed _____

     _____.

2. One type of animal **camouflage** is   *Possible response:* the polar bear's white fur _____

     _____.

3. A **decent** person would help a lost child by   *Possible response:* trying to find his or her parents ___

     _____.

4. If I had my own **kingdom**, it would be   *Possible response:* peaceful and fun _____

     _____.

5. Something that makes me **nervous** is   *Possible response:* speaking in front of large groups ___

     _____.

6. My ideal **quest** would be   *Possible response:* an adventure in the rainforest to find a new species of animal _

     _____.

7. Something I can **recite** from memory is   *Possible response:* the Pledge of Allegiance _____

     _____.

8. One thing that helps people **survive** in the wilderness is   *Possible response:* a tent for shelter

     _____.

Name _____

Mind Map

Use the mind map to show when you as an **individual** can make a difference within the world, your community, your family, and your own life. As you read the selections in this unit, add new ideas.

Answers will vary.

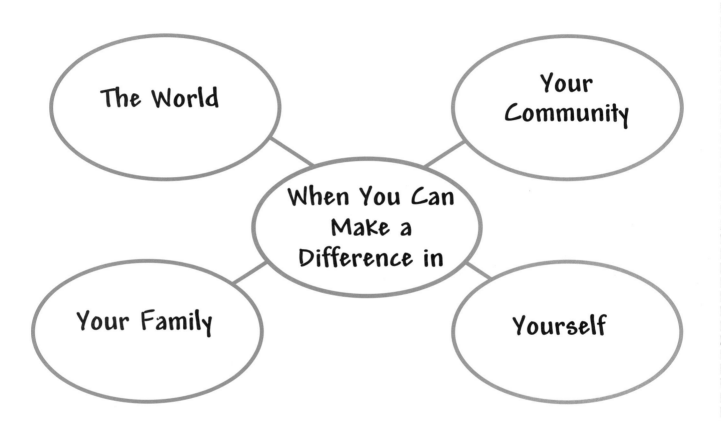

Academic Vocabulary

Think about an **individual** you admire. When did this **individual** make a difference? Use the word **individual** in your answer.

Answers will vary.

_____

_____

_____

_____

Text Structure: Chronological Order and Problem and Solution

A. Read the passage. Look for clues that show the organization.

> At the end of the year, everyone at Emma's company received a bonus. Emma decided to donate her bonus money to a school. First, she did some research. Next, she talked to some teachers at the local school. Then, she observed the children in the classrooms. Finally, Emma made a decision. She donated her bonus money to the school so it could purchase new computer equipment.

Circle how the passage is organized. **(In Chronological Order)**   **By Problem and Solution**

Tell how you know. *Possible response:* The events are written in order. The time words used are *first, next, then,* and *finally.*

B. Read the passage. Look for clues that show the organization.

> Emma wanted to help the students at a local school. They needed new computer equipment, but Emma did not have enough money to buy it. Then, at the end of the year, Emma received a bonus from her employer. Emma decided to donate her bonus money to the school. The school was able to buy the computer equipment. Emma knew that she had made the right decision!

Circle how the passage is organized.   **In Chronological Order**   **(By Problem and Solution)**

Tell how you know. *Possible response:* The problem is that Emma wanted to help a local school buy more computer equipment, but she didn't have much money. The solution is that Emma donated her bonus money to the school. The school was able to buy the computer equipment needed.

Academic Vocabulary

Write the steps you would take to **organize** a neighborhood fund raiser.

Answers will vary.

Focus on Vocabulary

Name _____

Use Word Parts

Some Word Parts
Suffix: *-able* means "can do"
Suffix: *-ful* means "full of"
Prefix: *anti-* means "against"
Prefix: *un-* means "not"

▶ Read the passages. Follow these steps.

1. Look closely at the word to see if you know any of the parts.
2. Cover any prefixes and suffixes. Think about the meaning of the base word.
3. Uncover the prefixes and suffixes and determine their meanings.
4. Put the meanings of the word parts together to define the whole word. Be sure the meaning makes sense in the passage.

A. Follow the directions above. Write the meaning of each underlined word.

> César Chávez was a Mexican American man whose actions changed the lives of many farm workers. As a boy, Chávez picked fruits and vegetables on farms in California. He faced <u>unsafe</u> working conditions and low pay. Chávez knew this was wrong. When he grew up, Chávez fought for more <u>acceptable</u> working conditions and higher pay. Chávez's <u>successful</u> efforts brought about change.

unsafe _not safe_

acceptable _can be accepted_

successful _full of success_

B. Follow the directions above. Write the meaning of each underlined word.

> Nelson Mandela wants to end segregation and make South Africa a <u>peaceful</u> place. He has devoted his life to this goal. For many years, he worked with the government to bring equality to South Africa. Mandela won the Nobel Peace Prize in 1993. This prize is awarded to individuals who use <u>antiwar</u> words and ideas to create peace. Mandela is one of the most <u>memorable</u> leaders in the world.

peaceful _full of peace_

antiwar _against war_

memorable _can be remembered_

Academic Vocabulary

I have to **focus** very hard when I _____

Possible response: practice shooting the basketball into the hoop

_____ .

70 Unit 3 Making a Difference

© National Geographic Learning, a part of Cengage Learning, Inc.

Critical Viewing Guide

▶ Take Notes

A. View the video. Take notes on at least three things that you learned.

Answers will vary.

_____

_____

_____

_____

_____

_____

_____

▶ Analyze the Video

B. Review your notes to help answer these questions.

1. Write two sentences to explain what was in the video.

   Answers will vary.

   _____

   _____

2. What was the most interesting thing you learned?

   Answers will vary.

   _____

   _____

3. Explain the ways some **individuals** worked for equal rights for everyone during the Civil Rights Movement.

   Answers will vary.

   _____

   _____

   _____

Learn Key Vocabulary

Name _____

The Civil Rights Movement: Key Vocabulary

A. Study each word. Circle a number to rate how well you know it. Then complete the chart.

Rating Scale	**1** I have never seen this word before.	**2** I am not sure of the word's meaning.	**3** I know this word and can teach the word's meaning to someone else.

▲ Rosa Parks believed in **equality**. She fought **prejudice** to help gain **civil rights** for African Americans.

Key Words	Check Understanding	Deepen Understanding
❶ civil rights (siv-ul rīts) *noun* Rating: 1 2 3	☐ guidelines on how to be polite ☒ basic rights and freedoms	Example: _____ *Possible response:* the right to peacefully protest
❷ determined (dē-**tur**-mind) *adjective* Rating: 1 2 3	☒ working hard to make something happen ☐ protecting the rights of others	Example: _____ *Possible response:* a marathon runner who completes a race
❸ equality (ē-**kwal**-i-tē) *noun* Rating: 1 2 3	☐ having popular opinions that are shared by others ☒ having the same rights as other people or groups	Example: _____ *Possible response:* paying the same salary to men and women for completing the same job
❹ integrate (**in**-ti-grāt) *verb* Rating: 1 2 3	☐ to enter a contract ☒ to bring together	Example: _____ *Possible response:* to invite both school friends and neighborhood friends to a party

Name _____

> ## Did You Know?
>
> **Segregation** comes from a Latin word which means "to separate from the herd or flock." Today the term usually refers to people rather than animals.

Key Words	Check Understanding	Deepen Understanding
❺ prejudice (**prej**-ū-dis) *noun* **Rating:** 1 2 3	☒ an unfair opinion about a person, group, or race ☐ the bad experiences of a group of people	Example: _____ *Possible response:* a false belief that all people with brown hair are lazy _____ _____
❻ protest (**prō**-test) *verb* **Rating:** 1 2 3	☐ to give a speech in support of a candidate ☒ to show disagreement	Example: _____ *Possible response:* to join a rally supporting fair wages for workers _____ _____
❼ segregation (**seg**-ri-**gā**-shun) *noun* **Rating:** 1 2 3	☒ the division of people into separate groups ☐ the southern part of a town or city	Example: _____ *Possible response:* having separate schools for girls and boys _____ _____
❽ separate (**sep**-u-rut) *adjective* **Rating:** 1 2 3	☒ apart from others ☐ part of a group	Example: _____ *Possible response:* red marbles and blue marbles in different bags _____ _____

B. Use at least two of the Key Vocabulary words. Write about a time you were treated unfairly. Tell how you handled the problem.

Answers will vary.

_____

_____

Text Structure: Chronological Order

Complete the Time Line as you read "The Movement Begins," "Separate but Equal," and "Brown v. Board of Education" in "The Civil Rights Movement."

Time Line

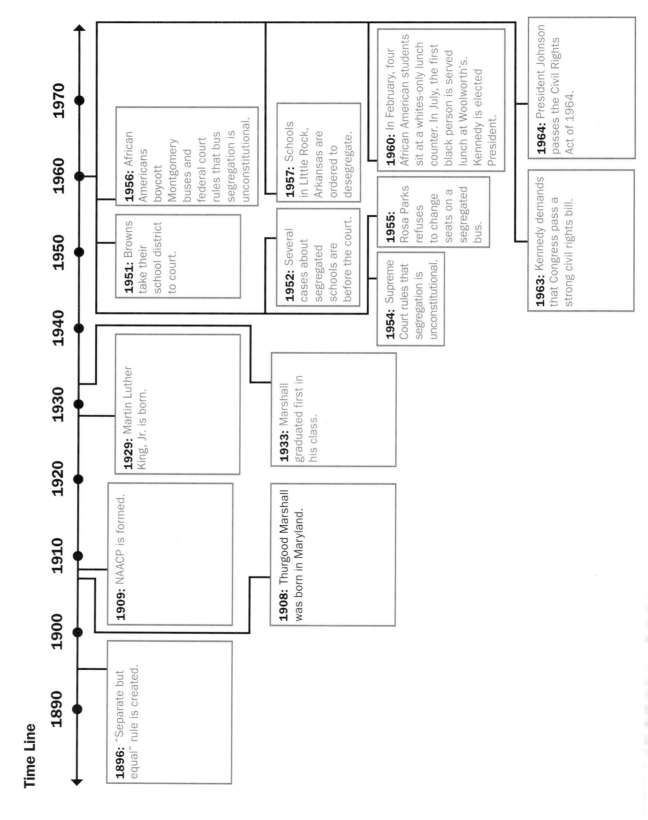

1890   1900   1910   1920   1930   1940   1950   1960   1970

1896: "Separate but equal" rule is created.

1908: Thurgood Marshall was born in Maryland.

1909: NAACP is formed.

1929: Martin Luther King, Jr. is born.

1933: Marshall graduated first in his class.

1951: Browns take their school district to court.

1952: Several cases about segregated schools are before the court.

1954: Supreme Court rules that segregation is unconstitutional.

1955: Rosa Parks refuses to change seats on a segregated bus.

1956: African Americans boycott Montgomery buses and federal court rules that bus segregation is unconstitutional.

1957: Schools in Little Rock, Arkansas are ordered to desegregate.

1960: In February, four African American students sit at a whites-only lunch counter. In July, the first black person is served lunch at Woolworth's. Kennedy is elected President.

1963: Kennedy demands that Congress pass a strong civil rights bill.

1964: President Johnson passes the Civil Rights Act of 1964.

Name _____

The Civil Rights Movement

Key Vocabulary

Civil Rights	prejudice
determined	protested
equality	segregation
integrate	separate

A. Read the paragraph.
Write a Key Vocabulary word in each blank.
Reread the paragraph to make sure the words make sense.

The ___Civil Rights___ Movement brought about many changes. Americans had to find ways to ___integrate___ all people into society. They could not enforce ___segregation___ by offering ___separate___ services for different races. People of all races ___protested___ together. They were ___determined___ to bring about social ___equality___. Today ___prejudice___ and problems still exist. People still need to work together to build understanding and find solutions.

B. Write complete sentences to answer these questions about "The Civil Rights Movement."

1. What can be done to build understanding and help prevent **prejudice**?

Answers will vary.

_____

_____

_____

_____

_____

2. Why is school **integration** important to build understanding?

Possible response: Classmates from many different backgrounds can build relationships that carry over into daily life.

_____

_____

_____

_____

_____

_____

_____

Vocabulary Study

Use Word Parts: Prefixes

Prefix	Meaning
de-	removal, reversal
dis-	the opposite of
non-	not
in-	not
re-	again
un-	not

▶ Follow the steps below to figure out the meaning of each word.

1. Find the word parts.
2. Analyze each of these word parts.
3. Put the meanings together to understand the whole word.
4. Then write a sentence for the word.

1. **unable** _not able_

   Sentence: _Possible response: I was unable to solve the puzzle because it was too hard._

2. **disprove** _the opposite of prove_

   Sentence: _Possible response: The scientist tried to disprove a theory by making a new discovery._

3. **regain** _gain again_

   Sentence: _Possible response: Chris tried to regain his position on the team because he missed playing soccer._

4. **nonfiction** _not fiction_

   Sentence: _Possible response: I like nonfiction books because I can learn about true events._

5. **inadequate** _not adequate_

   Sentence: _Possible response: His response to the question was inadequate because he did not provide all of the information._

6. **defrost** _to remove frost_

   Sentence: _Possible response: My father wanted to defrost the chicken that was in the freezer._

7. **nonstop** _not making any stops_

   Sentence: _Possible response: I knew my nonstop flight would be boring so I brought a book with me._

8. **readmit** _to admit again_

   Sentence: _Possible response: Her family had to readmit her to the hospital when she got sick again._

9. **disregard** _to not pay attention to_

   Sentence: _Possible response: Please disregard what I said because I was wrong._

Name _____

The Civil Rights Movement:
Academic Vocabulary Review

Academic Vocabulary

analyze   individual

evidence   organize

focus

A. Draw a line to match the word with its meaning.

Word	Definition
1. **analyze**	facts or details that support a conclusion
2. **evidence**	to separate something into parts and study it
3. **focus**	to put things in a certain order
4. **individual**	one person
5. **organize**	to pay attention to something

B. Complete each sentence.

1. A scientist might **analyze** _Possible response: data_ .

2. One type of **evidence** a detective might look for is _Possible response: fingerprints_ .

3. If you look out the classroom window, you could **focus** on _Possible response: clouds in the sky_ .

4. One of the most interesting **individuals** I know is _Answers will vary._ .

5. One way to **organize** a list is to _Possible response: put it in alphabetical order_ .

C. What is the best way to **organize** your desk? How does this help you to **focus**?

Answers will vary.

_____

_____

_____

Name _____

Critical Viewing Guide

▶ Take Notes

A. View the video. Take notes on at least three things that you learned.

Answers will vary.

_____

_____

_____

_____

_____

_____

_____

▶ Analyze the Video

B. Review your notes to help answer these questions.

1. Write two sentences to explain what was in the video.

Answers will vary.

_____

_____

2. What was the most interesting thing you learned?

Answers will vary.

_____

_____

3. How did one **individual**, Martin Luther King, Jr., work to end segregation?

Answers will vary.

_____

_____

_____

Learn Key Vocabulary

Name _____

Martin's Big Words: Key Vocabulary

A. Study each word. Circle a number to rate how well you know it. Then complete the chart.

Rating Scale	**1** I have never seen this word before.	**2** I am not sure of the word's meaning.	**3** I know this word and can teach the word's meaning to someone else.

▲ Dr. Martin Luther King, Jr., was a leader in the Civil Rights **Movement**. His March on Washington speech still **influences** activists today.

Key Words	Check Understanding	Deepen Understanding
❶ admire (ad-**mir**) *verb* **Rating:** 1 2 3	When you **admire** someone, you _____ them. (like) envy	Who is someone you admire? Explain why. _____ *Possible response:* I admire my grandmother because she worked hard to bring our family to the United States. _____
❷ arrest (u-**rest**) *noun* **Rating:** 1 2 3	A _____ makes **arrests**. (police officer) mayor	Why might someone be placed under arrest? _____ *Possible response:* A person might be placed under arrest for stealing. _____ _____
❸ convince (kun-**vins**) *verb* **Rating:** 1 2 3	To **convince** someone is to _____ them. annoy (persuade)	How would you convince someone to quit smoking? *Possible response:* I would tell him/her about the benifits of quitting, such as better health. _____ _____
❹ influence (in-**flü-uns**) *verb* **Rating:** 1 2 3	If you **influence** people, you make them _____ with you. (agree) argue	Who has influenced you? Explain. _____ *Possible response:* My biology teacher influenced me to think about a career in nursing. _____ _____

Name _____

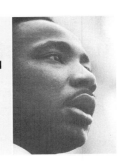

Dr. Martin Luther King, Jr., **convinced** many people that it is best to solve **problems** without violence. ▶

Key Words	Check Understanding	Deepen Understanding
5 movement (müv-munt) *noun* **Rating:** 1 2 3	A **movement** is a _____ of people who work to make a change. distrust (group)	How can a movement be successful? _____ *Possible response:* A movement can be successful if it has a lot of people who will work hard to reach the common goals. _____
6 peace (pēs) *noun* **Rating:** 1 2 3	**Peace** is freedom from _____. (war) people	Do you think world peace is possible? Explain. _____ *Possible response:* No, I think nations will always find a reason to fight. _____ _____
7 preach (prēch) *verb* **Rating:** 1 2 3	To **preach** is to urge people to _____ something. (believe) protest	What message would you preach to a younger student? Explain. *Possible response:* I would preach the importance of organization because it is easier to stay focused in class when you are organized. _____
8 problem (prah-blum) *noun* **Rating:** 1 2 3	It is best to _____ a **problem**. ignore (solve)	What problem have you solved in the last month? *Possible response:* I replaced the batteries in my alarm which solved my problem of waking up late. _____ _____

B. Use at least two of the Key Vocabulary words. Write about a person who influences you in a positive way.

Answers will vary.

_____

_____

Name _____

Text Structure: Chronological Order

Complete the Sequence Chain as you read "Martin's Big Words." Choose the most important events in Martin's life.

Sequence Chain

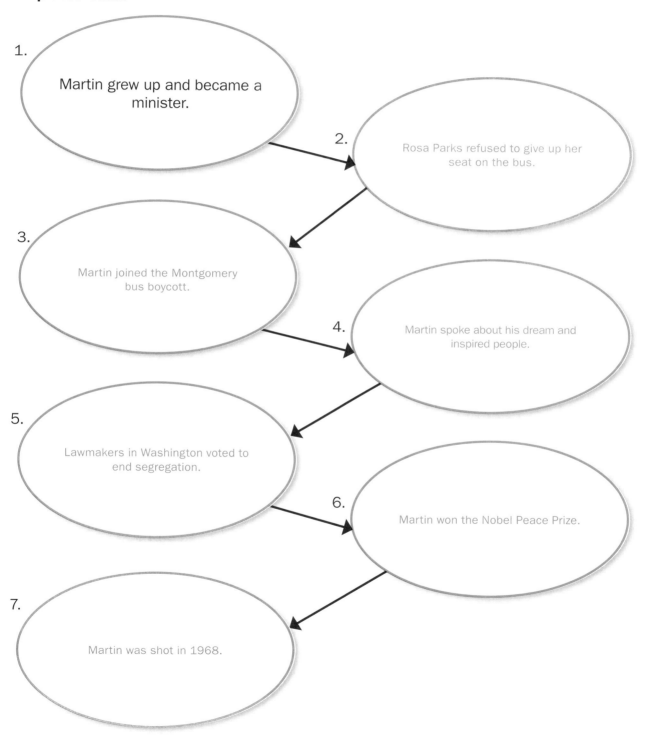

1. Martin grew up and became a minister.

2. Rosa Parks refused to give up her seat on the bus.

3. Martin joined the Montgomery bus boycott.

4. Martin spoke about his dream and inspired people.

5. Lawmakers in Washington voted to end segregation.

6. Martin won the Nobel Peace Prize.

7. Martin was shot in 1968.

Martin's Big Words

A. Read the paragraph.
Write a Key Vocabulary word in each blank.
Reread the paragraph to make sure the words make sense.

Dr. Martin Luther King, Jr., had a major ____influence____ on the success of the Civil Rights ____Movement____.

Millions of people heard him ____preach____ his message of ____peace____ and equality. He wanted to

solve many ____problems____ and was ____convinced____ he could make the world a better place. He was even

willing to be ____arrested____ for his beliefs. It is easy to see why so many people ____admire____ Dr. King.

B. Write complete sentences to answer these questions about "Martin's Big Words" and the "I Have a Dream" speech.

1. What do you **admire** about Dr. Martin Luther King, Jr.?

   Answers will vary.

   _____

   _____

   _____

   _____

   _____

2. Do you think Dr. King's message in his "I Have a Dream" speech is still meaningful today? Why or why not?

   Answers will vary.

   _____

   _____

   _____

   _____

   _____

Use Word Parts: **Suffixes**

▶ Follow the steps below to figure out the meaning of each word.

Suffix	Meaning
-tion	condition or action
-or	one who does an action
-ness	state of
-ly	like; in the manner of
-ic	like; nature of

1. Cover the suffix and look at the base word.
2. Think about the meaning of the base word.
3. Uncover the suffix. How does the suffix affect the base word?
4. Write the meaning of the whole word.
5. Then write a sentence for the word.

1. **darkness** _the state of being dark_

   Sentence: _Possible response: I tripped and fell in the darkness._

2. **poorly** _in a poor manner_

   Sentence: _Possible response: I played the flute poorly until I started practicing more often._

3. **director** _one who directs_

   Sentence: _Possible response: The choir director told us what to do._

4. **collection** _the action of collecting_

   Sentence: _Possible response: The collection of our test papers took a few minutes._

5. **historic** _in the nature of history_

   Sentence: _Possible response: I like to visit historic sites and museums._

6. **happiness** _the state of being happy_

   Sentence: _Possible response: Some scientists believe happiness can keep you healthy._

7. **sincerely** _in a sincere manner_

   Sentence: _Possible response: I sincerely apologized for being late._

8. **instructor** _one who instructs_

   Sentence: _Possible response: Our lab instructor helped us with our science projects._

9. **poetic** _like poetry_

   Sentence: _Possible response: Dr. King gave a poetic speech._

Martin's Big Words: Academic Vocabulary Review

A. Use your own words to tell what each Academic Vocabulary word means.

1. **focus** _Possible response: to pay attention to something_ _____

2. **individual** _Possible response: something that is separate from other things_ _____

3. **organize** _Possible response: to arrange things in a certain order_ _____

B. Use each Academic Vocabulary word in a sentence. You may use two words in one sentence.

1. _Answers will vary._ _____

_____

2. _Answers will vary._ _____

_____

3. _Answers will vary._ _____

_____

C. What **individual** inspires you?

Answers will vary. _____

_____

Build Background

Critical Viewing Guide

▶ **Take Notes**

A. View the images. Take notes on at least three things that you learned.

Answers will vary.

_____

_____

_____

_____

_____

_____

_____

_____

▶ **Analyze the Images**

B. Review your notes to help answer these questions.

1. Write two sentences to explain what was in the images.

   Answers will vary.

   _____

   _____

   _____

2. What was the most interesting thing you learned?

   Answers will vary.

   _____

   _____

   _____

3. What are some ways that an **individual** can help in the community?

   Answers will vary.

   _____

   _____

   _____

   _____

   _____

Learn Key Vocabulary

Speaking Up: Key Vocabulary

A. Study each word. Circle a number to rate how well you know it.
Then complete the chart.

| Rating Scale | **1** I have never seen this word before. | **2** I am not sure of the word's meaning. | **3** I know this word and can teach the word's meaning to someone else. |

▲ Students who get **involved** in their school or community improve their **leadership** skills.

Key Words	Check Understanding	Deepen Understanding
❶ challenge (**chal**-unj) *noun* **Rating: 1 2 3**	Circle the synonym for **challenge**. (**difficulty**) strength	It is a challenge to learn a new language because *Possible response: you need to learn a whole new* way to express your thoughts and feelings .
❷ contribute (kun-**trib**-yūt) *verb* **Rating: 1 2 3**	Circle the synonym for **contribute**. (**give**) take	If I could contribute to any cause, I would _____ *Possible response: volunteer my time or money to* a hospital .
❸ involved (in-**vahlvd**) *adjective* **Rating: 1 2 3**	Circle the synonym for **involved**. angry (**active**)	I would like to get involved with _____ *Possible response: a club that brings international* students together .
❹ leadership (**lēd**-ur-ship) *noun* **Rating: 1 2 3**	Circle the synonym for **leadership**. comfort (**guidance**)	The skills needed for leadership are _____ *Possible response: communication and problem-* solving skills .

Name _____

These students take **positive** actions to **contribute** to their community. ▶

Key Words	Check Understanding	Deepen Understanding
❺ negative (**neg**-u-tiv) *adjective* **Rating:** 1 2 3	Circle the synonym for **negative**. good (bad)	I have a negative opinion of _____ *Possible response:* people who talk loudly at the movies _____ .
❻ overcome (ō-vur-**kum**) *verb* **Rating:** 1 2 3	Circle the synonym for **overcome**. traveled (beat)	One difficulty I have overcome is _____ *Possible response:* my childhood fear of the dark _____ .
❼ positive (**pahz**-u-tiv) *adjective* **Rating:** 1 2 3	Circle the synonym for **positive**. (good) bad	Some positive features of our school include _____ *Possible response:* small class sizes, a computer lab, and after-school activities _____ .
❽ promote (pru-**mōt**) *verb* **Rating:** 1 2 3	Circle the synonym for **promote**. criticize (publicize)	If I wanted to promote bicycle safety, I would _____ *Possible response:* tell everyone to wear helmets and follow the rules of the road _____ .

B. Use at least two of the Key Vocabulary words. Write about a time you got involved in your school or community.

Answers will vary.

_____

_____

_____

Name _____

Text Structure: Problem and Solution

Complete the Problem-and-Solution Chain as you read "Student Works to End Bullying" and "Making Change Happen."

Problem-and-Solution Chain

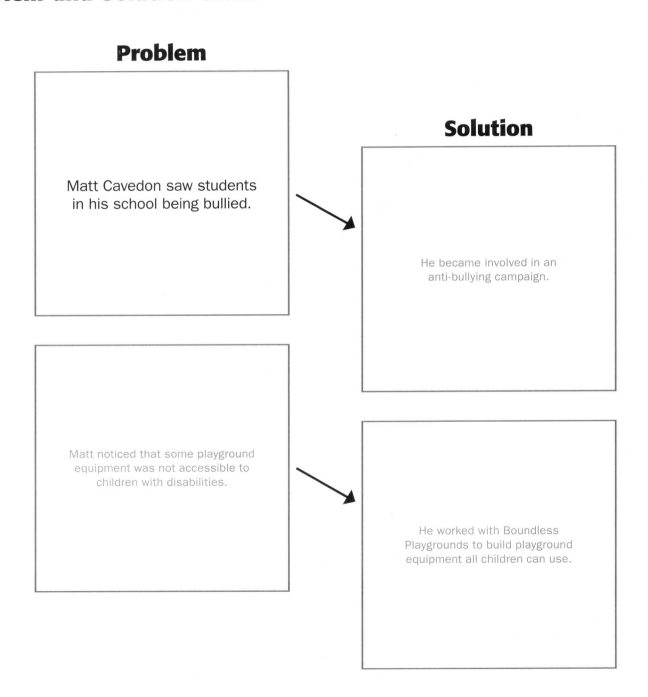

Problem

Matt Cavedon saw students in his school being bullied.

Solution

He became involved in an anti-bullying campaign.

Matt noticed that some playground equipment was not accessible to children with disabilities.

He worked with Boundless Playgrounds to build playground equipment all children can use.

Speaking Up

Key Vocabulary

challenges	negative
contributes	overcome
involved	positive
leadership	promote

A. Read the paragraph.
Write a Key Vocabulary word in each blank.
Reread the paragraph to make sure the words make sense.

Eve Vang and Matt Cavedon both have had to rise above ___challenges___, or difficulties. Other people might find it hard to ___overcome___ these problems to reach their goals. Each of them ___contributes___ to the community to make life better. They inspire others to change their ___negative___ attitudes. They think that it is important for everyone to get ___involved___ and help people. Their ___leadership___ skills ___promote___ actions that bring about ___positive___ results.

B. Write complete sentences to answer these questions about "Speaking Up."

1. What do you admire about people like Eve Vang and Matt Cavedon?

Answers will vary.

_____

_____

_____

_____

_____

_____

2. What did Eve Vang and Matt Cavedon do to make a difference in their communities?

Answers will vary.

_____

_____

_____

_____

_____

_____

_____

Vocabulary Study

Name _____

Use Word Parts

▶ Follow the steps below to predict the meaning of each word.

1. Break the word into parts.
2. Determine the meaning of each word part.
3. Put the meanings together to predict the meaning of the word. Write the definition.
4. Then use the word in a sentence.

Word Part	Meaning
-able	can be or is
-ly	in this way; way of being
re-	again
-tion	the act of
un-	not; the opposite of
under-	below; not enough

1. **unnecessary** _not necessary_

   Sentence: _Possible response: My mother thought it was unnecessary when I bought 15 comic books._

2. **adorable** _is adored_

   Sentence: _Possible response: I think puppies are adorable because they have big paws and floppy ears._

3. **protection** _the act of protecting_

   Sentence: _Possible response: Our umbrellas gave us protection from the rain._

4. **falsely** _being false_

   Sentence: _Possible response: The store owner falsely accused the man of stealing from the store._

5. **underpaid** _not paid enough_

   Sentence: _Possible response: Michael believes he is underpaid at his job so he is going to ask his boss for a raise._

6. **reheat** _to heat again_

   Sentence: _Possible response: Selena needed to reheat the pizza because it was cold._

7. **underground** _below the ground_

   Sentence: _Possible response: Animals like to go underground because it is a safe place to hide._

8. **rebuild** _to build again_

   Sentence: _Possible response: I had to rebuild my tower of blocks when my little brother knocked it down._

9. **automation** _the act of making something automatic_

   Sentence: _Possible response: Computers helped to make factory automation possible._

90 Unit 3 Making a Difference   © National Geographic Learning, a part of Cengage Learning, Inc.

Speaking Up: Academic Vocabulary Review

A. Draw a line to connect the beginning of each sentence to its ending.

1. Can we **convince** everyone	what will happen in the future.
2. I want to **focus** on	can make a difference.
3. Hector can **predict**	one subject at a time.
4. I must **organize**	the words by listing them alphabetically.
5. Even one **individual**	to vote for Maddie?

B. Write the Academic Vocabulary words next to their definitions.

1. to pay attention to something   focus _____

2. to persuade   convince _____

3. to guess about or tell what will happen   predict _____

4. to arrange things in a certain order   organize _____

5. one person   individual _____

SPEECHES *on the* LITTLE ROCK NINE

by DWIGHT D. EISENHOWER & BILL CLINTON

INTRODUCTION On September 23, 1957, nine African American high school students entered Little Rock's Central High School, ready to learn. Prior to 1957, African American and white students attended separate schools. These nine students were part of an integration plan ordered by the U.S. Supreme Court. Outside the school, a mob of violent protesters gathered, threatening the students' safety. Two days later President Dwight D. Eisenhower sent U.S. Army troops to escort the students to school. To explain his actions to the nation, he gave the following address. Forty years later, Bill Clinton told the nation that we've come a long way but still have a long way to go regarding racial harmony.

From **President Dwight D. Eisenhower's Radio and TV Address to the Nation, September 24, 1957**

2   Good Evening, My Fellow Citizens: For a few minutes this evening I want to speak to you about the serious situation that has arisen in Little Rock. To make this talk I have come to the President's office in the White House. I could have spoken from Rhode Island, where I have been staying recently, but I felt that, in speaking from the house of Lincoln, of Jackson and of Wilson, my words would better convey both the sadness I feel in the action I was compelled today to take and the firmness with which I intend to pursue this course until the orders of the Federal Court at Little Rock can be executed without unlawful interference.

3 E.1   In that city, under the **leadership** of **demagogic extremists,** disorderly mobs have **deliberately** prevented the carrying out of proper orders from a Federal Court. Local authorities have not eliminated that violent opposition and, under the law, I yesterday issued a Proclamation calling upon the mob to disperse.

4   This morning the mob again gathered in front of the Central High School of Little Rock, obviously for the purpose of again preventing the carrying out of the Court's order relating to the admission of Negro children to that school.

5   Whenever normal agencies prove inadequate to the task and it becomes necessary for the Executive Branch of the Federal Government to use its powers and

Key Vocabulary
● **leadership** *n.*, the ability to direct or guide other people

In Other Words
demagogic extremists people who use emotion to promote unpopular ideas or actions
deliberately purposefully

authority to uphold Federal Courts, the President's responsibility is inescapable. **In accordance with** that responsibility, I have today issued an Executive Order directing the use of troops under Federal authority to aid in the execution of Federal law at Little Rock, Arkansas. This became necessary when my Proclamation of yesterday was not observed, and the obstruction of justice still continues.

6   It is important that the reasons for my action be understood by all our citizens. As you know, the Supreme Court of the United States has decided that separate public educational **facilities** for the races are inherently unequal and therefore **compulsory** school **segregation** laws are unconstitutional.

7   Our personal opinions about the decision have no bearing on the matter of enforcement; the responsibility and authority of the Supreme Court to interpret the Constitution are very clear. Local Federal Courts were instructed by the Supreme Court to issue such orders and decrees as might be necessary to achieve admission to public schools without regard to race—and with all deliberate speed.

8   During the past several years, many communities in our Southern States have instituted public school plans for gradual progress in the enrollment and attendance of school children of all races in order to bring

". . . Southern States have instituted public school plans for gradual progress in the enrollment and attendance of school children of all races . . ."

themselves into compliance with the law of the land.

9   They thus demonstrated to the world that we are a nation in which laws, not men, are supreme. I regret to say that this truth—the cornerstone of our liberties—was not observed in this instance …

10   The interest of the nation in the proper fulfillment of the law's requirements cannot yield to opposition and demonstrations by some few persons. Mob rule cannot be allowed to override the decisions of our courts …

11   And so, with deep confidence, I call upon the citizens of the State of Arkansas to assist in bringing to an immediate end all interference with the law and its processes. If resistance to the Federal Court orders ceases at once, the further presence of Federal troops will be unnecessary and the City of Little Rock will return to its normal habits of **peace** and order and **a blot upon** the fair name and high honor of our nation in the world will be removed.

12   Thus will be restored the image of America and of all its parts as one nation, indivisible, with liberty and justice for all.

Key Vocabulary
- **segregation** *n.*, the division of people into groups based on race
- **peace** *n.*, agreement among people

In Other Words
In accordance with To go with
facilities places
compulsory required
a blot upon the negativity on

From President Bill Clinton's Speech at Central High School Little Rock, Arkansas September 25, 1997

13   On this beautiful, sunshiny day, so many wonderful words have been spoken with so much conviction, I am reluctant to add to them. But I must ask you to remember once more and to ask yourselves, what does what happened here 40 years ago mean today? What does it tell us, most importantly, about our children's tomorrows?

14   On September 4th, 1957, Elizabeth Eckford walked to this door for her first day of school, utterly alone. She was turned away by people who were afraid of change, instructed by ignorance, hating what they simply could not understand. And America saw her, haunted

and taunted for the simple color of her skin, and in the image we caught a very disturbing glimpse of ourselves. We saw not "one Nation under God, indivisible, with liberty and justice for all," but two Americas, divided and unequal …

J.3

15 … Imagine, all of you, what it would be like to come to school one day and be shoved against lockers, tripped down stairways, taunted day after day by your classmates, to go all through school with no hope of going to a school play or being on a basketball team or learning in simple peace …

16 Forty years later, what do you young people in this audience believe we have learned? Well, 40 years later, we know that we all benefit—all of us—when we learn together, work together, and come together. That is, after all, what it means to be an American.

> "… Forty years later, we know there are still more doors to be opened …"

17 Forty years later, we know, **notwithstanding some cynics,** that all our children can learn, and this school proves it. Forty years later, we know when the constitutional rights of our citizens are threatened, the National Government must guarantee them. Talk is fine, but when they are threatened, you need strong laws faithfully enforced and upheld by independent courts.

18 Forty years later, we know there are still more doors to be opened, doors to be opened wider, doors we have to keep from being shut again now. Forty years later, we know freedom and **equality** cannot be realized without responsibility for self, family, and the duties of citizenship, or without a commitment to building a community of shared destiny and a genuine sense of belonging.

19 Forty years later, we know the question of race is more complex and more important than ever, embracing no longer just blacks and whites, or blacks and whites and Hispanics and Native Americans, but now people from all parts of the Earth coming here to **redeem** the promise of America.

20 Forty years later, frankly, we know we're bound to come back where we started. After all the weary years and silent tears, after all the stony roads and bitter rides, the question of race is, in the end, still **an affair of the heart.** But if these are our lessons, what do we have to do? First, we must all **reconcile.** Then we must all face the facts of today. And finally we must act.

Key Vocabulary
- **equality** *n.*, having the same rights as other people

In Other Words
notwithstanding some cynics even though there are doubters
redeem benefit from
an affair of the heart an emotional issue
reconcile be friends

▶ Read for Understanding

A. What kind of texts are these? How do you know?

Possible response: speeches; They are the words spoken to the public by two presidents.

B. Write a sentence that tells the topic of the selection.

Possible response: The texts are mostly about racial equality in the Little Rock schools and how to accomplish it.

▶ Reread and Summarize

C. On **Practice Book** pages 92–95, circle the 3–5 most important words in each section. Make notes about why you chose each word. Why is the word important?

1. Section 1: (paragraphs 1–5)

   Answers will vary.

2. Section 2: (paragraphs 6–12)

   Answers will vary.

3. Section 3: (paragraphs 13–15)

   Answers will vary.

4. Section 4: (paragraphs 16–20)

   Answers will vary.

D. Use your topic sentence from above and your notes to write a summary of the selection.

Possible response: Eisenhower speaks about why he chose to send the National Guard to Little Rock to allow the African American children to go to school. Clinton speaks about what the Little Rock Nine meant to the country and the racial problems our country still faces today.

▶ Reread and Analyze

E. Analyze how the speaker presents problems and solutions.

1. Reread paragraphs 3–5 on **Practice Book** page 92 What are the problems? What are the solutions? Underline your answers.

   Answers will vary. Possible response: Problem: Mobs have prevented students from integrating at the Little Rock schools.

   Solution: Eisenhower sent federal troops to Central High School to make sure African American students could attend.

2. Underline phrases and sentences on **Practice Book** pages 92–95 that show problems and solutions. Explain how the solutions can remove the problems.

   Answers will vary.

F. Analyze how there can be more than one solution to a problem.

1. Reread paragraph 6 on **Practice Book** page 93. What event happened? Why is this a problem? Then look for two different solutions in paragraphs 8 and 11. Underline those solutions.

   Answers will vary. Possible response: Problem: Separate schools were unequal, so segregation was declared

   unconstitutional. Solutions: Communities can find their own way to make sure schools are integrated gradually. Citizens can

   make sure integration is carried out.

2. Identify other solutions to the issue of segregation you notice on **Practice Book** pages 92–95. Explain how the solutions and problems are organized.

   Answers will vary.

▶ Reread and Analyze

G. Analyze how the speaker supports his solutions.

1. Reread paragraphs 9 and 10 on **Practice Book** page 93. What reasons does Eisenhower give for his solution of sending troops to the school? What sentence did you think was most persuasive?

   Answers will vary. Possible response: Eisenhower believes that laws, not men, are supreme and that the students'

   liberties were not protected. He also believes that the federal courts should not be beaten by mob rule. This sentence was

   especially persuasive: "Mob rule cannot be allowed to override the decisions of our courts."

2. Identify the sentence on **Practice Book** pages 92–95 that you thought was especially persuasive. Tell why you thought it was convincing.

   Answers will vary.

   _____

H. Analyze how the speaker presents problems and solutions.

1. President Bill Clinton's speech was given 40 years later. Reread paragraphs 18 and 19 on **Practice Book** page 95. What new problems related to race does he mention? Then reread paragraph 20. What solutions does Clinton suggest?

   Answers will vary. Possible response: Problem: More doors need to be opened for real freedom and equality, and

   freedom doesn't come easily. Equality is complex and must include many cultures. Solution: We must reconcile,

   face facts, and take action.

2. In the **Practice Book**, underline examples of problems Clinton mentions. Tell which part speaks to you effectively.

   Answers will vary.

   _____

▶ Discuss and Write

I. Synthesize your ideas about problem-and-solution text structure.

1. With the class, discuss how the speakers presented problems and solutions and used them to structure the text. Have students list examples as they discuss.

Answers will vary. Possible response: Eisenhower told about his solution but then told of other ways communities and

citizens could solve the problem. Clinton told about racial problems we still face and how to address them.

2. Choose a paragraph from the text. Write a paragraph about how each speaker developed his ideas about problems and solutions. Use the questions below to organize your thoughts.

   · What is the problem? What is the solution?

   · What sentences develop the speaker's ideas most effectively? Why?

   · How does this paragraph help you understand ideas in the rest of the speech?

Answers will vary.

▶ Connect with (GUIDING QUESTION)

J. Discuss the Guiding Question: When can one individual make a difference?

1. What did Eisenhower think about integration?

Possible response: Eisenhower tried to be objective. He focused on supporting the court's decision.

2. How is that different from Clinton's attitude about integration?

Possible response: Clinton clearly supported school integration and was against segregation.

3. What sentences gave you clues about each president's attitude? Underline those sentences.

Possible responses: Eisenhower: "Our personal opinions about the decision have no bearing on the matter of enforcement."

Clinton: "We saw not 'one Nation under God, indivisible, with liberty and justice for all,' but two Americas, divided and unequal."

4. How did each president suggest American citizens could make a difference?

Possible responses: Eisenhower wanted citizens to support the law. Clinton wanted people to reconcile, face facts about

racism, and act.

Academic Vocabulary Review

Academic Vocabulary	
analyze	individual
convince	organize
evidence	predict
focus	

A. Circle the word that best fits into each sentence.

1. People try to (**convince** / **predict**) the outcome of an election.

2. Scientists found (**evidence** / **individual**) of water on the planet Mars.

3. I will (**analyze** / **focus**) on ways to help other people.

4. Mr. Tuan assigned a task to each (**individual** / **evidence**) in the class.

B. Read each statement. Circle **Yes** or **No** to answer.

1. One way to **organize** books is to arrange them by subject.   **Yes**   **No**

2. If you **convince** someone, they will not believe you.   **Yes**   **No**

3. If you **analyze** your test results, you can prepare better next time.   **Yes**   **No**

C. Answer the questions in complete sentences.

1. How could you **organize** students as they line up?

   Answers will vary.

   _____

2. Write about one **individual** who has made a difference in your life.

   Answers will vary.

   _____

3. How could you **convince** a friend not to do something that is dangerous?

   Answers will vary.

   _____

4. Write about one thing you would like to **focus** on during school this year.

   Answers will vary.

   _____

Key Vocabulary Review

A. Read each sentence. Circle the word that best fits into each sentence.

1. The police officer made several (**arrests**)/**problems**).

2. The team that was most (**negative** / (**determined**)) scored the most goals.

3. ((**Segregation**)/ **Prejudice**) is the division of people into groups based on race.

4. The class president led a student (**movement**)/ **challenge**) to end locker searches.

5. Twenty students and two teachers are (**overcome** / (**involved**)) in the after-school program.

6. When a group of people have the same rights as everyone else, they have (**equality**)/ **leadership**).

7. I would like to (**promote**)/ **convince**) a message of tolerance in our school.

8. The athletes formed two (**negative** / (**separate**)) teams so they could play a match.

B. Use your own words to write what each Key Vocabulary word means. Then write a synonym for each word.

Word	My Definition	Synonym
1. **admire**	*Possible response: to like someone*	*Possible response: respect*
2. **contribute**	*Possible response: to donate time or money*	*Possible response: give*
3. **convince**	*Possible response: to make someone believe something*	*Possible response: persuade*
4. **influence**	*Possible response: to change how people think*	*Possible response: affect*
5. **integrate**	*Possible response: to join things together*	*Possible response: combine*
6. **negative**	*Possible response: something bad*	*Possible response: unpleasant*
7. **positive**	*Possible response: something good*	*Possible response: favorable*
8. **problem**	*Possible response: a tough situation*	*Possible response: difficulty*

Unit 3 Key Vocabulary

admire	contribute	influence	movement	positive	promote
arrest	convince	integrate	negative	preach	protest
challenge	determined	involved	overcome	prejudice	segregation
civil rights	equality	leadership	peace	problem	separate

C. Use each word and at least one other Key Vocabulary word in a sentence.

1. **challenge**

   Possible response: It will be a challenge to achieve world peace.

   _____

2. **prejudice**

   Possible response: A fair society must overcome its prejudices.

   _____

3. **leadership**

   Possible response: I moved into a leadership role as I got more involved with the club.

   _____

4. **civil rights**

   Possible response: Civil rights are basic rights and freedoms that promote equality.

   _____

5. **overcome**

   Possible response: I have overcome my fear of heights and now I don't have this problem anymore.

   _____

6. **protest**

   Possible response: The activist influenced others to protest the unfair law.

   _____

7. **preach**

   Possible response: Dr. Martin Luther King, Jr., preached a message of equality.

   _____

8. **peace**

   Possible response: I admire people who promote peace in their relationships.

   _____

Mind Map

Use the mind map to write about things that might be different if you lived in another **location** . As you read the selections in this unit, add new ideas you learn about these **locations** .

Answers will vary.

At Home in Different Worlds

On Another Planet	In a Space Station	In a New Location on Earth

---

Academic Vocabulary

Think about a place you would like to live. What makes this **location** special? Use the word **location** in your answer.

Answers will vary.

_____

_____

_____

_____

Focus on Reading

Analyze Connections

Read the passage.
Underline the signal words.

Words that Signal Similarities	Words that Signal Differences
all	but
both	unlike
also	although
too	different
similarly	in contrast
just as	on the other hand

> There are eight planets in our solar system. Mercury, Venus, Earth, and Mars are made primarily of rock and metal. Jupiter, Saturn, Uranus, and Neptune, on the other hand, are mostly made of gases. Both Earth and Mars have moons that rotate around them, but they don't have as many moons as Jupiter, Saturn, Uranus, and Neptune. All eight planets orbit the sun, but each takes a different length of time. Earth orbits in one year; in contrast, Jupiter takes more than eleven years. Unlike either Earth or Jupiter, Neptune takes more than 165 years to orbit the sun.

Fill out the Comparison Chart below to show connections and signal words.

Comparison Chart

Ideas	Signal Words	Similar or Different?
Mercury, Venus, Earth, and Mars are made of rock and metal. Jupiter, Saturn, Uranus, and Neptune are mostly made of gases.	on the other hand	different
Earth and Mars have moons that rotate around them.	Both	similar
Earth and Mars don't have as many moons as Jupiter, Saturn, Uranus, or Neptune.	but	different
Eight planets orbit the sun.	All	similar
Earth, Jupiter, and Neptune take different amounts of time to orbit the sun.	but, different, in contrast, Unlike	different

Academic Vocabulary

Develop an idea that would **effectively** help you remember the order of the planets from the sun: Mercury, Venus, Earth, Mars, Jupiter, Saturn, Uranus, and Neptune. Explain your idea.

Answers will vary.

_____

_____

Focus on Vocabulary

Use Context Clues

▶ Read the passage. Follow these steps to help make the meaning of the new words obvious.

1. Use the topic of your reading to narrow down possible meanings for the unfamiliar word.
2. Reread the sentence where the word appears. Look for signal words that point to a definition, a restatement, or an example.
3. Use the sentences around the word to help figure out its meaning.

Type of Clue	How It Works	Signal Words
Definition or Restatement	The context tells the definition of the word or restates the meaning using other words.	*called, which is, or, in other words*
Examples	The unknown word may be listed as an example of something familiar. Or, you may find familiar examples of the unknown word.	*for example, like, such as, including*

Follow the directions above. Write the meaning of each underlined word.

> When I visited my sister in New York City this summer, I could not believe how <u>erroneous</u>, or wrong, my ideas of big-city life were! I thought that we would ride everywhere in taxis, but instead, we walked everywhere. After we went to the grocery store, we had to carry everything back to her apartment! My arms were aching from the tremendous weight of the bags. When we arrived at her apartment building, my sister didn't use a key. She rang a <u>buzzer</u>, which is like a doorbell. The building caretaker, called the <u>concierge</u>, let us inside. In her apartment, I expected to see an <u>expansive</u> view from the window, including all of the famous New York City buildings. Instead, I looked out on an ordinary red brick wall. Then I met my sister's neighbor, Mrs. Worsham. I thought she would be an <u>eccentric</u>, like the strange characters on my favorite television show. However, she seemed just like my own neighbor back home. Life in the big city just wasn't what I expected it to be.

erroneous <u>wrong</u>

buzzer <u>a ringer that makes noise</u>

concierge <u>a caretaker of a building</u>

expansive <u>including many things</u>

eccentric <u>a strange character</u>

Academic Vocabulary

It was **obvious** that my science project was going to win first place at the science fair because

<u>it was the neatest and most interesting project at the fair</u>

_____ .

Build Background

Critical Viewing Guide

▶ Take Notes

A. View the video. Take notes on at least three things that you learned.

Answers will vary.

_____

_____

_____

_____

_____

_____

_____

▶ Analyze the Video

B. Review your notes to help answer these questions.

1. Write two sentences to explain what was in the video.

Answers will vary.

_____

_____

2. What was the most interesting thing you learned?

Answers will vary.

_____

_____

3. How does the **location** of a planet affect its temperature? Why is this important?

Answers will vary.

_____

_____

_____

_____

Learn Key Vocabulary

Here, There, and Beyond: Key Vocabulary

A. Study each word. Circle a number to rate how well you know it. Then complete the chart.

Rating Scale	**1** I have never seen this word before.	**2** I am not sure of the word's meaning.	**3** I know this word and can teach the word's meaning to someone else.

▲ There are eight planets in our **solar system**. Only Earth has an **atmosphere** that supports human life.

Key Words	Check Understanding	Deepen Understanding
❶ atmosphere (**at**-mu-sfir) *noun* **Rating:** 1 2 3	Earth's **atmosphere** is underwater. Yes (No)	Earth's atmosphere contains _____ *Possible response:* nitrogen and oxygen _____ _____ _____ .
❷ energy (**en**-ur-jē) *noun* **Rating:** 1 2 3	**Energy** is the force that makes things work. (Yes) No	Two types of energy are _____ *Possible response:* solar power and nuclear energy _____ _____ _____ .
❸ feature (**fē**-chur) *noun* **Rating:** 1 2 3	The keyboard is an important **feature** of a computer. (Yes) No	Two features of good writing are _____ *Possible response:* logical organization and careful word choice _____ _____ .
❹ measurement (**mezh**-ur-ment) *noun* **Rating:** 1 2 3	When you take the **measurements** of something, you fix it. Yes (No)	I could use a meter stick to find the measurements of *Possible response:* a desk in the classroom _____ _____ _____ .

Name _____

Astronomers study different **features** of stars. Size and color are both **measurements** used to describe stars. ▶

Key Words	Check Understanding	Deepen Understanding
❺ rotation (rō-tā-shun) *noun* **Rating:** 1 2 3	The top layer of Earth is its **rotation**. Yes (No)	The rotation of Earth _____ *Possible response:* causes night and day _____ _____ _____ .
❻ solar system (sō-lur **sis**-tem) *noun* **Rating:** 1 2 3	Both the sun and Earth are a part of the **solar system**. (Yes) No	A model of the solar system would include _____ *Possible response:* the sun and eight planets _____ _____ _____ .
❼ solid (**sah**-led) *adjective* **Rating:** 1 2 3	A **solid** object will spill if you are not careful with it. Yes (No)	Two examples of solid objects are _____ *Possible response:* tables and chairs _____ _____ _____ .
❽ surface (**sur**-fes) *noun* **Rating:** 1 2 3	We walk on the **surface** of Earth. (Yes) No	If you look at the surface of Earth from an airplane, you might see _____ *Possible response:* land, water, or trees _____ _____ .

B. Use at least two of the Key Vocabulary words. Describe the physical features of the area where you live, such as mountains, lakes, or trees.

Answers will vary. _____

_____

_____

Name _____

Compare and Contrast

Complete the Comparison Chart as you read "Here, There, and Beyond."

Comparison Chart

What Is Being Compared	How They Are Alike	How They Are Different
Planets closest to the sun	They have similar surfaces and high densities. They are smaller than other planets, and they don't have many moons.	They have different atmospheres and temperatures. They are different sizes and distances from the sun. They have different surface features. Only Earth has life.
Planets farthest from the sun	Their atmospheres are mostly made of gases. They have many moons and rings. They are larger than other planets.	They have different surface features and are different distances from the sun. They move differently through space. They have different colors, sizes, and temperatures.
Asteroids and meteoroids	They are chunks, not planets. Their sizes can vary.	Asteroids move around the sun, but meteoroids do not follow a pattern.
Dwarf planets and comets	Both are icy objects that move around the sun.	Pluto has a small rocky center covered with ice, while comets are made of ice, gas, dust, and rock. Comets can form comas, or gas tails.

Here, There, and Beyond

A. Read the paragraph.
Write a Key Vocabulary word in each blank.
Reread the paragraph to make sure the words make sense.

Eight planets are in _____rotation_____ around our sun, the source of their _____energy_____ .
These fascinating planets are the main _____features_____ of our _____solar system_____ , along with moons and
asteroids. The planets closest to the sun are the most like Earth because they are _____solid_____ , not
murky swirls of gas. The top layers, or _____surfaces_____ , of these planets are uneven and rocky. By any
scale or _____measurement_____ , Earth is the liveliest planet in our solar system because of the life it sustains.
The _____atmospheres_____ of the other planets are impossible for humans to breathe.

B. Write complete sentences to answer these questions about "Here, There, and Beyond."

1. What would you include in a weather report about Jupiter?

   Answers will vary.

   _____

   _____

   _____

   _____

   _____

2. If you could visit one of the outer planets, which would you choose? Why?

   Answers will vary.

   _____

   _____

   _____

   _____

   _____

Vocabulary Study

Use Context Clues: Definition, Example, and Restatement

Type of Clue
A definition clue gives the meaning of the word.
An example names things that are familiar or like the unknown word.
A restatement restates the meaning using other words.

▶ Follow the steps below to figure out the meaning of each word.

1. Read the sentence and look at the underlined word.
2. Use context clues, such as a definition, example, or restatement, to figure out the meaning of the underlined word.
3. Write the meaning of the word.

1. A paper towel <u>absorbs</u>, or soaks up, spilled liquids.

   absorbs _soaks up_

2. The <u>scarab</u>, which is a type of beetle, was worshipped by the Ancient Egyptians.

   scarab _a type of beetle_

3. A weaver uses a <u>loom</u>, which is a machine used for weaving thread or yarn into cloth.

   loom _a machine used for weaving_

4. Use a small pointed tool, such as an <u>awl</u>, to make a hole in the wood.

   awl _a pointed tool_

5. Bologna, Italy, is famous for its <u>porticoes</u>, which are covered porches or walkways that lead to the entrance of a building.

   porticoes _covered porches or walkways_

6. There are many famous landmarks that are <u>obelisks</u>, such as the Washington Monument in Washington, D.C. An obelisk is a tall and narrow structure that comes to a point at the top.

   obelisk _a tall and narrow structure that comes to a point at the top_

7. A hammer has a flat head that is used to <u>strike</u>, or hit, an object.

   strike _hit_

8. A <u>ferry</u>, or boat used for transportation, brings people from Seattle to Bainbridge Island in Washington.

   ferry _a boat used to transport people_

Academic Vocabulary

Name _____

Here, There, and Beyond: Academic Vocabulary Review

A. Use your own words to tell what each Academic Vocabulary word means. Then write a synonym for each word.

Vocabulary	My Definition	Synonym
1. **compare**	look for similarity or difference	contrast
2. **definition**	the meaning of a word	meaning
3. **effectively**	done in a way that works well	successfully; well
4. **location**	a place where a person is	place
5. **obvious**	easy to see or understand	clear

B. Read each statement. Circle **Yes** or **No** to answer.

1. When you **compare** things, you look for ways they are alike. (Yes) No

2. The **definition** of a word shows how it is spelled in every language. Yes (No)

3. When you work **effectively**, you get good results. (Yes) No

4. One **obvious** feature of an elephant is its trunk. (Yes) No

5. When you describe your **location**, you tell how you are feeling. Yes (No)

C. **Compare** two objects in your classroom.

Answers will vary.

_____

_____

_____

Critical Viewing Guide

▶ Take Notes

A. View the video. Take notes on at least three things that you learned.

Answers will vary.

_____

_____

_____

_____

_____

_____

_____

▶ Analyze the Video

B. Review your notes to help answer these questions.

1. Write two sentences to explain what was in the video.

Answers will vary.

_____

_____

_____

2. What was the most interesting thing you learned?

Answers will vary.

_____

_____

_____

3. How different would your life be if you lived in a **location** like the International Space Station?

Answers will vary.

_____

_____

_____

_____

_____

Learn Key Vocabulary

Name _____

Earth and Space: Key Vocabulary

A. Study each word. Circle a number to rate how well you know it. Then complete the chart.

Rating Scale	**1** I have never seen this word before.	**2** I am not sure of the word's meaning.	**3** I know this word and can teach the word's meaning to someone else.

▲ **Astronauts** often **experience** many difficulties while working in space.

Key Words	Check Understanding	Deepen Understanding
❶ **astronaut** (**as**-tre-not) *noun* **Rating:** 1 2 3	☒ a person who travels to space ☐ a person who builds space shuttles	List three things that an astronaut needs. _____ *Possible response:* a spacesuit, a space shuttle, crewmates _____ _____
❷ **element** (**e**-lu-munt) *noun* **Rating:** 1 2 3	☒ a part of a whole ☐ a whole made up of many parts	List three elements of your favorite sandwich. *Possible response:* bread, ham, cheese _____ _____ _____
❸ **essential** (i-**sen**-shul) *adjective* **Rating:** 1 2 3	☐ uncommon ☒ absolutely necessary	List three essential things for people. _____ *Possible response:* food, water, clothing _____ _____ _____
❹ **experience** (ik-**spir**-ē-ens) *verb* **Rating:** 1 2 3	☒ to live through an event ☐ to read about something that happened	List three things you would like to experience. *Possible response:* fly on a plane, see the ocean, meet my great-grandfather _____ _____

Space exploration is **essential** if we are to better understand the **universe**. ▶

Key Words	Check Understanding	Deepen Understanding
⑤ process (**prah**-ses) *noun* **Rating:** 1 2 3	☐ the ultimate goal of a project ☒ a series of steps that lead to a result	List three things that happen in the process of getting your hair cut. _____ *Possible response:* wash hair, sit in barber's chair, barber trims your hair _____
⑥ routine (rü-**tēn**) *noun* **Rating:** 1 2 3	☒ a series of actions that you repeat ☐ the steps you take to break a habit	List three steps to your daily morning routine. *Possible response:* wake up to the alarm, choose clothes, wash my face _____ _____
⑦ similarity (si-mu-**lair**-u-tē) *noun* **Rating:** 1 2 3	☐ a way we tell things apart ☒ a way in which things are alike	List three similarities between cats and dogs. *Possible response:* they are both pets, they both walk on four legs, they both have fur _____ _____
⑧ universe (**yu**-nu-vers) *noun* **Rating:** 1 2 3	☐ the sun and planets ☒ everything in space	List three things in the universe. _____ *Possible response:* Earth, stars, moon _____ _____ _____

B. Use at least two of the Key Vocabulary words. Write whether you would like to be an astronaut. Explain why or why not.

Answers will vary. _____

_____

_____

Determine Author's Purpose

Read "Earth and Space." Fill out the Author's Purpose Chart to show facts or imaginary characters that give you clues about the author's purpose.

Author's Purpose Chart

Purpose:
to inform

Fact: More than fifty years ago, NASA began planning the first explorations of space.
Fact: Astronauts from many different countries work together on the International Space Station.
Fact: Gravity pulls us to the ground.
Fact: Astronauts feel weightless in space.
Fact: In low gravity, astronauts get taller and blood shifts from the lower part of the human body to the top.

Earth and Space

A. Read the paragraph.
Write a Key Vocabulary word in each blank.
Reread the paragraph to make sure the words make sense.

I am an ____astronaut____ aboard the International Space Station. It is amazing to ____experience____ a life out of this world! The space station has all the ____elements____ needed to sustain life. Of course, some ____essential____ everyday activities, like eating and sleeping, become a ____routine____ once you do them over and over. Amazingly, there are many ____similarities____ that make living on Earth and in space alike. However, the ____process____ of going to work is completely different, and the tasks I perform are actually very exciting. I think that I have the best job in the ____universe____!

B. Write complete sentences to answer these questions about "Earth and Space."

1. What would you put in a care package to an **astronaut** on the International Space Station?

Answers will vary.

_____

_____

_____

_____

_____

2. If you were an **astronaut** on the International Space Station, what would be the most difficult part of your job?

Answers will vary.

_____

_____

_____

_____

_____

Understand Jargon and Specialized Language

▶ Follow the steps below to understand the meaning of jargon or specialized language.

    1. Read the sentence and look at the underlined word.
    2. Use context clues to figure out the meaning of the underlined word in each sentence.
    3. Write the meaning of the underlined word.

1. The television station will present, or broadcast, the president's message to a large audience tonight.

    broadcast   to present on a television station

2. The helicopter landed on a helipad, which is a flat, clearly marked surface.

    helipad   a flat, clearly marked surface

3. The book is copyrighted, or protected by law, so you cannot make copies of it without permission.

    copyrighted   protected by a law so that no copies can be made

4. The doctor held an instrument to my chest and listened to my heartbeat through earphones placed in his ears. This instrument is called a stethoscope.

    stethoscope   an instrument that hears sounds in the chest and sends them into the ear of the doctor

5. The captain asked if all of his crew were on deck, or on the ship.

    on deck   on the ship

6. The news anchor delivered the news to the crowd of people.

    anchor   a person who delivers the news

7. The traveler enjoys French cuisine, or food cooked in the French style.

    cuisine   a style of cooking

8. To make a milkshake, scoop milk and ice cream into a blender and press the button so the machine mixes the ingredients together.

    blender   a machine used to mix ingredients together

Academic Vocabulary

Name _____

Earth and Space: Academic Vocabulary Review

Academic Vocabulary

effectively	purpose
location	unique
obvious	relate

A. Draw a line to match each Academic Vocabulary word with its meaning.

Word	Definition
1. **effectively**	easily seen or understood
2. **location**	to show how things are connected
3. **obvious**	a reason for doing something
4. **relate**	done in a way that gets results
5. **purpose**	the place where a person is
6. **unique**	special or different

B. Write an Academic Vocabulary word to complete each sentence.

1. Raj works very _____effectively_____ with others.

2. Blair paints in a style that is _____unique_____ to her.

3. It was _____obvious_____ which of the wrestlers was stronger.

4. The _____purpose_____ of the experiment is to find out which eraser works best.

5. Give me your exact _____location_____ so I can find you.

C. Use **obvious** and **purpose** in a sentence.

Answers will vary.

_____

_____

_____

Build Background

Critical Viewing Guide

▶ **Take Notes**

A. View the images. Take notes on at least three things that you learned.

Answers will vary.

_____

_____

_____

_____

_____

_____

_____

▶ **Analyze the Images**

B. Review your notes to help answer these questions.

1. Write two sentences to explain what was in the images.

   Answers will vary.

   _____

   _____

2. What was the most interesting thing you learned?

   Answers will vary.

   _____

   _____

3. What makes a **location** feel like home? Give some examples of **locations** that feel like home to you.

   Answers will vary.

   _____

   _____

   _____

Learn Key Vocabulary

Name _____

Indian Summer Sun: Key Vocabulary

A. Study each word. Circle a number to rate how well you know it. Then complete the chart.

Rating Scale	**1** I have never seen this word before.	**2** I am not sure of the word's meaning.	**3** I know this word and can teach the word's meaning to someone else.

▲ It is important to **concentrate** when you work on a bicycle. The smallest **adjustment** can affect how the bicycle rides.

Key Words	Check Understanding	Deepen Understanding
❶ **adjustment** (u-**just**-ment) *noun* **Rating:** 1 2 3	Circle the synonym for **adjustment**. habit (**change**)	Example: _____ *Possible response:* waking up earlier to walk a new dog
❷ **concentrate** (**kon**-sen-trāt) *verb* **Rating:** 1 2 3	Circle the synonym for **concentrate**. (**focus**) order	Example: _____ *Possible response:* when you turn off the radio to study for a test
❸ **couple** (**kup**-ul) *noun* **Rating:** 1 2 3	Circle the synonym for **couple**. single (**pair**)	Example: _____ *Possible response:* my sister and brother-in-law
❹ **ignore** (ig-**nor**) *verb* **Rating:** 1 2 3	Circle the synonym for **ignore**. tease (**overlook**)	Example: _____ *Possible response:* to not answer a question

Name _____

> ### Did You Know?
> Early Roman philosopher Lucius Annaeus Seneca described luck as "what happens when preparation meets **opportunity**." Do you agree with his **perspective**?

Key Words	Check Understanding	Deepen Understanding
❺ opportunity (op-ur-**tü**-ni-tē) *noun* **Rating:** 1 2 3	Circle the synonym for **opportunity**. profession (possibility)	Example: _____ *Possible response:* the chance to meet your favorite author _____ _____
❻ perspective (pur-**spek**-tiv) *noun* **Rating:** 1 2 3	Circle the synonym for **perspective**. (outlook) prediction	Example: _____ *Possible response:* your beliefs about an important issue, such as education _____ _____
❼ refuse (ri-**fūz**) *verb* **Rating:** 1 2 3	Circle the synonym for **refuse**. (deny) punish	Example: _____ *Possible response:* to reject help from a friend _____ _____ _____
❽ remind (ri-**mīnd**) *verb* **Rating:** 1 2 3	Circle the synonym for **remind**. forget (mention)	Example: _____ *Possible response:* to help someone remember an appointment _____ _____

B. Use at least two of the Key Vocabulary words. Write about an adjustment you made.

Answers will vary. _____

_____

_____

Name _____

Compare Structures of Texts

Read the passage. List text structures from "Almost Evenly Divided" and "Indian Summer Sun" in the chart.

Comparison Chart

Genre	Text Structure	Text Structure	Text Structure	Text Structure
Short Story "Indian Summer Sun"	Characters: laugh at the narrator's accent	Plot: Narrator tries to relate to classmates	Dialogue: in Spanish and English	Character: narrator's feelings
Poetry "Almost Evenly Divided"	Rhythm: The last two words in lines 8 and 9 have the same rhythm.	Repetition: Repeats ser *mujer puertorriqueña*	Repetition: Repeats the title, *almost evenly divided*	Similar Words: *17 ½ years* and *20 ½ years* sound similar

Selection Review

Indian Summer Sun

Key Vocabulary

adjustment	opportunity
concentrate	perspective
couple	refuse
ignore	remind

A. Read the paragraph.
Write a Key Vocabulary word in each blank.
Reread the paragraph to make sure the words make sense.

I really liked Cristina, the new girl in school, but she used to ___ignore___ me no matter what

I did. She sat behind me in math, and whenever I moved my desk or made some other ___adjustment___,

she didn't seem to notice me. I needed to find a chance to talk to her, but I couldn't seem to get an

___opportunity___. Then my sister decided to have a party. I was afraid Cristina would ___refuse___,

so I was glad to find out that she could come. I kept having to ___remind___ myself to breathe when

she agreed to go for a walk. I also had to ___concentrate___ really hard to understand her Puerto Rican

accent. I think we made a really nice ___couple___, but that's just my own personal ___perspective___.

I wonder what Cristina thinks.

B. Write complete sentences to answer these questions about "Indian Summer Sun."

1. How does Cristina's experience **remind** you of a time when you felt out of place?

   Answers will vary.

   _____

   _____

   _____

   _____

2. If you were Cristina's algebra teacher, what might you have done to make
   her **adjustment** easier?

   Answers will vary.

   _____

   _____

   _____

   _____

Understand Denotation and Connotation

▶ Follow the steps below to understand the connotation of the underlined word in each sentence.

1. Read the sentence and think about the feelings associated with the underlined word.
2. Write whether the underlined word has a positive or negative connotation.
3. Write your own sentence with the connotation for the underlined word.

1. The stubborn athlete ignored the advice of his coach and did not practice the skill. _negative_

   Sentence: _Answers will vary but must show a negative connotation._

2. My grandmother is very sophisticated and will only buy the best clothing. _positive_

   Sentence: _Answers will vary but must show a positive connotation._

3. My brother convinced me to help him wash the dishes. _positive_

   Sentence: _Answers will vary but must show a positive connotation._

4. The book was so interesting that I could not stop reading it. _positive_

   Sentence: _Answers will vary but must show a positive connotation._

5. I could barely keep my eyes open because the speech was so dull. _negative_

   Sentence: _Answers will vary but must show a negative connotation._

6. The student was motivated to study for the test and get a good grade. _positive_

   Sentence: _Answers will vary but must show a positive connotation._

7. Heath climbed the long steep hill and felt like he conquered a great challenge when he

   reached the top. _positive_

   Sentence: _Answers will vary but must show a positive connotation._

8. The pair of sunglasses was not expensive, but they were flimsy and kept slipping

   off my nose. _negative_

   Sentence: _Answers will vary but must show a negative connotation._

Academic Vocabulary

Name _____

Academic Vocabulary

connotation   effectively
effect   obvious

Indian Summer Sun: Academic Vocabulary Review

A. Use your own words to tell what each Academic Vocabulary word means.

Word	Meaning
1. **connotation**	*Possible response:* the feelings associated with a word
2. **effect**	*Possible response:* the result of an action or cause
3. **effectively**	*Possible response:* done in a way that works or gets results
4. **obvious**	*Possible response:* easily seen or understood

B. Complete the sentences.

1. One **connotation** for the word *vacation* is _Possible response: a positive one_ _____ .

2. One thing I can do **effectively** is _Possible response: clean my room_ _____ .

3. One thing that is **obvious** about me is _Possible response: that I like bright colors_ _____ .

4. When I stay up late, one **effect** is _Possible response: that I am cranky_ _____ .

From So You're Going to MARS

by Arthur C. Clarke

1 So you're going to Mars? That's still quite an adventure—though I suppose that in another ten years no one will think twice about it. Sometimes it's hard to remember that the first ships reached Mars scarcely more than half a century ago and that our colony on the planet is less than thirty years old. (By the way, don't use that word when you get there. Base, settlement, or whatever you like—but not colony, unless you want to hear the ice tinkling all around you.)

2 I suppose you've read all the forms and tourist literature they gave you at the Department of Extraterrestrial Affairs. But there's a lot you won't learn just by reading, so here are some pointers and background information that may make your trip more enjoyable. I won't say it's right up to date— things change so rapidly, and it's a year since I got back from Mars myself but on the whole you'll find it pretty reliable. …

3 If you haven't booked your passage yet, remember that the cost of the ticket varies considerably according to the relative positions of Mars and Earth. That's a complication we don't have to worry about when we're travelling from country to country on our own globe, but Mars can be six times farther away at one time than at another. Oddly enough, the shortest trips are the most expensive since they involve the greatest changes of speed as you hop from one orbit to the other. And in space, speed, not

Science Background

Earth and Mars travel around the sun in different orbital paths. Mars's orbital path is about 1.5 times as long as Earth's, and the two planets will be at different points along their orbital paths at any given time. Therefore, the distance between Earth and Mars is constantly changing.

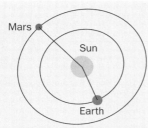

distance, is what costs money. ...

4   Now that we've brought up the subject of money, I'd better remind you that the Martian economy is quite different from all those on Earth. Down here, it doesn't cost you anything to breathe, even though you've got to pay to eat. But on Mars the very air has to be synthesized—they break down the **oxides in the ground** to do this—so every time you fill your lungs someone has to **foot the bill**. Food production is planned in the same way—each of the cities, remember, is a carefully balanced ecological system, like a well-organized aquarium. No parasites can be allowed, so everyone has to pay a basic tax which entitles them to air, food and the shelter of the domes.

F.2
The tax varies from city to city, but averages about ten Terradollars a day. Since everyone earns at least twenty times as much as this, they can all afford to go on breathing. ...

5   You'll land, of course, at Port Lowell: besides being the largest settlement on Mars it's still the only place that has the facilities for handling spaceships. From the air the plastic pressure domes look like a cluster of bubbles—a very pretty sight when the Sun catches them. Don't be alarmed if one of them is deflated. That doesn't mean that there's been an accident. The domes are let down at fairly frequent intervals so that **the envelopes** can be checked for leaks. If you're lucky you may see one being pumped up—it's quite impressive.

In Other Words
oxides in the ground surface materials that contain oxygen
foot the bill pay for it
the envelopes the coverings of the domes

6 After two months in a spaceship, even Port Lowell will seem a mighty metropolis. (Actually, I believe its population is now well over twenty thousand.) You'll find the people energetic, inquisitive, forthright—and very friendly, unless they think you're **trying to be superior.**

7 It's a good working rule never to criticize anything you see on Mars. As I said before, they're very proud of their achievements and after all you are a guest, even if a paying one.

8 Port Lowell has practically everything you'll find in a city on Earth, though of course on a smaller scale. You'll come across many reminders of "home." For example, the
F.2 main street in the city is Fifth Avenue—but surprisingly enough you'll find Piccadilly Circus where it crosses Broadway.

9 The port, like all the major settlements, lies in the dark belt of **vegetation** that roughly follows the equator and occupies about half the southern hemisphere. The northern hemisphere is almost all desert—the red oxides that give the planet its ruddy color. Some of these desert regions are very beautiful; they're far older than anything on the **surface** of our Earth, because there's been little weathering on Mars to wear down the rocks—at least since the seas dried up, more than 500 million years ago.

10 You shouldn't attempt to leave the city until you've become quite accustomed to living in an oxygen-rich, low-pressure **atmosphere.** You'll have grown **fairly well acclimatized** on the trip, because the air in the spaceship will have been slowly adjusted to conditions on Mars. Outside the domes, the pressure of the natural Martian atmosphere is about equal to that on the top of Mount Everest—and it contains **practically** no oxygen. So when you go out you'll have to wear a helmet, or travel in one of those pressurized jeeps they call "sand fleas."

11 Wearing a helmet, by the way, is nothing like the nuisance you'd expect it to be. The equipment is very light and compact and, as long as you don't do anything silly, is quite foolproof. As it's very unlikely that you'll ever go out without an experienced guide, you'll have no need to worry. Thanks to the low gravity, enough oxygen for twelve hours' normal working can be carried quite easily—and you'll never be away from shelter as long as that.

H.2
12 Don't attempt to imitate any of the locals you may see walking around without

---

Key Vocabulary
- **surface** *n.*, the outside, or top layer, of an object
- **atmosphere** *n.*, air that surrounds a planet

In Other Words
trying to be superior
  acting like you are better than them
vegetation plants
fairly well acclimatized
  ready to enter the atmosphere of Mars
practically almost

oxygen gear. They're second-generation colonists and are used to the low pressure. They can't breathe the Martian atmosphere any more than you can, but like the old-time native pearl divers they can make one lungful last for several minutes when necessary. Even so, it's a silly sort of trick and they're not supposed to do it.

13   As you know, the other great obstacle to life on Mars is the low temperature. The highest thermometer reading ever recorded is somewhere in the eighties, but that's quite exceptional. In the long winters, and during the night in summer or winter, it never rises above freezing. And I believe the record low is minus one hundred and ninety!

14   Well, you won't be outdoors at night, and for the sort of **excursions** you'll be doing, all that's needed is a simple thermosuit. It's very light, and traps the body heat so effectively that no other source of warmth is needed.

15   No doubt you'll want to see as much of Mars as you can during your stay. There are only two methods of transport outside the cities—sand fleas for short ranges and aircraft for longer distances. Don't misunderstand me when I say "short ranges"—a sand flea with a full charge of power cells is good for a couple of

> " ... you'll want to see as much of Mars as you can ... "

thousand miles, and it can do eighty miles an hour over good ground. Mars could never have been explored without them. You can survey a planet from space, but in the end someone with **a pick and shovel** has to do the dirty work filling in the map.

16   One thing that few visitors realize is just how big Mars is. Although it seems small beside the Earth, its land area is almost as great because so much of our planet is covered with oceans. So it's hardly surprising that there are vast regions that have never been properly explored, particularly around the **poles**. Those stubborn people who still believe that there was once **an indigenous** Martian civilization pin their hopes on these great blanks. Every so often you hear rumors of some wonderful archaeological discovery in the wastelands, but nothing ever comes of it. ...

17   Well, that's all I've got to say, except to wish you a pleasant trip. Oh, there *is* one other thing. My boy collects stamps, and I rather let him down when I was on Mars. If you could drop me a few letters while you're there—there's no need to put anything in them if you're too busy—I'd be much obliged. He's trying to collect a set of space-mail covers postmarked from all the Martian Cities, and if you could help—thanks a lot!

H.2

In Other Words
excursions trips
a pick and shovel tools to
    explore land surfaces
poles points on opposite sides of
    the planet
an indigenous a native

◗ Read for Understanding

A. From what kind of text is this passage taken? How do you know?

Possible response: science fiction; The story is about people living on and traveling to Mars, which is not true now but seems

possible to be true sometime.

B. Write a sentence that tells the topic of the selection.

Possible response: This text is mostly about what it's like to visit Mars.

◗ Reread and Summarize

C. On **Practice Book** pages 128–131, circle the 3–5 most important words in each section. Make notes about why you chose each word. Why is the word important?

1. Section 1: (paragraphs 1–3)

Answers will vary.

2. Section 2: (paragraphs 4–5)

Answers will vary.

3. Section 3: (paragraphs 6–11)

Answers will vary.

4. Section 4: (paragraphs 12–17)

Answers will vary.

D. Use your topic sentence from above and your notes to write a summary of the selection.

Possible response: This science fiction story describes what it is like to visit Mars now that a civilization has been established

there. It tells about the environment and the living conditions on Mars and compares them to Earth.

▶ Reread and Analyze

E. Make inferences and provide support for those inferences.

1. Reread paragraphs 1 and 2 on **Practice Book** page 128. When does this story take place, and what do you know about the narrator?

   Answers will vary. Possible response: This story takes place at least thirty to fifty years in the future. The narrator has

   been to Mars, is willing to share information, and is a father.

2. Underline key words and phrases on **Practice Book** pages 128–131 that helped you answer these questions. Decide whether each piece of evidence or support is reliable.

   Answers will vary. Possible response: I underlined the years mentioned in paragraph 1. I noticed that the writer mentioned

   being back from Mars in paragraph 2.

F. Make another inference and provide supporting evidence.

1. Reread paragraphs 4 and 8 on **Practice Book** pages 129 and 130. Are the colonists on Mars influenced by the society on Earth? Explain.

   Answers will vary. Possible response: Yes, because they have to pay taxes, and some of the streets are named after

   places on Earth.

2. Underline support for your inference on **Practice Book** pages 128–131. Then tell what other prior knowledge or logic you used to make an inference.

   Answers will vary. Possible response: I underlined "the tax varies from city to city." I know that people on Earth have to

   pay taxes, so I bet the colonists got that idea from Earth. I also underlined some street names on Mars that are named after

   places on Earth.

▶ Reread and Analyze

G. Analyze the evidence you used and the inferences you made.

1. Reread paragraphs 6 and 7 on **Practice Book** page 130. How would you describe the colonists on Mars?

   Answers will vary. Possible response: The colonists are energetic, curious, and friendly. They are proud of the society they

   have built and don't appreciate criticism or comparisons.

2. What evidence on **Practice Book** pages 128–131 supports your answer? Decide whether this evidence provides strong support for your inference.

   Answers will vary. Possible response: The text says the people of Mars are "energetic, inquisitive, forthright—and very

   friendly, unless they think you're trying to be superior." It also warns you not to criticize things you see on Mars because the

   colonists are very proud of it.

H. Make an inference and provide support for inferences.

1. Reread paragraphs 12 and 16 on **Practice Book** pages 130 and 131. What kind of people do you think come to Mars? What is one reason they come?

   Answers will vary. Possible response: The people who live on Mars are adventurous and like to live on the edge.

   They want to explore the unknown.

2. On **Practice Book** pages 130–131, underline evidence that supports your inference. Then share your ideas and evidence with a partner. Decide whether each other's inferences are supported.

   Answers will vary. Possible response: The text mentions that sometimes colonists like to walk around without oxygen gear,

   which is very risky. Later, it mentions that people who come to Mars often hope to explore the "vast regions" that have never

   been explored, and they "pin their hopes" on those "wastelands."

▶ Discuss and Write

I. Synthesize your ideas about making inferences.

1. With the class, make inferences about the society and people on Mars. List inferences as you discuss them.

   Answers will vary. Possible responses: The people on Mars have quickly built a functional society. Mars welcomes tourists,

   and there are many things for a visitor to do. The terrain, the temperature, and the air on Mars present challenges.

   _____

2. Choose one of the inferences you made about the society or people on Mars. Write a paragraph about your inference and the evidence that supports it. Use the questions below to organize your thoughts.

   · What inference did you make?

   · What are two pieces of evidence?

   · How strong is your supporting evidence?

   · How did this inference help you understand the text?

   Answers will vary. _____

   _____

   _____

   _____

   _____

   _____

▶ Connect with ⬤GUIDING QUESTION

J. Discuss the Guiding Question: How can your location affect the way you live?

1. How is life on Mars different from life on Earth? Give two examples.

   Possible responses: The air is not breathable, so people have to pay to breathe. It is very cold, so special transportation is

   needed to explore the terrain.

2. Imagine you were traveling to Mars. Think about everyday things you do. How would that be different on Mars? What questions would you ask the narrator about life for you on Mars?

   Answers will vary. _____

Unit 4 Review

Academic Vocabulary Review

Academic Vocabulary

characteristic	effect	purpose
compare	effectively	relate
connotation	location	unique
definition	obvious	

A. Use Academic Vocabulary words to complete the paragraph.

Many people like to travel to new places. One _____purpose_____ of travel is to learn about other cultures. Every place, or _____location_____ , has special features, such as climate, architecture, and history. It's fun to _____compare_____ each new place with other places that you've visited before. Each special _____characteristic_____ makes a place one of a kind, or _____unique_____ . It's _____obvious_____ that traveling can be very educational.

B. Use your own words to write the meaning of each Academic Vocabulary word. Then write an example for each word.

Word	Meaning	Example
1. **connotation**	the feelings connected to a word	*Answers will vary.*
2. **definition**	the meaning of a word	*Answers will vary.*
3. **relate**	to show how things are connected	*Answers will vary.*

C. Respond to each item with a complete sentence.

1. Describe how you might **effectively** make a plan for a party.

   Answers will vary.

   _____

   _____

2. Describe one **effect** of a problem with your **location**.

   Answers will vary.

   _____

   _____

Key Vocabulary Review

A. Read the paragraph.
Write a Key Vocabulary word in each blank.
Reread the paragraph to make sure the words make sense.

A new baby in the home is a big ____adjustment____ for everyone. It's necessary, or ____essential____,

to keep a positive ____perspective____. Babies require a lot of attention and ____energy____. Their odd

schedules can put an entire family off its regular daily ____routine____, so it's important for everyone to

be flexible throughout the ____process____. It's also important to focus, or ____concentrate____, on the good

times, such as when the baby smiles and laughs for the first time. It can be a wonderful ____experience____ to

care for a child.

B. Write a sentence to relate each word pair.

1. **universe   solar system**

   Possible response: The solar system is a part of the universe.

   _____

2. **astronaut   atmosphere**

   Possible response: An astronaut travels outside Earth's atmosphere.

   _____

3. **solid   surface**

   Possible response: The surface of a rock is solid.

   _____

4. **ignore   refuse**

   Possible response: When you ignore people, you refuse to pay attention to them.

   _____

Unit 4 Key Vocabulary

adjustment	couple	experience	opportunity	remind	solar system
astronaut	element	feature	perspective	rotation	solid
atmosphere	energy	ignore	process	routine	surface
concentrate	essential	measurement	refuse	similarity	universe

C. Complete the sentences.

1. One **similarity** between a **couple** might be _____

   Possible response: that they both have brown hair

   _____ .

2. The **elements** in my favorite salad are _____

   Possible response: lettuce, cucumbers, carrots, cheese, and dressing

   _____ .

3. The most important **features** of a car include _____

   Possible response: the frame, an engine, a steering wheel, and tires

   _____ .

4. The last time I needed to use a **measurement** was _____

   Possible response: when I had to add exact amounts of flour, sugar, and baking soda to make cookies

   _____ .

5. An **opportunity** I hope to have is _____

   Possible response: to be an intern at my favorite radio station

   _____ .

6. When a friend **reminds** me to relax, I _____

   Possible response: try to take the advice with good humor

   _____ .

7. The Earth's **rotation** causes _____

   Possible response: our days and nights

   _____ .

Mind Map

Answer the questions about the **environment** on the mind map. As you read the selections in this unit, add new ideas you learn about things that are important to the **environment** .

Answers will vary.

What is a valuable part of the environment?	What has caused problems?	What are possible solutions?

Academic Vocabulary

Think about different animals in the **environment** . How would life be different without them? Use the word **environment** in your answer.

Answers will vary.

_____

_____

_____

_____

Name _____

Text Features
Features That Organize and Features That Show Information

Read the passage. Look for the text **features** that organize the text and provide additional information, including clues to the author's attitude toward the topic. Then answer the questions.

Giant Panda

There are only about 1,000 pandas left in the forests of southwestern China. They are in danger of becoming extinct. The panda eats about 35 pounds of bamboo per day. Pandas spend about 12 hours each day eating.

Loss of Habitat

The main reason the panda is in danger is because the forests in China are being cleared for farming, firewood, and timber. The panda is losing its habitat, and there is not enough bamboo for the panda to eat.

Panda Facts
• a type of mammal
• part of the bear family
• classified as an omnivore but eats mostly bamboo
• lives about 20 years in the wild
• weighs about 300 pounds

What text **features** are here? How does each one provide information and a clue about the author's attitude?

The text features are the headings and the chart. The headings stand out and they tell what the passage is about.

The headline "Loss of Habitat" presents a problem, which shows that the author cares about the panda's loss of

habitat. The chart lists more facts about the panda, which hint at why the author believes that people should help save the panda.

_____

_____

_____

Academic Vocabulary

Describe two **features** of a panda's habitat.

Answers will vary.

_____

_____

_____

Name _____

Use Context Clues: Multiple-Meaning Words

▶ Read the passages. Follow these steps.

1. Read each underlined word and guess what it might mean in the passage.
2. Read the sentences nearby to find clues to the word's meaning.
3. Reread the sentence with each meaning in place of the word.
4. Decide which meaning makes sense.

A. Follow the directions above. Write the meaning of each underlined word.

> Tree Musketeers is a children's group in California that helps protect the environment. The organization began in 1987 when a young girl named Tara Church planted trees in her California neighborhood. She wanted to improve the air quality, and trees help to clean the air. Today the group is also involved in other important environmental concerns, or issues, such as recycling.

group organization, club _____

quality degree of excellence _____

concerns issues _____

B. Follow the directions above. Write the meaning of each underlined word.

> When an animal is endangered, this means it may disappear forever. Many animals are endangered because their homes are being lost. Often, humans are responsible for this problem. People build houses where animals live and pollute the land with trash. People can help by not polluting. They can also volunteer with a group to clear trash from a forest or natural area near their home.

lost ruined, wiped out _____

responsible at fault, to blame _____

clear remove _____

Academic Vocabulary

Write about a time when you used **context** to help you understand something.

Possible response: I used context clues when I did not know the word _examine_. The context told me it means _look closely_.

_____

Build Background

Name _____

Critical Viewing Guide

▶ Take Notes

A. View the video. Take notes on at least three things that you learned.

Answers will vary.

_____

_____

_____

_____

_____

_____

_____

_____

▶ Analyze the Video

B. Review your notes to help answer these questions.

1. Write two sentences to explain what was in the video.

Answers will vary.

_____

_____

2. What was the most interesting thing you learned?

Answers will vary.

_____

_____

3. What did the video tell about how humans affect the **environment**?

Answers will vary.

_____

_____

_____

_____

A Natural Balance: Key Vocabulary

A. Study each word. Circle a number to rate how well you know it. Then complete the chart.

Rating Scale	**1** I have never seen this word before.	**2** I am not sure of the word's meaning.	**3** I know this word and can teach the word's meaning to someone else.

▲ Recent efforts to protect gray wolves have helped the **population** of this **species** recover.

Key Words	Check Understanding	Deepen Understanding
❶ classified (**klas**-u-fīd) *verb* Rating: 1 2 3	Scientists have **classified** plants but not animals. Yes ⬤No	Example: *Possible response:* placing land, water, and sea animals into groups
❷ endangered (en-**dān**-jurd) *adjective* Rating: 1 2 3	There are laws to protect **endangered** animals. ⬤Yes No	Example: *Possible response:* northern spotted owl
❸ environment (en-**vī**-run-ment) *noun* Rating: 1 2 3	The **environment** includes both living and nonliving things. ⬤Yes No	Example: *Possible response:* the people, buildings, animals, trains, cars, and plants in a city
❹ extinct (ik-**stingt**) *adjective* Rating: 1 2 3	You can only see **extinct** animals at the zoo. Yes ⬤No	Example: *Possible response:* dinosaurs

Name _____

Okapi live in remote **environments**. Their **population** faces threats from land loss and **illegal** hunting. ▶

Key Words	Check Understanding	Deepen Understanding
❺ illegal (i-**lē**-gul) *adjective* **Rating:** 1 2 3	It is **illegal** to ride your bike to school. Yes (**No**)	Example: _Possible response:_ shoplifting _____ _____ _____ _____
❻ pollution (pul-**lü**-shun) *noun* **Rating:** 1 2 3	It is best to reduce **pollution**. (**Yes**) No	Example: _Possible response:_ gas emissions from cars _____ _____ _____ _____
❼ population (pop-yu-**lā**-shun) *noun* **Rating:** 1 2 3	**Population** is the way an animal finds food. Yes (**No**)	Example: _Possible response:_ the number of people in a town _____ _____ _____
❽ species (**spē**-shēz) *noun* **Rating:** 1 2 3	Animals in a **species** share common traits. (**Yes**) No	Example: _Possible response:_ Indian and African elephants _____ _____ _____

B. Use at least two of the Key Vocabulary words. Write about the effect you have on the environment.

Answers will vary.

_____

_____

© National Geographic Learning, a part of Cengage Learning, Inc.

Analyze Author's Viewpoint

As you read "A Natural Balance," look for clues to the author's viewpoint, such as strong words that create clear feelings and opinion statements. Then put all of the information together and describe the author's viewpoint.

Viewpoint Diagram

Author's Purpose: to inform readers about how people endanger the environment

Clues from the Text:

- Opinion: "Activities like these greatly affect plants and animals in our environment."
- Strong words: *cut down, plow, empty waste*
- Opinion: "Sometimes our actions benefit the environment."
- Opinion: "Our activities can also harm plant and animal populations."
- Strong words: *over-hunting, pollution, dying out, endangered environment, in danger, lost forever*
- Opinion: "Some scientists think as many as 100 species become extinct every day."
- Opinion: "The scientists at FWS have a challenging job."
- Strong words: *in need of protection, disappear, survival*

Author's Viewpoint: The author believes that people need to work to save endangered species and their habitats.

A Natural Balance

A. Read the paragraph.
Write a Key Vocabulary word in each blank.
Reread the paragraph to make sure the words make sense.

Scientists watch the world around us, or the __environment__ , very closely. They study plant and animal __species__ to keep track of how they are doing. Changes because of __population__ growth, __illegal__ hunting, or water __pollution__ can cause problems. In some cases, plants and animals might disappear from the Earth, or become __extinct__ . They are put into a group, or __classified__ , as being __endangered__ . In some cases, protecting plants and animals can save them.

B. Write complete sentences to answer these questions about "A Natural Balance."

1. We cannot save every **species** on Earth. How do you think we should choose which plants and animals to save?

   Answers will vary.

   _____

   _____

   _____

   _____

   _____

2. Protecting the **environment** is everyone's job. What are some ways people can help?

   Possible response: People can use less energy and fuel, cut down on waste, recycle and reuse trash, and follow

   rules in wildlife habitats.

   _____

   _____

   _____

   _____

   _____

Name _____

Use Context Clues: Multiple-Meaning Words

▶ Follow the steps below to figure out the meaning of each word.

   1. Use context to figure out the meaning of each underlined word.
   2. Then use a different meaning of the word to write a new sentence.

1. I made a <u>plan</u> to finish my homework in time to watch television. _a scheme_____

  New sentence: _Answers will vary. (Plan should be used as a verb.)_____

2. Tom straightened the <u>cover</u> on the bed. _blanket_____

  New sentence: _Answers will vary. (Cover should be used as a verb.)_____

3. Jessica <u>felt</u> unhappy when she got a bad grade on her report. _to be emotionally affected by_____

  New sentence: _Answers will vary. (Felt should be used as a verb or as a noun, like when describing fabric.)_

4. The people will <u>crowd</u> the door so they can be the first to get inside. _to move forward in a group____

  New sentence: _Answers will vary. (Crowd should be used as a noun.)_____

5. Zhao Fei saw a <u>notice</u> on the door that said the store would be closed on Saturday. _note_____

  New sentence: _Answers will vary. (Notice should be used as a verb.)_____

6. Will the marble <u>sink</u> or float? _to fall below the surface_____

  New sentence: _Answers will vary. (Sink should be used as a noun.)_____

7. The light will <u>flash</u> three times in the window. _flicker_____

  New sentence: _Answers will vary. (Flash should be used as a noun.)_____

8. Ricardo bumped into the metal <u>post</u> on the sidewalk. _a pole_____

  New sentence: _Answers will vary. (Post should be used as a verb.)_____

9. The workers must be careful when they enter the coal <u>mine</u>. _an area dug out from the ground____

  New sentence: _Answers will vary. (Mine should be used as a possessive pronoun.)_____

10. Be sure the ladder is <u>stable</u> before you climb it. _not easily moved or changed_____

  New sentence: _Answers will vary. (Stable should be used as a noun.)_____

Academic Vocabulary

A Natural Balance: Academic Vocabulary Review

A. Use your own words to tell what each Academic Vocabulary word means.

1. **context** _Possible response: nearby words that help you figure out the meaning_

2. **environment** _Possible response: everything that is around you_

3. **feature** _Possible response: a noticeable part of something_

4. **image** _Possible response: a picture in your mind_

B. Replace the underlined word with an Academic Vocabulary word. Rewrite each sentence.

1. I can understand the new word on this page from the <u>words around it</u>.

   I can understand the new word on this page from the context.

2. I have <u>a picture in my mind</u> of how you will look when you are older.

   I have an image of how you will look when you are older.

3. One important responsibility as a citizen is to take care of the <u>things that surround us</u>.

   One important responsibility as a citizen is to take care of the environment.

4. One <u>noticeable part</u> of our school is its friendly people.

   One feature of our school is its friendly people.

C. What is an **image** you have in your mind that makes you want to protect the **environment**?

   Answers will vary.

   _____

   _____

   _____

Build Background

Critical Viewing Guide

▶ Take Notes

A. View the images. Take notes on at least three things that you learned.

Answers will vary.

_____

_____

_____

_____

_____

_____

▶ Analyze the Images

B. Review your notes to help answer these questions.

1. Write two sentences to explain what was in the images.

Answers will vary.

_____

_____

_____

2. What was the most interesting thing you learned?

Answers will vary.

_____

_____

_____

3. What did the images tell about threatened animals?

Answers will vary.

_____

_____

_____

_____

_____

Learn Key Vocabulary

Name _____

Siberian Survivors: Key Vocabulary

A. Study each word. Circle a number to rate how well you know it. Then complete the chart.

Rating Scale	**1** I have never seen this word before.	**2** I am not sure of the word's meaning.	**3** I know this word and can teach the word's meaning to someone else.

▲ Efforts to protect the natural **habitat** of Siberian tigers help this animal to **thrive**.

Key Words	Check Understanding	Deepen Understanding
❶ biologist (bī-**ol**-u-jist) *noun* Rating: 1 2 3	Circle the synonym for **biologist**. teacher (scientist)	My Definition: _____ *Possible response:* a person who studies living things
❷ expert (**ek**-spurt) *noun* Rating: 1 2 3	Circle the synonym for **expert**. beginner (professional)	My Definition: _____ *Possible response:* a person who knows the most about something
❸ habitat (**hab**-i-tat) *noun* Rating: 1 2 3	Circle the synonym for **habitat**. (home) forest	My Definition: _____ *Possible response:* the place where a plant or animal usually lives
❹ increase (in-**krēs**) *verb* Rating: 1 2 3	Circle the synonym for **increase**. ask (grow)	My Definition: _____ *Possible response:* to get bigger in number or size

Did You Know?
The World **Wildlife** Fund is an international organization dedicated to the protection of endangered species and their habitats.

Key Words	Check Understanding	Deepen Understanding
❺ poacher (pō-chur) *noun* Rating: 1 2 3	Circle the synonym for **poacher**. (hunter) activist	My Definition: *Possible response:* someone who hunts illegally
❻ shrink (shringk) *verb* Rating: 1 2 3	Circle the synonym for **shrink**. expand (decrease)	My Definition: *Possible response:* to make something smaller
❼ thrive (thrīv) *verb* Rating: 1 2 3	Circle the synonym for **thrive**. (succeed) fail	My Definition: *Possible response:* to grow strong and healthy
❽ wildlife (wīld-līf) *noun* Rating: 1 2 3	Circle the synonym for **wildlife**. jungle (animals)	My Definition: *Possible response:* animals that roam free

B. Use at least two of the Key Vocabulary words. Write about interesting animals you have seen.

Answers will vary.

_____

_____

Compare Viewpoints

Identify different viewpoints in "Siberian Survivors." Tell how the author responds to each viewpoint.

Viewpoints Chart

Other People's Viewpoints	Author's Response
Some people in Asia believe that tiger parts can be used to improve health. Almost every body part is used to make some kind of potion.	• The word *potion* causes a negative feeling. • The author disagrees with using tiger parts to improve health.
Poachers, people who hunt illegally, can make $15,000 from selling just one dead tiger.	• The word *poachers* causes a negative feeling. • The author disagrees with paying people to kill tigers.
Many people are moving in. They're cutting down trees and tiger habitat.	• The words *cutting down* causes a negative feeling. • The author disagrees with removing trees from the tiger habitat.
Many experts say we can manage forests in a cat-friendly way.	• The author says that this could allow people and tigers to use the same forests. • The author agrees with the experts.
Scientists are finding ways to protect Olga and other tigers.	• The author says that this is helping keep poachers out of the forest. • The author agrees with the scientists.

Selection Review

Siberian Survivors

Key Vocabulary

biologists	poachers
experts	shrinks
habitats	thrive
increase	wildlife

A. Read the paragraph.
Write a Key Vocabulary word in each blank.
Reread the paragraph to make sure the words make sense.

____Biologists____ are scientists who study living things. When the number of animals ____shrinks____, or decreases, ____wildlife____ may be at risk. Teams of ____experts____ work to save the Siberian tiger. They want to be sure the Siberian tigers survive and ____thrive____. They can point out dangers like development and pollution that destroy tiger ____habitats____. They help catch illegal hunters called ____poachers____. Many people must work together so that the number of Siberian tigers will ____increase____.

B. Write complete sentences to answer these questions about "Siberian Survivors."

1. Why is it easier for people to think about saving the Siberian tiger than it is for them to save a species of insect or bat or bug-eating plant?

   Possible response: Tigers are familiar, people think they are amazing creatures, and the cubs are cute. It is harder to

   get people to care about an unfamiliar species.

   _____

   _____

   _____

   _____

2. What can we learn about saving endangered **wildlife** from studying Siberian tiger populations?

   Possible response: We can learn about things that affect species numbers, find ways to manage habitat, and apply what we

   know to saving other species.

   _____

   _____

   _____

   _____

Use Context Clues: Multiple-Meaning Words Across Content Areas

▶ Read the sentence. Follow these steps.

   1. Use context to determine which meaning makes the most sense.
   2. Circle the correct meaning.

1. The farm <u>yields</u> enough fruit for our needs.

   a. to give up or surrender

   (b.) to give forth or produce

2. Travelers crowded the <u>terminal</u>.

   a. to last for a definite period

   (b.) a building that contains passengers

3. My teacher said my <u>composition</u> was the best in my English Literature class.

   (a.) a short essay

   b. makeup or structure

4. Adnan only took a <u>fraction</u> of the cake and left the rest for his friends.

   a. a mathematical expression

   (b.) a very small amount

5. The <u>pitcher</u> at the game was amazing.

   (a.) a person who throws the ball to a batter

   b. a container used to hold and pour liquids

6. The government protected the Native Americans' <u>reservation</u> so they could rebuild their town.

   (a.) a tract of land set aside for a special purpose

   b. a doubt about something

7. The river <u>deposited</u> sand along the shoreline.

   a. to deliver and leave an item

   (b.) to lay down or leave behind by a natural process

Academic Vocabulary

Siberian Survivors: Academic Vocabulary Review

Academic Vocabulary	
context	research
environment	

A. Draw a line to match the Academic Vocabulary word with its meaning.

Word	Definition
1. **context**	the surrounding text near a word that helps explain its meaning
2. **environment**	a collection of information about something
3. **research**	everything that surrounds us

B. Answer the questions in complete sentences.

1. What is something you would like to change about your **environment**?

   Answers will vary.

   _____

2. How does the **context** of a word help you understand it better?

   Answers will vary.

   _____

3. What is one way you could do more **research** about tigers?

   Answers will vary.

   _____

Build Background

Critical Viewing Guide

▶ Take Notes

A. View the video. Take notes on at least three things that you learned.

Answers will vary.

_____

_____

_____

_____

_____

_____

_____

_____

▶ Analyze the Video

B. Review your notes to help answer these questions.

1. Write two sentences to explain what was in the video.

   Answers will vary.

   _____

   _____

2. What was the most interesting thing you learned?

   Answers will vary.

   _____

   _____

3. Why do you think people like Mireya Mayor work to save the **environment**?

   Answers will vary.

   _____

   _____

   _____

Mireya Mayor: Explorer/Correspondent:
Key Vocabulary

A. Study each word. Circle a number to rate how well you know it. Then complete the chart.

▲ These scientists hope to raise **awareness** of fox **conservation**.

Rating Scale	**1**	**2**	**3**
	I have never seen this word before.	I am not sure of the word's meaning.	I know this word and can teach the word's meaning to someone else.

Key Words	Check Understanding	Deepen Understanding
❶ awareness (u-**wair**-nes) *noun* **Rating:** 1 2 3	☒ knowledge of something ☐ freedom of expression	Why is it helpful to have an awareness of how people feel? _Possible response: It is helpful to have an_ awareness of how people feel in order to understand their actions and motivations _____ .
❷ conservation (kon-sur-**vā**-shun) *noun* **Rating:** 1 2 3	☐ a dangerous place ☒ careful protection of something	What is one conservation effort that your community can make? _Possible response: My community could_ protect the natural park areas that surround our homes _____ .
❸ discovery (dis-**kuv**-ur-ē) *noun* **Rating:** 1 2 3	☐ a sample taken to a lab ☒ something seen for the first time	What is an example of a discovery? _____ _Possible response: An example of a discovery is_ when early humans first learned how to make and control fire _____ .
❹ document (**dok**-yu-ment) *verb* **Rating:** 1 2 3	☒ to provide facts ☐ to open a file	How would you document a research paper? _____ _Possible response: I would include supportive facts in_ the footnotes and a bibliography of my sources _____ _____ .

Name _____

An **explorer** takes photographs to **document** his **expedition**. ▶

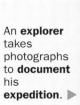

Key Words	Check Understanding	Deepen Understanding
❺ ensure (en-**shur**) *verb* Rating: 1 2 3	☒ to make certain ☐ to announce publicly	How can you ensure that a bicycle is safe to ride? *Possible response*: You can check to see if the pedals and handlebars are working and that the tires have plenty of air _____ .
❻ establish (i-**stab**-lish) *verb* Rating: 1 2 3	☒ to start something ☐ to end something	What program would you like to establish at your school? *Possible response:* I would like to establish a program that teaches students how to run a successful Internet business _____ .
❼ expedition (ek-spu-**di**-shun) *noun* Rating: 1 2 3	☐ papers required to leave the country ☒ a trip made for a specific purpose	What is an example of an expedition? _____ *Possible response:* An example of an expedition is a trip made to collect plant samples from the rainforest _____ .
❽ explorer (ek-**splor**-ur) *noun* Rating: 1 2 3	☒ someone who travels to discover new information ☐ someone who makes speeches	What qualities should an explorer have? _____ *Possible response:* An explorer should be brave, quick-thinking, and have a sense of adventure _____ .

B. Use at least two of the Key Vocabulary words. Write about a time you explored a new place.

Answers will vary.

_____

_____

_____

Analyze Author's Viewpoint

Read "Mireya Mayor: Explorer/Correspondent." Notice what the author
includes and leaves out. Tell what this shows about the author's viewpoint.

Author's Viewpoint Chart

Author's Decision	What the Decision Tells About the Author's Viewpoint
The author decided to tell how Mayor became interested in primates.	This decision shows that the author admires Mayor's work.
The author decided to include a quote from Mayor about how her television work resulted in a cure for a human disease.	This decision shows that the author believes that Mayor's television series has had a big impact.
The author decided to describe how Mayor worked hard to gain protection of the mouse lemur's habitat in Madagascar.	This decision shows that the author thinks that Mayor is very dedicated to her cause.

Mireya Mayor: Explorer/Correspondent

Key Vocabulary

awareness	ensure
conservation	establish
discoveries	expedition
documents	explorer

A. Read the paragraph.
Write a Key Vocabulary word in each blank.
Reread the paragraph to make sure the words make sense.

Mireya Mayor is an _____explorer_____ who travels the world. Each trip, or _____expedition_____ , she takes has

a purpose. She wants to raise _____awareness_____ about species at risk. She wants to promote ideas about

_____conservation_____ and how to protect wildlife. Mayor _____documents_____ her _____discoveries_____ , or findings, on

film. She has used her work to _____establish_____ , or start, funds to save wildlife. Mayor's work will

_____ensure_____ the survival of many species that would be lost without her help.

B. Write complete sentences to answer these questions about "Mireya Mayor: Explorer/Correspondent."

1. If you could travel someplace in the world on a **conservation expedition**, where would you go, and why?

   Answers will vary.

   _____

   _____

   _____

   _____

2. Why do you think people like Mireya Mayor are doing such important work?

   Possible response: They are helping people understand the world so that they can appreciate it and

   help protect it.

   _____

   _____

   _____

   _____

Vocabulary Study

Use Context Clues: Jargon

▶ Read the sentence. Follow these steps.

1. Use context to figure out the meaning of each word or phrase.
2. Then write the meaning in your own words.
3. Use a dictionary if you need more help.

1. My teacher asked us to complete the exercises at the end of the chapter.

    exercises _questions or activities_____

2. My parents only let me spend one hour per day on the Web.

    Web _the Internet_____

3. The substitute who taught us today was very nice and let our class play a game.

    substitute _a temporary teacher_____

4. The basketball player fouled out and could only watch the rest of the game.

    fouled out _to be ejected from a game_____

5. The grounder skipped through the infield and past the first baseman.

    grounder _a ball hit on the ground_____

6. Ernesto thought the movie was the coolest one he had ever seen.

    coolest _best_____

7. My older brother starts his new job next week and says he will be rolling in the dough very soon!

    rolling in the dough _to have a lot of money_____

8. Melinda is such a ham that she tells jokes to every new person she meets and laughs like they are

    the funniest jokes in the world.

    ham _a performer who exaggerates_____

9. Click the mouse twice to start the computer program.

    mouse _a control device connected to a computer_____

Mireya Mayor: Explorer/Correspondent:
Academic Vocabulary Review

A. Write the Academic Vocabulary words next to the correct definition.

1. the surrounding text near a word or phrase _context_____

2. something that is definite or particular _specific_____

3. something that stands out or is noticeable _feature_____

4. everything that surrounds you _environment_____

B. Use Academic Vocabulary words to finish the paragraph.

Do you wish you could remember things better? Scientists have done a lot of research on the topic of memory. One way to remember something is to form a mental image of it in your mind. First, think of the ____specific____ thing you would like to remember. Then, focus closely on it. Notice a special ____feature____ that makes it stand out. Also look at the ____context____, or things around it. When you pay attention to these details, you will remember people and things in your ____environment____ more easily.

C. If you could be a famous explorer or scientist, what **specific environment** or animal would you like to study? Tell why.

Answers will vary.

_____

_____

_____

WILDERNESS LETTER

David E. Pesonen   December 3, 1960
Wildland Research Center, Agricultural Experiment Station

Dear Mr. Pesonen:

1
E.1   I believe that you are working on the wilderness **portion** of the Outdoor Recreation Resources Review Commission's report. If I may, I should like to **urge** some arguments for wilderness preservation . . . What I want to speak for is not so much the wilderness uses, valuable as those are, but the wilderness idea, which is a resource in itself . . .

2   Something will have gone out of us as a people if we ever let the remaining wilderness be destroyed; if we permit the last **virgin forests** to be turned into comic books and plastic cigarette cases; if we drive the few remaining members of the wild **species** into zoos or to extinction; if we pollute the last clear air and dirty the last clean streams and push our paved roads through the last of the silence, so that never again will Americans be free in their own country from the noise, the exhausts, the stinks of human and automotive waste. And so that never again can we have the chance to see ourselves single, separate, vertical and individual in the world, part of the **environment** of trees and rocks and soil, brother to the other animals, part of the natural world and competent to belong in it. Without any remaining wilderness we are committed wholly, without chance for even momentary reflection and rest, to a **headlong drive** into our technological termite-life, the Brave New World of a completely man-controlled environment. We need wilderness preserved—as much of it as is still left, and as many kinds—because it was the challenge against which our character as a people was formed. The reminder and the reassurance that it is still there is good for our spiritual health even if we never once in ten years set foot in it. It is good for us when we are young, because of the incomparable sanity it can bring briefly, as vacation and rest, into our insane lives. It is important to us when we are old simply because it is there—important, that is, simply as idea.

3   . . . That is the reason we need to put into effect, for its preservation, some other principle than the principles of **exploitation** or "usefulness" or even recreation. We simply need that wild country available to us, even if we never do more than drive to its edge and look in. For it can be a means of reassuring ourselves of our sanity as creatures, a part of the geography of hope.

Very sincerely yours,
Wallace Stegner

"We need wilderness preserved."

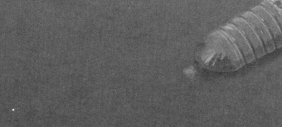

Key Vocabulary
- **species** *n.*, a related group
- **environment** *n.*, everything that surrounds you

Cultural Reference
Brave New World is a science fiction novel about a dark future world where people have lost many of their freedoms.

In Other Words
portion part
urge strongly recommend
virgin forests woods that have never been cut
headlong drive movement forward
exploitation unfair use of

Name _____

▶ Read for Understanding

A. What kind of text is this? How do you know?

Possible response: letter; It has the parts of the letter, including the address, date, salutation, and closing.

B. Write a sentence that tells the topic of the selection.

Possible response: This text is mostly about Wallace Stegner's opinions on the wilderness and why it should be preserved.

▶ Reread and Summarize

C. On **Practice Book** page 164, circle the 3–5 most important words in each section. Make notes about why you chose each word. Why is the word important?

1. Section 1: (paragraph 1)

   Answers will vary.

2. Section 2: (paragraph 2)

   Answers will vary.

3. Section 3: (paragraph 3)

   Answers will vary.

D. Use your topic sentence from above and your notes to write a summary of the selection.

Possible response: Wallace Stegner writes a letter to the Wildland Research Center to share his belief that the wilderness

should be preserved. He thinks the presence of the wilderness is important to us as a people. He believes the wilderness

keeps us sane and gives us hope.

◑ Reread and Analyze

E. Analyze the author's viewpoint.

1. Reread paragraph 1. What is the author's main idea? Underline it. What conflicting idea does he mention? How does Stegner respond to it?

   Answers will vary. Possible response: Main idea: The wilderness should be preserved because the idea of wilderness is

   important. Conflicting idea: The wilderness should be preserved because it is useful. Stegner disagrees with this.

   _____

2. Underline phrases and sentences on **Practice Book** page 164 that show the author's viewpoint. Explain how each sentence develops or refines the concept.

   Answers will vary.

   _____

F. Analyze how the author persuades readers to agree with his viewpoint.

1. Reread paragraph 2. What parts are especially persuasive, and why? Does the author appeal to logic, ethics, emotions, or a combination of the three?

   Answers will vary. Possible response: Emotion: "Something will have gone out of us as a people if we ever let the remaining

   wilderness be destroyed." Logic: "Without any remaining wilderness we are committed . . . to a headlong drive into our technological

   termite-life . . ." Ethics: "The reminder and reassurance that [the wilderness] is still there is good for our spiritual health . . ."

2. Underline persuasive phrases or sentences on **Practice Book** page 164. Label them with the techniques the author uses.

   Answers will vary.

   _____

▶ **Discuss and Write**

G. Synthesize your ideas about the author's viewpoint.

1. With the class, discuss the conflicting, or opposing, idea that the author presents. Have them tell how he responds to it.

Possible response: Stegner doesn't like the idea of preserving the wilderness because it is useful to people and can be

"exploited." He doesn't write much about this idea, but he clearly disagrees with it.

2. Choose a sentence or phrase in the letter that you found particularly persuasive. Write a paragraph about why it was effective. Use the questions below to organize your thoughts.

   · Which sentence or phrase did you choose? Why?

   · What words did you think were especially persuasive?

   · Did this sentence appeal to your emotions, logic, or ethics?

   · How does this sentence or phrase contribute to the rest of the letter?

Answers will vary.

▶ **Connect with** (GUIDING QUESTION)

H. Discuss the Guiding Question: What makes the environment so valuable?

1. What valuable parts of the wilderness does Stegner mention?

   Possible responses: virgin forests, clear air, silence, animals

2. Why does Stegner believe people need the wilderness?

   Possible response: The wilderness gives people hope and sanity, and it allows them to relax.

Academic Vocabulary Review

Academic Vocabulary	
context	image
environment	research
feature	specific

A. Circle the Academic Vocabulary word that best fits into each sentence.

1. The Russian taiga is an example of a/an (**environment** / **image**).

2. When you explain your ideas, include (**specific** / **research**) details.

3. Clara has a clear (**image** / **context**) of ways to improve her campus.

4. If you don't understand my words, think about the (**feature** / **context**).

B. Define each Academic Vocabulary word. Then give an example.

Word	My Definition	Examples
1. **feature**	*Possible response*: part of something that stands out	*Answers will vary.*
2. **image**	*Possible response*: mental picture	*Answers will vary.*
3. **research**	*Possible response*: a collection of information	*Answers will vary.*

C. Answer the questions. Use complete sentences.

1. Describe a **specific** time when you noticed something new in your **environment**.

   Answers will vary.

   _____

   _____

   _____

2. Tell about a text **feature** or an **image** that helped you understand something important in one of the selections you read during this unit.

   Answers will vary.

   _____

   _____

   _____

   _____

Key Vocabulary Review

A. Use these Key Vocabulary words to complete the paragraph.

explorer	**document**	**illegal**	**species**
expedition	**habitats**	**poachers**	**wildlife**

The _____explorer_____ began her journey early in the morning. This trip was not her first _____expedition_____.

As a scientist, she often traveled to different _____habitats_____ to study the _____wildlife_____ there. Today,

she hoped to find signs of people and not animals. There had been several reports of _____illegal_____

hunting in the area. The explorer set out to _____document_____ these claims. She knew _____poachers_____ could

pose a serious threat to the local elephant _____species_____. She was determined to stop their unlawful

activity. If there was evidence of poaching, she would find it.

B. Use your own words to write what each Key Vocabulary word means. Then write a synonym and antonym for each word.

Word	My Definition	Synonym	Antonym
1. **awareness**	*Possible response:* an understanding	*Possible response:* knowledge	*Possible response:* ignorance
2. **conservation**	*Possible response:* a protection of something	*Possible response:* preservation	*Possible response:* destruction
3. **establish**	*Possible response:* to start something new	*Possible response:* begin	*Possible response:* end
4. **expert**	*Possible response:* someone who knows a lot about a subject	*Possible response:* professional	*Possible response:* amateur
5. **extinct**	*Possible response:* no longer living	*Possible response:* dead	*Possible response:* alive
6. **increase**	*Possible response:* to get bigger	*Possible response:* grow	*Possible response:* decrease
7. **shrink**	*Possible response:* to get smaller	*Possible response:* decrease	*Possible response:* enlarge
8. **thrive**	*Possible response:* to grow strong and healthy	*Possible response:* flourish	*Possible response:* weaken

Unit 5 Key Vocabulary

awareness	discovery	environment	explorer	increase	shrink
biologist	document	establish	extinct	poacher	species
classified	endangered	expedition	habitat	pollution	thrive
conservation	ensure	expert	illegal	population	wildlife

C. Complete the sentences.

1. A **biologist** is someone who _____

   Possible response: studies living things

   _____ .

2. Scientists probably **classified** animals in order to _____

   Possible response: study them in groups and relate facts about their common traits

   _____ .

3. The light bulb was an important **discovery** because_____

   Possible response: it provides people with quick, easy, reliable, and constant light

   _____ .

4. One way to protect an **endangered** species is to _____

   Possible response: stop illegal hunting of the animal

   _____ .

5. Doctors should try to **ensure** _____

   Possible response: the safety and comfort of their patients

   _____ .

6. The **environment** includes living and nonliving things, such as _____

   Possible response: people, buildings, plants, and animals

   _____ .

7. One example of **pollution** is _____

   Possible response: an oil spill

   _____ .

8. It is important to have a balance of human **population** and natural resources because _____

   Possible response: we do not want to run out of the things we need to survive

   _____ .

Name _____

Mind Map

Use the mind map to write about **conflict** and resolution. As you read the selections in this unit, add new ideas you learn about **conflict**.

Answers will vary.

Academic Vocabulary

Think about things that could cause a **conflict**. What would be some ways to avoid **conflict**? Use the word **conflict** in your answer.

Answers will vary.

_____

_____

_____

_____

Determine Author's Purpose

A. Read the passage. Look at the word choices to figure out the author's purpose.

> Franklin Delano Roosevelt was born in New York in 1882. He was interested in politics. He went to school and was elected into the state senate. When Roosevelt was 39, he became ill. The illness left him unable to use his legs. He stayed in politics and became the governor of New York. In 1933, Roosevelt was elected president of the United States.

Circle the author's purpose.   **to entertain**   (**to inform**)

Tell how you know. _Possible response:_ The author uses words that emphasize fact, not emotion.

B. Read the passage. Look at the word choices to figure out the author's purpose.

> Last week Laura's class began their research projects on the United States presidents. Laura was excited to do her research on Franklin Delano Roosevelt. Yesterday, the students each had to give a speech to present the information they had learned. When Laura was called to the front of the class, she suddenly got the hiccups. At the end of each sentence, instead of pausing, she hiccupped. She was glad that she had found so much interesting information about Roosevelt because the class definitely paid attention to her speech that day!

Circle the author's purpose.   (**to entertain**)   **to inform**

Tell how you know. _Possible response:_ The author uses words that create moods and emotions to keep the reader interested.

Academic Vocabulary

What is the **purpose** of friendship? How do you think friends should treat each other?

Possible response: The purpose of friendship is to have someone to talk to and spend time with. Friends should always be honest with each other and treat each other with respect.

Focus on Vocabulary

Go Beyond the Literal Meaning

▶ Read the passages. Follow these steps to figure out the meanings of the underlined phrases and sentence.

1. Decide whether a literal meaning could be correct.
2. Look at the figurative language to see what is being compared.
3. Think about what the comparison could mean.
4. Decide what feeling or image the writer is trying to create.

A. Follow the directions above. Write the meaning of each underlined phrase.

> Anger can make us feel down in the dumps. What should we do when we feel angry? Communication is to anger as lotion is to a rash. First, listen to the other person, and try to understand where he is coming from. Then, tell the person your own feelings, too. Avoid making things worse by talking out of turn or raising your voice. Work together to come up with a solution you are both happy with.

down in the dumps _feeling sad or upset_

Communication : anger :: lotion : rash _Talking helps resolve a problem just as lotion helps soothe a rash._

where he is coming from _his point of view_

talking out of turn _interrupting someone_

B. Follow the directions above. Write the meaning of each underlined phrase.

> The summer is my favorite time of year. This is when I visit my Aunt Helen. She lives next to a lake that is clear as glass and sparkles in the sunlight. The large maple trees in her backyard wave their arms to keep me cool. We have a blast staying up late. I can forget all of my troubles at Aunt Helen's house.

clear as glass _smooth and reflective_

wave their arms _the branches and leaves move in the breeze_

have a blast _have a great time_

Academic Vocabulary

Your friend never uses the **literal** meaning of words. So what would your friend say about a very hot day?

Possible responses: The sun's rays strike like spears; I'm sweating buckets; The sun is an electric blanket set too high;

The heat punched me in the face.

Critical Viewing Guide

▶ Take Notes

A. View the images. Take notes on at least three things that you learned.

Answers will vary.

_____

_____

_____

_____

_____

_____

_____

▶ Analyze the Images

B. Review your notes to help answer these questions.

1. Write two sentences to explain what was in the images.

Answers will vary.

_____

_____

_____

2. What was the most interesting thing you learned?

Answers will vary.

_____

_____

_____

3. What can cause a **conflict** between different groups of people?

Answers will vary.

_____

_____

_____

_____

_____

Learn Key Vocabulary

Nadia the Willful: Key Vocabulary

A. Study each word. Circle a number to rate how well you know it. Then complete the chart.

Rating Scale	**1** I have never seen this word before.	**2** I am not sure of the word's meaning.	**3** I know this word and can teach the word's meaning to someone else.

▲ A **willful** attitude does not solve conflicts. This family **forbids** negative comments when they discuss their problems.

Key Words	Check Understanding	Deepen Understanding
❶ banish (**ban**-ish) *verb* **Rating:** 1 2 3	To **banish** is to request information. **Yes** (**No**)	Give an example of a reason to banish someone. *Possible response:* because he or she broke an important law _____ _____
❷ forbid (fur-**bid**) *verb* **Rating:** 1 2 3	The law **forbids** stealing. (**Yes**) **No**	Give an example of something you would forbid. *Possible response:* I would forbid stealing. _____ _____ _____
❸ grief (grēf) *noun* **Rating:** 1 2 3	It is best to comfort someone in **grief**. (**Yes**) **No**	Give an example of a time when you might feel grief. *Possible response:* if I lost somebody close to me _____ _____ _____
❹ memory (**me**-mu-rē) *noun* **Rating:** 1 2 3	**Memory** is another word for photograph. **Yes** (**No**)	Give an example of a childhood memory. _____ *Possible response:* when my little brother was born _____ _____ _____

Key Vocabulary, continued

A properly trained dog can be taught to **obey** without the use of **punishment**. ▶

Key Words	Check Understanding	Deepen Understanding
⑤ obey (ō-bā) *verb* **Rating:** 1 2 3	A good dog **obeys** its owner. (Yes) No	Give an example of someone you would obey. *Possible response:* a police officer
⑥ punishment (**pun**-ish-ment) *noun* **Rating:** 1 2 3	Most people enjoy **punishments**. Yes (No)	Give an example of a harsh punishment. _____ *Possible response:* getting grounded for a month
⑦ recall (rē-kawl) *verb* **Rating:** 1 2 3	To **recall** means to remember. (Yes) No	Give an example of something you might recall. *Possible response:* the date of an important event for a history test
⑧ willful (**wil**-ful) *adjective* **Rating:** 1 2 3	A **willful** child is a stubborn child. (Yes) No	Give an example of someone who is willful. _____ *Possible response:* someone who will not listen to good advice

B. Use at least two of the Key Vocabulary words. Write about a conflict you experienced. Explain how you solved the problem.

Answers will vary.

_____

_____

Compare Viewpoints

Fill in the chart as you read "Nadia the Willful."

Reader's Viewpoint Chart

What One Character Thinks/Feels:	What Another Character Thinks/Feels:	My Viewpoint:
Tarik thinks nothing can be done to deal with Nadia's temper.	Hamed thinks that Nadia's temper can be changed by laughing and teasing her.	Answers will vary.
Tarik is sad but accepts that his son is dead.	Nadia refuses to accept that her brother is gone.	Answers will vary.
Nadia thinks they should talk about Hamed because it makes everyone feel better.	Tarik thinks that no one should speak of Hamed because he is gone.	Answers will vary.
Nadia refuses to stop talking about her brother because that is how she remembers him.	Tarik changes his viewpoint and feels better when he hears about his son. He realizes it is helpful and comforting to talk about him.	Answers will vary.

Nadia the Willful

A. Read the paragraph.
Write a Key Vocabulary word in each blank.
Reread the paragraph to make sure the words make sense.

It was hard for Nadia the _____Willful_____ to _____obey_____ her father's decree. Nadia felt the

same sorrow and _____grief_____ that her father felt, but when she talked about Hamed, it helped Nadia

keep his _____memory_____ alive. Nadia risked her father's _____punishment_____ and openly shared tales and

memories and spoke Hamed's _____forbidden_____ name. She was glad to risk being _____banished_____ to the

desert because it meant she could _____recall_____ happy times with Hamed.

B. Write complete sentences to answer these questions about "Nadia the Willful."

1. How can sharing stories and memories help you **recall** a loved one?

Answers will vary.

_____

_____

_____

_____

_____

_____

2. What other names besides "Nadia the Willful" would fit Nadia's personality?

Possible response: Nadia could be called Nadia the Brave, Nadia the Loyal, or Nadia the Faithful Daughter and Sister.

_____

_____

_____

_____

Name _____

Simile, Metaphor, Personification, and Analogy

▶ Follow the steps below to identify the figurative language in each sentence.

1. Read the sentence carefully.
2. Decide if the figurative language is a simile, metaphor, personification, or analogy.
3. Write the meaning of the sentence.

Types of Figurative Language
A **simile** uses *like*, *as*, or *than* to compare two things.
A **metaphor** compares things without using *like* or *as*.
Personification gives human qualities to non-human things.
An **analogy** shows how ideas are related to each other.

1. Her dress was <u>as blue as the sky</u>.

   Type of figurative language: simile _____

   Sentence meaning: The dress is very blue. _____

2. The car barreled down the street <u>with an angry growl</u>.

   Type of figurative language: personification _____

   Sentence meaning: The car made a loud noise. _____

3. The young boy's eyes were <u>stuck like glue</u> to the television.

   Type of figurative language: simile _____

   Sentence meaning: The boy could not stop looking at the television. _____

4. Her bicycle is <u>as important to her as wings are to a bird</u>.

   Type of figurative language: analogy _____

   Sentence meaning: She needs her bicycle as much as a bird needs its wings. _____

5. <u>Her smile was the sun</u> during a dark day.

   Type of figurative language: metaphor _____

   Sentence meaning: Her smile made the day seem better. _____

6. The <u>bright, friendly moon guided me through</u> the forest.

   Type of figurative language: personification _____

   Sentence meaning: A person used the moonlight to see in the forest. _____

Nadia the Willful: Academic Vocabulary Review

A. Use your own words to tell what each Academic Vocabulary word means.

Word	My Definition
1. **compare**	*Possible response:* to see how things are alike or different
2. **conflict**	*Possible response:* a problem or disagreement
3. **literal**	*Possible response:* the exact meaning of a word
4. **purpose**	*Possible response:* the reason for doing something

B. Circle the Academic Vocabulary word that best fits each sentence.

1. Preston will explain the (**purpose** / **conflict**) of his experiment.

2. Who can tell the (**conflict** / **literal**) meaning of this word?

3. We will discuss the (**conflict** / **purpose**) between the two countries.

4. If you (**compare** / **literal**) the two artists, you can judge who is best.

Build Background

Name _____

Critical Viewing Guide

▶ **Take Notes**

A. View the video. Take notes on at least three things that you learned.

Answers will vary.

_____

_____

_____

_____

_____

_____

_____

▶ **Analyze the Video**

B. Review your notes to help answer these questions.

1. Write two sentences to explain what was in the video.

Answers will vary.

_____

_____

_____

2. What was the most interesting thing you learned?

Answers will vary.

_____

_____

_____

3. What are some skills that are important to ending **conflict**? Explain.

Answers will vary.

_____

_____

_____

_____

Learn Key Vocabulary

Name _____

Passage to Freedom: Key Vocabulary

A. Study each word. Circle a number to rate how well you know it. Then complete the chart.

| Rating Scale | **1** I have never seen this word before. | **2** I am not sure of the word's meaning. | **3** I know this word and can teach the word's meaning to someone else. |

▲ A rescue team seeks **permission** to **approach** the shore.

Key Words	Check Understanding	Deepen Understanding
❶ agreement (a-**grē**-ment) *noun* Rating: 1 2 3	☐ a safe place ☒ an understanding about something	Give an example of an agreement you have with somebody. *Possible response:* I have an agreement with my neighbor that I will feed her cats and pick up her mail while she is away.
❷ approach (u-**prōch**) *verb* Rating: 1 2 3	☒ to come closer ☐ to step quietly	Why should you approach a stray dog carefully? *Possible response:* You should approach a stray dog carefully because it could bite you.
❸ diplomat (**dip**-lō-mat) *noun* Rating: 1 2 3	☒ a person who represents his/her government ☐ a person who disagrees with government policy	Would you like to be a diplomat? Why or why not? *Possible response:* Yes, I would enjoy a job where I can travel and represent my country.
❹ insist (in-**sist**) *verb* Rating: 1 2 3	☐ to care for ☒ to demand	Is it a good idea to insist on your beliefs? Explain. *Possible response:* It is good to be firm in your beliefs, but you should not insist upon them to the point of not listening to others.

Key Words	Check Understanding	Deepen Understanding
❺ issue (i-shü) *verb* **Rating: 1 2 3**	☒ to give or hand out ☐ to take	If you could issue one item to all people, what would it be? *Possible response:* I would issue everybody a warm blanket so that they would never be cold.
❻ permission (pur-**mish**-un) *noun* **Rating: 1 2 3**	☐ reckless behavior ☒ allowing something to happen	Would you give a child permission to drive a car? Explain. *Possible response:* No, because children are too small and too young to drive safely.
❼ refugee (ref-yu-jē) *noun* **Rating: 1 2 3**	☒ a person who must leave his or her home to be safe ☐ a person with many belongings	What are some challenges a refugee might face? *Possible response:* Refugees might find it difficult to leave their home safely, move their belongings, and learn a new way of life.
❽ translate (trans-lāt) *verb* **Rating: 1 2 3**	☐ to relate ideas from different sources ☒ to explain in another language	Have you ever translated something in order to help someone? Explain. *Possible response:* Yes, I translate articles in the Sunday newspaper for my grandfather.

B. Use at least two of the Key Vocabulary words. Write about a time you did not agree with a rule or law.

Answers will vary.

_____

_____

_____

Evaluate Historical Fiction

A. Read the passage. Identify factual and fictional elements in "Passage to Freedom."

T Chart

Facts	Fiction
Possible response: ...my family and I went to a Hanukkah celebration for the first time.	*Possible response:* That boy looked into my father's eyes...
Possible response: I was five years old.	*Possible response:* In the mornings, birds sang in the trees.
Possible response: In 1940, my father was a diplomat representing the country of Japan.	*Possible response:* Little did we know that the real soldiers were coming our way.
Possible response: Houses and churches around us were hundreds of years old.	*Possible response:* My mother...woke...us up, telling us to get dressed quickly.
Possible response: Outside, I saw hundreds of people crowded around the gate in front of our house.	*Possible response:* "What do they want?" I asked my mother.
Possible response: My father...asked the crowd to choose five people to come inside and talk.	*Possible response:* "They have come to ask for your father's help," she replied.

Key Vocabulary

agreement	issue
approached	permission
diplomat	refugees
insist	translate

Passage to Freedom

A. Read the paragraph.
Write a Key Vocabulary word in each blank.
Reread the paragraph to make sure the words make sense.

Chiune Sugihara was a ___diplomat___ who worked for the Japanese government and lived in

Lithuania. He needed to get ___permission___ to ___issue___ visas so that people could travel to Japan.

When a crowd of Jewish ___refugees___ came to ask for his help, he had his assistant ___translate___

what he was saying into a language the crowd understood. Five men ___approached___ Sugihara to beg for

his help. The Nazis would ___insist___ that everyone in the crowd be killed if Sugihara did not act

to save them. Sugihara couldn't reach an ___agreement___ with the Japanese government. Even so, with

courage and daring, Sugihara did what he had to do.

B. Write complete sentences to answer these questions about "Passage to Freedom."

1. If Sugihara was your father, would you have encouraged him to
   issue visas to the **refugees**? Explain your answer.

   Answers will vary.

   _____

   _____

   _____

   _____

   _____

2. Why did Sugihara's decision take courage?

   Answers will vary.

   _____

   _____

   _____

   _____

   _____

Vocabulary Study

Idioms

▶ Follow the steps below to figure out the meaning of each idiom.

   1. Read each sentence.
   2. Think about the meaning of the underlined words.
   3. Write the meaning of each underlined idiom.

1. The teacher said she had <u>run out of</u> patience with the class.

   Meaning: _no more of_ _____

2. I cannot remember her name <u>for the life of me</u>.

   Meaning: _no matter how hard I try_ _____

3. My mother told me to apologize to my friend so our fight would not <u>drag on</u>.

   Meaning: _last too long_ _____

4. The college graduate was <u>living it up</u> in the big city.

   Meaning: _having a great time_ _____

5. My friend told me my idea was like a <u>breath of fresh air</u>.

   Meaning: _something new and different_ _____

6. He gave me <u>his two cents' worth</u>, even though I did not ask for his opinion.

   Meaning: _opinion, point of view_ _____

7. Emily said she <u>would not be caught dead</u> wearing that sweater.

   Meaning: _would never do_ _____

8. I need to <u>hit the books</u> so I can do well on the test tomorrow.

   Meaning: _study hard_ _____

9. Jack <u>ran into</u> an old friend at the mall.

   Meaning: _met unexpectedly_ _____

Academic Vocabulary

conflict	purpose
evaluate	response
literal	

Passage to Freedom: Academic Vocabulary Review

A. Match each Academic Vocabulary word with its meaning.

Word	Definition
1. **conflict**	the exact meaning of a word
2. **evaluate**	a reason for doing something
3. **literal**	to decide on the quality of something
4. **purpose**	a reply to something that has happened or been said
5. **response**	a problem or disagreement

B. Read each statement. Circle **Yes** or **No** to answer.

1. When you agree with someone, you have a **conflict**.   Yes   (No)

2. When you answer someone, you give a **response**.   (Yes)   No

3. When you **evaluate** something, you decide how good it is.   (Yes)   No

4. When you use a word in a **literal** way, you use its exact meaning.   (Yes)   No

5. When you explain the **purpose** for something, you give a reason for it.   (Yes)   No

C. Answer the questions in complete sentences.

1. When you have a **conflict** with a friend, what is one way you can resolve it?

   Answers will vary.
   _____

   _____

2. Write about something you own that has a useful **purpose**.

   Answers will vary.
   _____

   _____

Critical Viewing Guide

▶ Take Notes

A. View the video. Take notes on at least three things that you learned.

Answers will vary.

_____

_____

_____

_____

_____

_____

_____

▶ Analyze the Video

B. Review your notes to help answer these questions.

1. Write two sentences to explain what was in the video.

   Answers will vary.

   _____

   _____

2. What was the most interesting thing you learned?

   Answers will vary.

   _____

   _____

3. What are some ways that a **conflict** can affect people?

   Answers will vary.

   _____

   _____

   _____

   _____

   _____

Learn Key Vocabulary

Zlata's Diary: Key Vocabulary

A. Study each word. Circle a number to rate how well you know it. Then complete the chart.

Rating Scale	**1** I have never seen this word before.	**2** I am not sure of the word's meaning.	**3** I know this word and can teach the word's meaning to someone else.

▲ Reporters attempt to show the **impact** of **conflicts** around the world.

Key Words	Check Understanding	Deepen Understanding
❶ conflict (**kon**-flikt) *noun* **Rating: 1 2 3**	Circle the synonym for **conflict**. compromise (struggle)	My Definition: _____ *Possible response:* a fight between people _____ _____ _____
❷ desperate (**des**-pu-rit) *adjective* **Rating: 1 2 3**	Circle the synonym for **desperate**. angry (hopeless)	My Definition: _____ *Possible response:* having lost all hope _____ _____ _____
❸ destroy (di-**stroi**) *verb* **Rating: 1 2 3**	Circle the synonym for **destroy**. create (ruin)	My Definition: _____ *Possible response:* to completely damage _____ _____ _____
❹ humanity (hū-**man**-i-tē) *noun* **Rating: 1 2 3**	Circle the synonym for **humanity**. (goodwill) communication	My Definition: _____ *Possible response:* compassion and generosity towards all others _____ _____

Key Words	Check Understanding	Deepen Understanding
❺ impact (**im**-pakt) *verb* **Rating:** 1 2 3	Circle the synonym for **impact**. (**influence**) **display**	My Definition: _____ *Possible response:* to have an effect _____ _____ _____
❻ innocent (**in**-u-sent) *adjective* **Rating:** 1 2 3	Circle the synonym for **innocent**. **illegal** (**blameless**)	My Definition: _____ *Possible response:* having no guilt _____ _____ _____
❼ politics (**pol**-i-tiks) *noun* **Rating:** 1 2 3	Circle the synonym for **politics**. (**civics**) **business**	My Definition: _____ *Possible response:* government affairs _____ _____ _____
❽ reality (**rē**-a-lu-tē) *noun* **Rating:** 1 2 3	Circle the synonym for **reality**. **ability** (**actuality**)	My Definition: _____ *Possible response:* what actually goes on in life _____ _____ _____

B. Use at least two of the Key Vocabulary words. Write about a frightening experience you have had.

Answers will vary. _____

_____

_____

Name _____

Analyze Author's Viewpoint

Read the passage. Look for clues to the author's viewpoint.

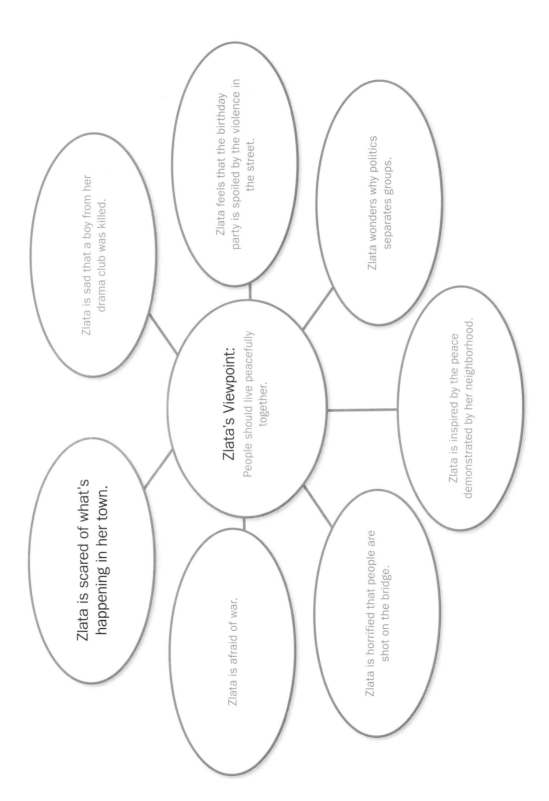

Mind Map

Zlata is sad that a boy from her drama club was killed.

Zlata feels that the birthday party is spoiled by the violence in the street.

Zlata wonders why politics separates groups.

Zlata's Viewpoint: People should live peacefully together.

Zlata is inspired by the peace demonstrated by her neighborhood.

Zlata is scared of what's happening in her town.

Zlata is afraid of war.

Zlata is horrified that people are shot on the bridge.

Selection Review

Zlata's Diary

Key Vocabulary

conflict	impacted
desperate	innocent
destroy	politics
humanity	reality

A. Read the paragraph.
Write a Key Vocabulary word in each blank.
Reread the paragraph to make sure the words make sense.

Zlata felt ____desperate____ about the ____conflict____ ripping her country apart. The war ____impacted____

everyone she knew. She saw many ____innocent____ people suffering or dying. She thought the

____politics____ conducted by adults would ____destroy____ or ruin many lives. By publishing her book,

the rest of ____humanity____ would see the war from her point of view. The world would understand her

____reality____ as a child in Sarajevo.

B. Write complete sentences to answer these questions about "Zlata's Diary."

1. Why do you think a diary brings comfort at a difficult time such as war?

_____Answers will vary._____

_____

_____

_____

_____

_____

2. Do you think Zlata would have expressed her thoughts differently if she
had known they would be published? How would she have done it?

_____Answers will vary._____

_____

_____

_____

_____

_____

Shades of Meaning and Word Choice

▶ Follow these steps to create a Synonym Scale for each underlined word.

1. Read the sentence. Look at the underlined word.
2. Think of three synonyms for the underlined word. Use a dictionary or thesaurus to help you.
3. Write the word and three synonyms on the scale. Arrange the words in order from the weakest to the strongest meanings.

1. He chewed his food at the dinner table.

| nibbled | chewed | chomped | devoured |

2. Julio received a good grade on his test.

| good | great | excellent | fabulous |

3. She was happy to find her missing necklace.

| pleased | happy | thrilled | ecstatic |

4. He ran down the street to the park.

| skipped | jogged | ran | sprinted |

5. Lisa stared at her friends' concert tickets.

| looked | stared | gaped | ogled |

6. It was a hot day at the beach.

| warm | hot | sweltering | scorching |

7. The snow was cold when I touched it.

| cool | cold | frigid | icy |

8. She yelled when she saw her favorite musician.

| yelled | shouted | screamed | shrieked |

Academic Vocabulary	
conflict	purpose
literal	scale

Zlata's Diary: Academic Vocabulary Review

A. Write the Academic Vocabulary words next to their definitions.

1. a graphic organizer that shows how items relate _Scale_____

2. the exact meaning of a word _literal_____

3. the reason for doing something _purpose_____

4. a problem or disagreement _conflict_____

B. Complete each sentence with an Academic Vocabulary word.

1. If we talk about our differences, we will not have a _____conflict_____.

2. When I say, "That's great," I mean it in a _____literal_____ way.

3. Use the map _____scale_____ to find the distance to Cuba.

4. Our teacher explained the _____purpose_____ of the project.

C. Use each pair of Academic Vocabulary words in a sentence.

1. **conflict**   **literal**

   Answers will vary.
   _____
   _____
   _____

2. **purpose**   **scale**

   Answers will vary.
   _____
   _____

PROTECTING HUMAN RIGHTS

by Marty Schmitt and the United Nations

1   Nesse Godin was 13 years old when the Nazis occupied her town in Lithuania during World War II. Because she and her family were Jewish, they were sent to a concentration camp. By the end of the war, over 6 million people would die in similar camps. Once the stories of Holocaust survivors like Nesse Godin were made public, world leaders vowed to never let something like this happen again. The United Nations, an organization of 51 nations, established a Commission on Human Rights to decide which rights all people should have.

THE UNIVERSAL DECLARATION OF HUMAN RIGHTS

2   The members of this commission came from different cultural backgrounds, but they worked together to create a "common standard of achievement for all people and all nations." On December 10, 1948, the UN General Assembly approved the commission's Universal Declaration of Human Rights.

3   The Declaration is organized into 30 articles, each of which addresses a different type of right. Together, the articles describe everyday rights such as the right to life, work, travel, education, medical care, self-expression, participation in government, and many others.

THE IMPACT OF HUMAN RIGHTS

4   The declaration has had an impact on people and governments. For example, during the 1960s–1980s, countries around the world pressured the Republic of South Africa to grant human rights to its non-white population. E.1 Many countries refused to trade with South Africa, and the country was barred from participating in the Olympic Games from 1964–1990.

5   In 1994, South Africa finally gave in to the pressure and held elections in which all people could vote. The people elected Nelson Mandela, a leader of the African population, as president. This action showed the power of human rights.

6   The declaration is part of the International Bill of Rights, **a legally binding agreement** signed by the majority of the world's countries. It has also inspired more than 80 other international human rights treaties and declarations. According to the United Nations, the declaration remains "the first **pillar** of twentieth-century human rights law and the **cornerstone** of the universal human rights movement." This will continue to be a pillar of law in the twenty-first century.

Historical Background

From 1939 to 1945, Germany, Italy, and Japan formed the Axis Powers of World War II. Dictator Adolph Hitler led Nazis, also known as the National Socialist German Workers' Party. They were responsible for the Holocaust during which they set up camps to imprison and kill approximately six million Jewish people.

In Other Words

a legally binding agreement an agreement that can be enforced by a court of law
pillar building block
cornerstone foundation

Universal Declaration of Human Rights: The First Five Articles

7 **ARTICLE 1.**

F.2 All human beings are born free and equal in dignity and rights. They are **endowed with reason and conscience** and should act towards one another in a spirit of brotherhood.

8 **ARTICLE 2.**

F.2 Everyone is entitled to all the rights and freedoms set forth in this Declaration, without distinction of any kind, such as race, color, sex, language, religion, political or other opinion, national or social origin, property, birth or other status. Furthermore, no distinction shall be made on the basis of the political, jurisdictional or international status of the country or territory to which a person belongs, whether it be independent, trust, non-self-governing or under any other limitation of **sovereignty**.

9 **ARTICLE 3.**

F.2 Everyone has the right to life, liberty and **security of person**.

10 **ARTICLE 4.**

F.2 No one shall be held in slavery or servitude; slavery and the slave trade shall be prohibited in all their forms.

11 **ARTICLE 5.**

F.2 No one shall be subjected to torture or to cruel, inhuman or degrading treatment or punishment.

In Other Words
endowed with reason and conscience able to think and to make good choices
sovereignty independence of its citizens
security of person personal safety

▶ Read for Understanding

A. From what kind of text is this passage taken? How do you know?

Possible response: It is from an informational article and an official document. I noticed the authors, titles, headings, and image.

B. Write a sentence that tells the topic of the selection.

Possible response: This text is mostly about the U.N. Human Rights declaration and why it is important.

▶ Reread and Summarize

C. On **Practice Book** pages 196–197, circle the 3–5 most important words in each section. Make notes about why you chose each word. Why is the word important in the section?

1. Section 1: (paragraphs 1–3)

Answers will vary.

2. Section 2: (paragraphs 4–6)

Answers will vary.

3. Section 3: (paragraphs 7–11)

Answers will vary.

D. Use your topic sentence from above and your notes to write a summary of the selection.

Possible response: After the Holocaust, the U.N. made a resolution about the human rights of all people. The resolution says that everyone has certain basic rights. The resolution had an impact on many governments, such as South Africa who were pressured by the world's respect of the U.N. Declaration to give human rights to all its population, not just whites.

Name _____

▶ Reread and Analyze

E. Analyze and identify the author's viewpoint.

1. Reread paragraphs 4 and 5 on **Practice Book** page 196. What loaded words are used? What opinion do you see? What do these clues tell you about the author's viewpoint? Underline words and phrases to support your answer.

   Possible response: The words *refused* and *barred* are strong, negative words that show how the author disapproves of South

   Africa's refusal to grant human rights to all people. Later, the author says that "this action showed the power of human

   rights," which shows the author's opinion that the U.N. resolution is powerful.

2. Underline other words or sentences on **Practice Book** page 196 that give clues about the author's viewpoint.

   Answers will vary. Possible response: The word *finally* shows that the author thought that South Africa took too long to

   change its position on human rights. The last line of paragraph 6 shows the author's opinion that the U.N. Declaration will

   continue to be important in the future.

F. Analyze how viewpoint is shown in a document created by a group.

1. How is the text on **Practice Book** page 197 different from the one on page 196 as far as author's viewpoint?

   Possible response: There is more than one author for the Articles on page 197. Many people at the United Nations wrote it.

   The Articles show a large group's viewpoint in the rules they created.

2. In the Articles on page 197, there are no specific details like people's names, places, or dates. Who do you think the Articles are written for? How do you know? On **Practice Book** page 197, underline words and phrases of the Human Rights Declaration that support your response.

   Answers will vary. Possible responses: The Articles are written to people all over the world. They are written like a list of

   rules to everyone. They use words like *All human beings* and *Everyone*.

▶ Discuss and Write

G. Synthesize your ideas about author viewpoint.

1. With the class, discuss how the viewpoint of the article's author is similar to the viewpoint of the writers of the Human Rights Declaration. List the examples you discuss.

Answers will vary. Possible response: Both the author and the U.N. declaration agree that people should have basic human

rights and that they should be stated and enforced.

_____

_____

_____

2. Write a paragraph about the viewpoint of either the author of this article or the writers of the Human Rights Declaration.

   · What words or phrases gave you clues about a viewpoint?

   · Where is a viewpoint directly stated? Where do you have to make an inference to understand viewpoint? Explain.

Answers will vary.

_____

_____

_____

_____

_____

▶ Connect with (GUIDING QUESTION)

H. Discuss the Guiding Question: How should people overcome conflict?

1. Think of a current international conflict. How would the authors of the Human Rights Declaration respond to this conflict? What might they be concerned about?

Possible response: The authors of the Human Rights Declaration would probably want to know that no one is being

tortured or enslaved as a result of this conflict. They would want to make sure people's freedoms and rights are protected

on both sides of the conflict.

Academic Vocabulary Review

Academic Vocabulary

compare	literal
conflict	purpose
connection	response
evaluate	scale
identify	

A. Circle the Academic Vocabulary word that best fits into each sentence.

1. Our families are not related, but we share a strong (**connection** / **scale**).

2. We can (**compare** / **evaluate**) the size of a goat to a sheep.

3. I hope two countries will end their (**conflict** / **purpose**).

B. Define each Academic Vocabulary word. Then give an example.

Word	My Definition	Example
1. **purpose**	a reason for doing something	*Answers will vary.*
2. **response**	a reply to something	*Answers will vary.*
3. **scale**	a graphic organizer that shows how items are related	*Answers will vary.*

C. Answer the questions. Use complete sentences.

1. Do you **compare** historical people to yourself? Do you make **connections** between events you read about and your own life?

   Answers will vary.

   _____

   _____

2. **Identify** an important event in your life. **Evaluate** its effect on you.

   Answers will vary.

   _____

   _____

   _____

Key Vocabulary Review

A. Read each sentence. Circle the Key Vocabulary word that best fits into each sentence.

1. The police do not believe the criminal is (**innocent**)/ **willful**).

2. The umpire (**issued** /(**banished**)) the abusive coach from the game.

3. A (**refugee** /(**diplomat**)) is a person who represents his or her government.

4. We wrote subtitles to (**banish** /(**translate**)) the film into other languages.

5. I could not ((**recall**)/ **obey**) the answer to the test question.

6. The way to get food at a game is to (**destroy** /(**approach**)) the snack counter.

7. A stubborn person always ((**insists**)/ **forbids**) on his or her opinions.

8. The ((**refugee**)/ **diplomat**) fled her country to escape danger.

B. Use your own words to write what each Key Vocabulary word means.
   Then write a synonym and antonym for each word.

Word	My Definition	Synonym and Antonym
1. **conflict**	*Possible response:* a fight between people	*Possible response:* struggle, peace
2. **desperate**	*Possible response:* having lost all hope	*Possible response:* miserable, hopeful
3. **destroy**	*Possible response:* to ruin completely	*Possible response:* wreck, create
4. **grief**	*Possible response:* an extremely sad feeling	*Possible response:* sorrow, happiness
5. **issue**	*Possible response:* to hand out	*Possible response:* give, take
6. **punishment**	*Possible response:* a price paid for bad behavior	*Possible responses:* penalty, reward
7. **reality**	*Possible response:* what actually happens in life	*Possible response:* actuality, fantasy
8. **willful**	*Possible response:* not willing to change	*Possible response:* stubborn, flexible

---

Unit 6 Key Vocabulary

agreement	desperate	grief	insist	permission	recall
approach	destroy	humanity	issue	politics	refugee
banish	diplomat	impact	memory	punishment	translate
conflict	forbid	innocent	obey	reality	willful

C. Answer the questions in complete sentences.

1. What is your favorite childhood **memory**?

   Possible response: I like to remember when my uncle taught me how to ride a horse.

2. Would you enjoy a career in **politics**? Explain.

   Possible response: I would enjoy a career in politics because I like to take action and solve problems.

3. How can doctors show **humanity** to their patients?

   Possible response: Doctors can work hard to heal their patients and lessen their suffering.

4. Is it always right to **obey** someone in authority? Explain.

   Possible response: No, you should not obey an authority figure who wants you to hurt someone or do something wrong.

5. What do you have **permission** to do now that you could not do when you were younger?

   Possible response: Now I have permission to go to the movies by myself.

6. How can a coach **impact** the score of a game?

   Possible response: A coach can prepare his/her players to perform well and he/she can cheer them on as they play.

7. Should teachers **forbid** cell phones in class? Explain.

   Possible response: Yes, it is not easy to concentrate if someone nearby is talking or sending text messages.

8. How can you reach an **agreement** with someone who thinks differently than you do?

   Possible response: You can listen to their opinions, share your perspective, and attempt to compromise.

Mind Map

Use the mind map to write your ideas about what fairness means. As you read the selections in this unit, add new ideas you learn about fairness.

Answers will vary.

Academic Vocabulary

Think about a time when good **judgment** is needed. Why is it important to use good **judgment** when you are making a decision? Use the word **judgment** in your answer.

Answers will vary.

_____

_____

_____

_____

Compare Text Structures

A. Read the folk tale. Underline clues to the structure of the text.
Then answer the questions.

> Everyone in the village respected the wise old man. <u>Because</u> he did not speak much, they listened carefully to every word he said. Yet, <u>since</u> he was so quiet, they began to forget he was there. <u>As a result</u>, they stopped seeking his advice. <u>Due</u> to this change, problems began to arise in the village.

How is this text organized?   **chronological order text structure**   (**cause-and-effect text structure**)

What information is most important to the author?

How events affect each other is most important.

_____

B. Read the folk tale. Underline clues to the structure of the text.
Then answer the questions.

> Everyone in the village respected the wise old man. <u>Every morning</u>, people sat at his feet to listen to the few words of advice he offered. <u>For many years</u>, things went very well in the village. <u>On one stormy day</u>, the people failed to visit the old man. <u>Soon</u>, the villagers forgot the habit of listening to the old man. <u>By the end of the year</u>, problems began to arise in the village.

How is this text organized?   (**chronological order text structure**)   **cause-and-effect text structure**

What information is most important to the author?

The time order of events is most important.

_____

Academic Vocabulary

Explain why it is **logical** to seek advice from someone older than you.

Possible response: It is reasonable to assume that someone who has lived longer has more life experiences and has

learned more lessons.

_____

Focus on Vocabulary

Use Word Origins

▶ Read the passages. Follow these steps.

1. Study each underlined word. Look for a root word.
2. Think of a word you know that has a similar root.
3. Use this similarity to figure out the meaning.

Root	Source and Meaning	Examples
cred-	Latin, *credere* (to believe), about beliefs	incredible—unbelievable
leg-	Latin, *lex* (law), of or about law	legal—according to the law
posi-	Latin, *positus* (place), put in place or set down	deposit—to put down

A. Follow the directions above. Write the meaning of each underlined word.

> If you are eighteen years old and a citizen of the United States, you are legally allowed to vote. Voting gives people power within the government. People can vote for candidates who support their position on important issues. Unfortunately, many people do not always exercise their right to vote. Some people do not vote because they cannot decide on a credible candidate for the job. Others say that they are just too busy to vote. It is important to make time to vote.

legally   in a way that is legal or right by the law _____

position   a person's place or opinion on an issue _____

credible   believable _____

B. Follow the directions above. Write the meaning of each underlined word.

> Many states have a law that makes it illegal to talk on a cell phone while driving. Officials believe that holding your cell phone makes it difficult to concentrate on the road and is dangerous. Some people believe this is unfair. They are in opposition to this law. Others believe that this law is just. They give credit to lawmakers for making the roads safer.

illegal   not legal, against the law _____

opposition   the act of opposing or being set against _____

credit   recognition of believability _____

Academic Vocabulary

I like to learn about the **origin** of everyday products I use, such as a toothbrush or a comb.

When I try to find the **origin** , I need to _____

figure out where and how it was invented by looking in an encyclopedia or on the Internet _____ .

Build Background

Critical Viewing Guide

▶ Take Notes

A. View the images. Take notes on at least three things that you learned.

Answers will vary.

_____

_____

_____

_____

_____

_____

_____

_____

▶ Analyze the Images

B. Review your notes to help answer these questions.

1. Write two sentences to explain what was in the images.

   Answers will vary.

   _____

   _____

   _____

2. What was the most interesting thing you learned?

   Answers will vary.

   _____

   _____

   _____

3. What are some things people should consider when making a **judgment**? Why is it important to listen to all sides when making a **judgment**?

   Answers will vary.

   _____

   _____

   _____

   _____

Learn Key Vocabulary

Name _____

The Clever Magistrate: Key Vocabulary

A. Study each word. Circle a number to rate how well you know it. Then complete the chart.

Rating Scale	**1** I have never seen this word before.	**2** I am not sure of the word's meaning.	**3** I know this word and can teach the word's meaning to someone else.

▲ Lawyers present careful **arguments** to **plead** their case before a judge.

Key Words	Check Understanding	Deepen Understanding
❶ argument (ar-gyu-munt) *noun* **Rating:** 1 2 3	Circle the synonym for **argument**. agreement (**disagreement**)	My Definition: _____ *Possible response:* a difference of opinion between people
❷ complaint (kum-**plānt**) *noun* **Rating:** 1 2 3	Circle the synonym for **complaint**. request (**protest**)	My Definition: _____ *Possible response:* a statement of unhappiness
❸ damage (dam-ij) *noun* **Rating:** 1 2 3	Circle the synonym for **damage**. repair (**destruction**)	My Definition: _____ *Possible response:* harm caused by an accident
❹ furious (fyur-ē-us) *adjective* **Rating:** 1 2 3	Circle the synonym for **furious**. hot (**angry**)	My Definition: _____ *Possible response:* feeling very mad

Did You Know?

The term **relent** comes from a Middle English word that means "to melt or soften."

Key Words	Check Understanding	Deepen Understanding
❺ **inevitable** (i-**nev**-i-tu-bul) *adjective* **Rating:** 1 2 3	Circle the synonym for **inevitable**. endless (certain)	My Definition: _____ *Possible response:* something that will happen no matter what
❻ **mercy** (**mur**-sē) *noun* **Rating:** 1 2 3	Circle the synonym for **mercy**. (compassion) justice	My Definition: _____ *Possible response:* kindness to people in trouble
❼ **plead** (plēd) *verb* **Rating:** 1 2 3	Circle the synonym for **plead**. (beg) borrow	My Definition: _____ *Possible response:* to strongly ask for something
❽ **relent** (ri-**lent**) *verb* **Rating:** 1 2 3	Circle the synonym for **relent**. continue (stop)	My Definition: _____ *Possible response:* to finally stop

B. Use at least two of the Key Vocabulary words. Write about a time someone showed mercy to you.

Answers will vary.

_____

_____

_____

Determine Theme

Complete the Theme Chart as you read "The Clever Magistrate." Record clues that you find from the title, characters, setting, and plot. Then write the theme.

Theme Chart

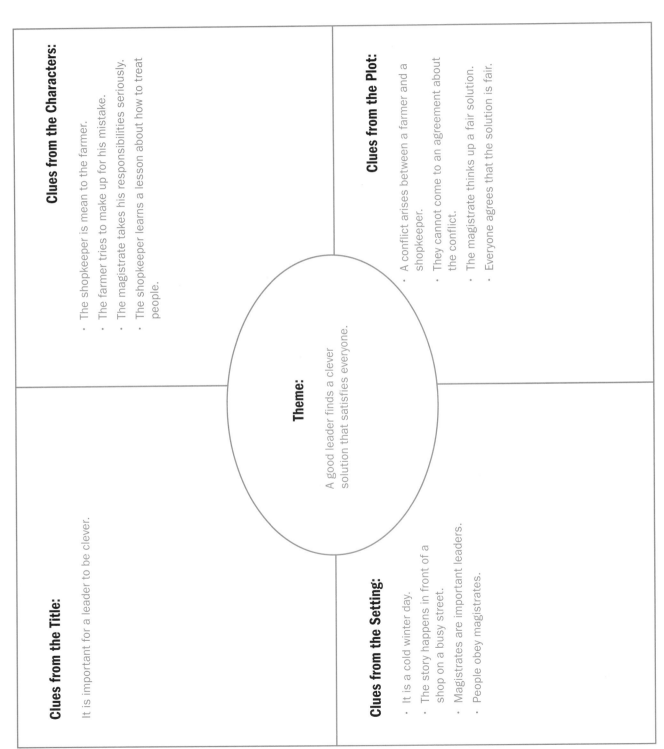

Clues from the Title:

It is important for a leader to be clever.

Clues from the Characters:

- The shopkeeper is mean to the farmer.
- The farmer tries to make up for his mistake.
- The magistrate takes his responsibilities seriously.
- The shopkeeper learns a lesson about how to treat people.

Clues from the Setting:

- It is a cold winter day.
- The story happens in front of a shop on a busy street.
- Magistrates are important leaders.
- People obey magistrates.

Clues from the Plot:

- A conflict arises between a farmer and a shopkeeper.
- They cannot come to an agreement about the conflict.
- The magistrate thinks up a fair solution.
- Everyone agrees that the solution is fair.

Theme:

A good leader finds a clever solution that satisfies everyone.

Name _____

The Clever Magistrate

A. Read the paragraph.
Write a Key Vocabulary word in each blank.
Reread the paragraph to make sure the words make sense.

When a farmer accidentally spilled some slop in front of a coat shop, the shopkeeper wanted the

farmer to clear away the ____damage____ . The farmer wanted to fetch a mop, which started an

____argument____ . The farmer begged and ____pleaded____ with the shopkeeper to be reasonable and

show ____mercy____ . The angry shopkeeper refused to be fair because he was so ____furious____ .

When the magistrate arrived, the shopkeeper ____relented____ . He had no additional ____complaints____ .

Once the clever magistrate was involved, the outcome was ____inevitable____ .

B. Write complete sentences to answer these questions about "The Clever Magistrate."

1. If you were a bystander, would you agree with the farmer or the shopkeeper?
   Explain your answer.

   Answers will vary.

   _____

   _____

   _____

   _____

   _____

   _____

2. What other ways could the magistrate have settled the **argument**?

   Answers will vary.

   _____

   _____

   _____

   _____

   _____

   _____

Vocabulary Study

Use Word Origins: Borrowed Words

▶ Follow the steps below to study these borrowed words.

1. Find each word in a dictionary.
2. Write the original language from which the word was borrowed.
3. Then write the definition of the word.

1. **menu** _French_ _____

   a listing of food available at a restaurant _____

2. **cargo** _Spanish_ _____

   goods loaded onto a ship, airplane, or vehicle _____

3. **tornado** _Spanish_ _____

   a funnel-shaped cloud with strong winds _____

4. **diploma** _Greek_ _____

   a document that certifies a person has completed a course of study _____

5. **grape** _French_ _____

   a fruit grown on a vine _____

6. **coyote** _Spanish_ _____

   a small, wolf-like carnivorous animal _____

7. **skeleton** _Greek_ _____

   the bones of a living thing that form the framework of the body _____

8. **ocean** _Greek_ _____

   a body of saltwater _____

9. **restaurant** _French_ _____

   a place where people go to eat _____

Academic Vocabulary

The Clever Magistrate: Academic Vocabulary Review

Academic Vocabulary	
culture	logical
definition	origin
judgment	structure

A. Use your own words to tell what each Academic Vocabulary word means.

1. **culture** _____ *Possible response:* the beliefs of a group of people

2. **judgment** _____ *Possible response:* ability to make good decisions

3. **logical** _____ *Possible response:* making sense

4. **origin** _____ *Possible response:* beginning of something

5. **structure** _____ *Possible response:* how parts of something are organized

6. **definition** _____ *Possible response:* the meaning of a word

B. Draw a line to match the beginning of each sentence with its ending

Beginning of Sentence	Ending of Sentence
1. Arrange the books on the shelf	do not use good **judgment**.
2. People who talk on the phone while they drive	is part of Native American **culture**.
3. Traditional dance	of civilization in social studies.
4. We learned about the **origin**	in a **logical** order.
5. Suki drew a picture to show the **structure**	is its **definition**.
6. The meaning of a word	of a plant cell.

Critical Viewing Guide

▶ Take Notes

A. View the video. Take notes on at least three things that you learned.

Answers will vary.

_____

_____

_____

_____

_____

_____

_____

▶ Analyze the Video

B. Review your notes to help answer these questions.

1. Write two sentences to explain what was in the video.

Answers will vary.

_____

_____

_____

2. What was the most interesting thing you learned?

Answers will vary.

_____

_____

_____

3. Why do you think the Constitution includes fair **judgment** for all?

Answers will vary.

_____

_____

_____

_____

Learn Key Vocabulary

Name _____

The Constitution: Key Vocabulary

A. Study each word. Circle a number to rate how well you know it. Then complete the chart.

Rating Scale	**1** I have never seen this word before.	**2** I am not sure of the word's meaning.	**3** I know this word and can teach the word's meaning to someone else.

▲ The Constitution outlines the laws of our **government**. These laws are the building blocks of **democracy** in the United States.

Key Words	Check Understanding	Deepen Understanding
❶ amend (u-**mend**) *verb* **Rating:** 1 2 3	To **amend** is to demand. Yes (No)	How can you amend a paper you write for class? *Possible response:* I can improve its organization, and I can correct spelling errors.
❷ delegate (**del**-i-get) *noun* **Rating:** 1 2 3	A **delegate** speaks for other citizens. (Yes) No	What is an advantage to having delegates? _____ *Possible response:* Delegates speak and act for many people, which saves time and avoids the chaos of having many people run a government or organization.
❸ democracy (di-**mok**-ru-sē) *noun* **Rating:** 1 2 3	People can vote in a **democracy**. (Yes) No	In what way do people participate in a democracy? *Possible response:* People participate in a democracy by voting on issues and candidates.
❹ government (**guv**-urn-ment) *noun* **Rating:** 1 2 3	A **government** has no leaders. Yes (No)	What might the United States be like without a government? _____ *Possible response:* The United States would probably be less organized, and the citizens would have fewer services.

Name _____

One symbol that **represents** American **independence** is the United States flag. ▶

Key Words	Check Understanding	Deepen Understanding
5 independence (in-di-**pen**-duns) *noun* **Rating:** 1 2 3	When you have **independence**, you have freedom. **(Yes)** No	Is independence important to you? Explain. _____ *Possible response:* Yes, I value independence because I want to be free to speak my mind and pursue my interests and desires.
6 interpret (in-**tur**-prut) *verb* **Rating:** 1 2 3	It is possible to **interpret** a poem in more than one way. **(Yes)** No	How would you interpret a smile from a friend? _____ *Possible response:* I would interpret a smile as a sign that my friend was happy to see me.
7 justice (**jus**-tis) *noun* **Rating:** 1 2 3	**Justice** is another word for kindness. Yes **(No)**	Why should a judge value justice? _____ *Possible response:* A judge should value justice because it is his or her job to decide what is fair according to the laws.
8 represent (rep-ri-**zent**) *verb* **Rating:** 1 2 3	When you **represent** someone, you judge them. Yes **(No)**	What qualities would you want in someone who represents you? _____ *Possible response:* I would want someone who represents me to be a good listener and to be persistent in finalizing my goals.

B. Use at least two of the Key Vocabulary words. Write about a time you felt someone or something was unfair.

Answers will vary.

_____

_____

Analyze Main Idea and Details

A. Read the section called "A Closer Look" and complete the Main-Idea Diagram.

Main-Idea Diagram

Main Idea: The Constitution consists of many parts to meet various specific needs.

Detail 1: The Preamble states the basic purposes of the new plan of the government.

Detail 2: The Seven Articles set out the powers of Congress, the President, and the federal courts.

Detail 3: The Amendments were added later.

Detail 4: The Legislative Branch, the Congress, passes the laws.

Detail 5: The Executive Branch, the President, is commander-in-chief of the military, makes treaties, and appoints ambassadors and judges.

Detail 6: The Judicial Branch, the Supreme Court and other federal courts, interprets the law.

Detail 7: The Constitution created three separate branches of government so each branch can help control the powers of the others.

B. Read the section called "The Amendments" and complete the Main-Idea Diagram.

Main-Idea Diagram

Main Idea: Amendments are changes to the Constitution that are difficult to make but meet specific needs.

Detail 1: The Bill of Rights is the first ten amendments that protect basic freedoms of individuals.

Detail 2: Seventeen more amendments were made after 1791 to create more freedom for all Americans.

Detail 3: The Constitution has been amended twenty-seven times and has lasted more than 200 years.

The Constitution

A. Read the paragraph.
Write a Key Vocabulary word in each blank.
Reread the paragraph to make sure the words make sense.

A group of ___delegates___ gathered together to write the Constitution. The colonists had just fought

the British to gain ___independence___ from King George's form of ___government___ . The Constitution created

a ___democracy___ , which means that the people have the power. People from every state ___represent___

citizens in Congress. Congress makes the laws, and the president carries out the laws. The Supreme

Court ___interprets___ the laws to ensure fairness and ___justice___ . If the Constitution needs to be

changed, the people can vote to ___amend___ it. This ensures that the United States will serve the

needs of its people for many years to come.

B. Write complete sentences to answer these questions about "The Constitution."

1. How does the Constitution protect people's freedom?

Possible response: It gives them the power to elect their leaders and representatives.

_____

_____

_____

_____

_____

2. Why did the founders choose a **democracy** for our way of **government** ?

Possible response: They wanted the government to be fair, to take care of its people, to be flexible, and to be strong.

_____

_____

_____

_____

_____

Vocabulary Study

Use Word Origins:
Greek, Latin, and Anglo-Saxon Roots

Root	Meaning	Related English Word
chron, Greek	time	chronological
dem, Greek	people	democracy
jud, Latin	judge	judicial
popul, Latin	people	population
riht, Anglo-Saxon	straight, direct	right

▶ Many English words have Greek, Latin, or Anglo-Saxon origins. Follow the steps below to figure out the meaning of each word.

1. Look at the chart to find the root. Write its meaning.
2. Then write the meaning of the whole word.
3. Check your answer in a dictionary.

1. **judgment**   **judg-:** _____judge_____ **-ment:** an act of

   an act of judging

2. **forthright**   **forth-:** forward **-right:** _____straight_____

   straightforward

3. **epidemic**   **epi-:** close in space or time **-dem-:** _____people_____ **-ic:** relating to

   relating to many people at the same time or in the same place

4. **popular**   **popul-:** _____people_____ **-ar:** of or relating to

   of the people

5. **synchronize**   **syn-:** same **-chron-:** _____time_____ **-ize:** to cause to occur

   to cause to occur at the same time

6. **demography**   **dem-:** _____people_____ **-ography:** a process of recording information

   recording information about people

7. **prejudice**   **pre-:** before **-jud-:** _____judge_____ **-ice-:** an action or state of being

   the act or state of judging before knowing

8. **populous**   **popul-:** _____people_____ **-ous:** full of

   full of people

Academic Vocabulary

The Constitution: Academic Vocabulary Review

Academic Vocabulary	
judgment	symbol
origin	

A. Match each Academic Vocabulary word with its meaning.

Word	Definition
1. **judgment**	an object or idea that stands for something else
2. **origin**	the source or beginning of something
3. **symbol**	the ability to make good decisions

B. Read each statement. Circle **Yes** or **No** to answer.

1. If you make good decisions, then you have good **judgment**.   (Yes)   No

2. The **origin** of something is its end.   Yes   (No)

3. The flag is a **symbol** of our country.   (Yes)   No

C. Use each Academic Vocabulary word in a sentence.

1. **judgment**

   Answers will vary.

   _____

2. **symbol**

   Answers will vary.

   _____

3. **origin**

   Answers will vary.

   _____

Critical Viewing Guide

▶ Take Notes

A. View the video. Take notes on at least three things that you learned.

Answers will vary.

_____

_____

_____

_____

_____

_____

_____

▶ Analyze the Video

B. Review your notes to help answer these questions.

1. Write two sentences to explain what was in the video.

Answers will vary.

_____

_____

_____

2. What was the most interesting thing you learned?

Answers will vary.

_____

_____

_____

3. In your **judgment**, what makes a good citizen?

Answers will vary.

_____

_____

_____

_____

Learn Key Vocabulary

Name _____

Kids Take Action: Key Vocabulary

A. Study each word. Circle a number to rate how well you know it. Then complete the chart.

Rating Scale	**1** I have never seen this word before.	**2** I am not sure of the word's meaning.	**3** I know this word and can teach the word's meaning to someone else.

▲ These students **volunteer** to help in their school's **campaign** to recycle.

Key Words	Check Understanding	Deepen Understanding
❶ **campaign** (kam-**pān**) *noun* **Rating:** 1 2 3	☐ an organized group of protesters ☒ a series of actions designed to bring about a goal	Example: _____ *Possible response:* the actions a person takes to become class president
❷ **citizen** (**sit**-u-zen) *noun* **Rating:** 1 2 3	☒ a member of a country ☐ a visitor	Example: _____ *Possible response:* a person born in the United States
❸ **debate** (di-**bāt**) *verb* **Rating:** 1 2 3	☒ to discuss different views about an issue ☐ to make an appeal to a judge	Example: _____ *Possible response:* to argue for or against a candidate
❹ **informed** (in-**formd**) *adjective* **Rating:** 1 2 3	☐ having an alternative plan ☒ having knowledge about something	Example: _____ *Possible response:* someone who reads about the candidates before he or she votes

Name _____

An **informed** candidate **debates** an issue. She hopes to **persuade** the audience. ▶

Key Words	Check Understanding	Deepen Understanding
❺ persuade (pur-**swād**) *verb* **Rating:** 1 2 3	☒ to convince ☐ to conquer	Example: _____ *Possible response:* to convince a classmate to agree with your opinion about a school rule _____ _____ _____
❻ petition (pu-**tish**-un) *noun* **Rating:** 1 2 3	☒ a written request ☐ a long speech	Example: _____ *Possible response:* a request you send to your city government to preserve the local parks _____ _____ _____
❼ support (su-**pōrt**) *noun* **Rating:** 1 2 3	☐ hope ☒ help	Example: _____ *Possible response:* the love and care children receive from their parents _____ _____ _____
❽ volunteer (vol-en-**tēr**) *verb* **Rating:** 1 2 3	☐ to build houses ☒ to work without pay	Example: _____ *Possible response:* to visit the elderly in a nursing home _____ _____ _____

B. Use at least two of the Key Vocabulary words. Write about a time you volunteered. Tell why you decided to help.

Answers will vary. _____

_____

_____

Unit 7 Fair Is Fair **223**

Relate Cause and Effect

Complete the Cause-and-Effect Chain as you read "Kids Take Action."

Cause-and-Effect Chain

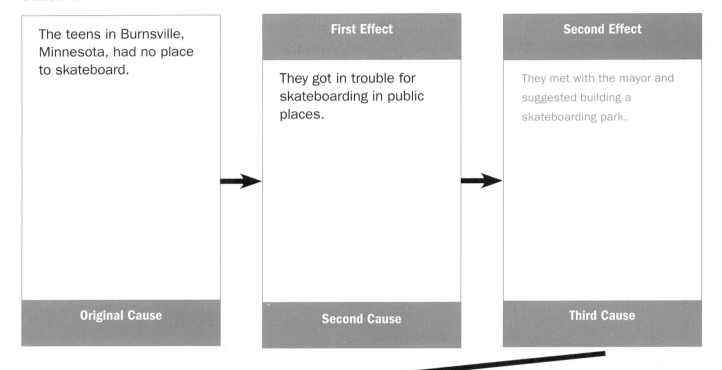

The teens in Burnsville, Minnesota, had no place to skateboard.

Original Cause

First Effect

They got in trouble for skateboarding in public places.

Second Cause

Second Effect

They met with the mayor and suggested building a skateboarding park.

Third Cause

Third Effect

The mayor gave them advice about how to build a skateboarding park.

Fourth Cause

Fourth Effect

They got support from people who lived in the area.

Fifth Cause

Fifth Effect

They gave a speech before the City Council, which voted in favor of the park.

Kids Take Action

A. Read the paragraph.
Write a Key Vocabulary word in each blank.
Reread the paragraph to make sure the words make sense.

> As a _____citizen_____ of the United States, you have the right to speak out and express an _____informed_____ opinion. You can _____debate_____ people who don't agree with your views. If you want to make changes in your community, you can _____volunteer_____ to pass around a _____petition_____ for people to sign. You can present your idea to the local government to _____persuade_____ the city council to vote in your favor. You can also start a _____campaign_____ by making speeches, writing letters, and making your voice heard. Other citizens who agree with you will give you _____support_____ for your idea and help you change your community.

B. Write complete sentences to answer these questions about "Kids Take Action."

1. What do you think is the best way to make your voice heard?

Answers will vary.

_____

_____

_____

_____

2. How can having an **informed** opinion help you in your own household?

Possible response: An informed opinion can help me state my views calmly and clearly and give reasons for my thinking

so that my parents have the information they need to make a decision.

_____

_____

_____

_____

Vocabulary Study

Name _____

Use Word Origins: Greek and Latin Mythology

Use the chart and a dictionary to write the meaning of each sentence.

epicurean	Epicurus was the founder of a school of philosophy and believed the goal in life should be pleasure.
iridescent	Zeus' messenger, Iris, traveled through the skies wearing a sparkling, rainbow-colored cape.
labyrinth	The Labyrinth was a confusing maze built to contain the monster Minotaur.
martial	March, the first month of the Roman calendar, was named after Mars, the god of war.
museum	The Muses, nine Greek goddesses, presided over arts and literature.
narcissism	Narcissus fell in love with himself after seeing his own reflection in a pool.

1. The art **museum** holds historic paintings and sculptures.

   The art museum is a place where you can go and see art.

2. The streets in Venice seem like a **labyrinth** since it is so easy to get lost.

   The streets in Venice are like a maze.

3. This website focuses on **epicurean** delights such as entertainment, food, and drink.

   The website focuses on pleasurable things.

4. The **narcissistic** girl looked at herself in the mirror every chance she got.

   The girl was very conceited and liked the way she looked.

5. **Martial** arts focus on training and practicing for combat.

   Martial arts teach you how to fight.

6. Insects' wings can seem **iridescent** in the sunlight.

   Insects' wings shine and shimmer in the light.

Academic Vocabulary

Academic Vocabulary

judgment	organize
logical	relate

Kids Take Action: Academic Vocabulary Review

A. Write the Academic Vocabulary word next to the correct definition.

Meaning	Word
1. the ability to make good decisions	judgment
2. to show how things are connected	relate
3. when something makes sense or is reasonable	logical
4. to arrange things in a certain order	organize

B. Write an Academic Vocabulary word to complete each sentence.

1. Please help me _____organize_____ this closet.

2. Irma showed good _____judgment_____ when she called 911.

3. Jose wants to know how wolves and dogs _____relate_____ to each other.

4. The answer she gave was clear and _____logical_____ .

C. What is a **logical** way to **organize** your music collection?

Answers will vary.
_____

_____

_____

from
The Words We Live By

by Linda R. Monk

WE THE PEOPLE . . .

1   These first three words of the Constitution are the most important. They clearly state that the people—not the king, not the legislature, not the courts—are the true rulers in American **government**. This principle is known as popular sovereignty.

2   But who are "We the People"? This question troubled the nation for centuries. As Lucy Stone, one of America's first **advocates** for women's rights, asked in 1853: "'We the People'? Which 'We the People'? The women were not included." Neither were white males who did not own property, Native Americans, or African Americans—slave or free.

E.1

Justice Thurgood Marshall, the first African American on the Supreme Court, described the limitation:

3   *For a sense of **the evolving nature of the Constitution**, we need look no further than the first three words of the document's preamble: 'We the people.' When the founding fathers used this phrase in 1787, they did not have in mind the majority of America's **citizens** . . .*

4   *The men who gathered in Philadelphia in 1787 could not . . . have imagined, nor would they have accepted, that the document they were drafting would one day be construed by a Supreme Court **to which had been appointed** a woman and the descendant of an African slave.*

Marshall was not the first African American to speak out about the phrase.

Key Vocabulary
- **government** *n.*, people who rule a country or state
- **citizen** *n.*, a person who lives in a country and has certain rights and duties

In Other Words
advocates supporters
the evolving nature of the Constitution the way the meaning of the Constitution can change
to which had been appointed that included

DOUGLASS
1818-1895

ANTHONY
1820-1906

GINSBURG
BORN·1933

NOT WE, THE WHITE PEOPLE
FREDERICK DOUGLASS

5   *We, the people—not we, the white people—not we, the citizens, or the legal voters—not we, the privileged class, and excluding all other classes but we, the people; not we, the horses and cattle, but we the people—the men and women, the human inhabitants of the United States, do **ordain** and establish this Constitution.*

WE, THE WHOLE PEOPLE
SUSAN B. ANTHONY

6   *It was we, the people; not we, the white male citizens; not yet we, the male citizens; but we, the whole people, who formed the Union. And we formed it, not to give the blessings of liberty, but to secure them; not to the half of ourselves and the half of our **posterity**, but to the whole people—women as well as men. And it is a downright mockery to talk to women of their enjoyment of the blessings of liberty while they are denied the use of the only means of securing them provided by this democratic-republican government—the ballot.*

GENTLEMEN OF THEIR TIME
JUSTICE RUTH BADER GINSBURG

7   *It **manifests** no disrespect for the Constitution to note that the **framers** were gentlemen of their time, and therefore had a distinctly limited vision of those who counted among "We the People." Not until the adoption of the post-Civil War Fourteenth Amendment did the word "equal," in relation to the stature of individuals, even make an appearance in the Constitution. But the equal dignity of all persons is nonetheless a vital part of our constitutional **legacy**, even if the culture of the framers held them back from perceiving that universal ideal. We can best celebrate that legacy by striving to form a "more perfect Union" for ourselves and the generations to come.*

8   Through the amendment process, more and more Americans were eventually included in the Constitution's definition of "We the People." After the Civil War, the Thirteenth Amendment ended slavery, the Fourteenth Amendment gave African Americans citizenship, and the Fifteenth Amendment gave black men the right to vote. In 1920, the Nineteenth Amendment gave women the right to vote nationwide.

F.1

In Other Words
ordain choose; demand
posterity future generations
manifests shows
framers creators of the Constitution
legacy history

◖ Read for Understanding

A. From what kind of text is this passage taken? How do you know?

Possible response: a textbook or social studies feature; it tells about history; it features the words of some important people

in history

B. Write a sentence that tells the topic of the selection.

Possible response: This text is mostly about the opening words to the U.S. Constitution and how the phrase, "We the People,"

has been interpreted throughout history.

◖ Reread and Summarize

C. On **Practice Book** pages 228–229, circle the 3–5 most important words in each section. Make notes about why you chose each word. Why is the word important in the section?

1. Section 1: (paragraphs 1–4)

   Answers will vary.

2. Section 2: (paragraph 5–7)

   Answers will vary.

3. Section 3: (paragraph 8)

   Answers will vary.

D. Use your topic sentence from above and your notes to write a summary of the selection.

Possible response: Although the Constitution is written for all the people as interpreted from the phrase, "We the people,"

the founding fathers did not count everyone equally. Not everyone was able to vote and enjoy the freedoms promised by the

Constitution. Women, African Americans, and even non-landowners did not feel they were considered part of the "We the people."

Frederick Douglass insisted that "We the people" included all people, even slaves. Susan B. Anthony insisted "We the people"

included women and that is why women should have the right to vote.

◗ Reread and Analyze

E. Analyze how the author introduces the main idea and supports it with details.

1. Reread paragraph 2 on **Practice Book** page 228. What main idea is introduced in this paragraph? Underline words and phrases to support your answer. Use evidence from the text to support your answer.

   Possible response: The U.S. Constitution says the country is to be governed by the people, but the founders didn't include

   women, African Americans, or others in that statement.

2. Underline remarks from Thurgood Marshall, Frederick Douglass, Susan B. Anthony, or Ruth Bader Ginsburg from **Practice Book** pages 228–229 that relate to this main idea.

   Answers will vary.

F. Analyze how the author supports the main idea with details.

1. Reread paragraph 8 on **Practice Book** page 229. How do the details in this paragraph support the main idea? Underline the words and phrases that support your answer. Use evidence from the text to support your answer.

   Possible response: The main idea is that because of amendments, more people were included in the Constitution's

   definition of "We the people." The details that support this are that Constitutional amendments gave women and African

   Americans the right to vote.

2. On **Practice Book** pages 228–229, underline other supporting details. Explain what they tell about the main idea.

   Answers will vary.

▶ Discuss and Write

G. Synthesize your ideas about the main idea of the article.

1. With the class, discuss how the writer supported the main idea. List the examples you discuss.

   Answers will vary. Possible responses: The author used the phrase "We the people" and explained that it didn't cover all

   people at first. Quotes from Thurgood Marshall, Frederick Douglass, Susan B. Anthony, and Ruth Badar Ginsburg were

   used to support this idea.

   _____

   _____

2. Write a paragraph about how the writer supported the main idea with details. Use the questions below to organize your thoughts.

   • What specific details did the writer include?

   • How do they support or extend the main idea?

   • How do they help you to better understand the main idea?

   Answers will vary.

   _____

   _____

   _____

   _____

▶ Connect with (GUIDING QUESTION)

H. Discuss the Guiding Question: What should you do when life is unfair?

1. What made Douglass, Anthony, and Ginsburg think not everyone was being considered when "We the people" was originally written?

   Possible response: Unconstitutional situations like slavery, lack of right to vote, and not being treated equally, led

   Douglass, Anthony, and Ginsburg to think that certain people were not be counted in "We the people."

2. How might Douglass, Anthony, or Ginsburg rewrite or add to the phrase, "We the people," to make it more fair?

   Answers will vary. Possible response: Douglass might write *We the people, including African Americans.* Anthony might

   write, *We the people, including women.* Ginsburg might write *We the people, who are all equal.*

Name _____

Academic Vocabulary Review

A. Circle the Academic Vocabulary word that best fits into each sentence.

1. You show good (**origin** / **judgment**) when you look before you cross the street.

2. Suni will (**organize** / **analyze**) the problem and find a fair solution.

3. I want to learn about my relatives in Cambodia and their (**symbol** / **culture**).

B. Write a short definition for each Academic Vocabulary word. Then give a synonym.

Word	My Definition	Synonym
1. **logical**	in a way that makes sense	*Possible response:* sensible
2. **organize**	to put things in a certain order	*Possible response:* arrange
3. **origin**	where something comes from	*Possible response:* beginning
4. **symbol**	something that stands for something else	*Possible response:* sign

C. Use an Academic Vocabulary word to complete each sentence.

1. The _____structure_____ of a birdhouse and a doghouse are similar.

2. One way the two buildings _____relate_____ is that each has an open doorway.

3. She explained the school parking rules in a clear and _____logical_____ way.

4. We need to research the _____origin_____ of our town for our history report.

5. The Statue of Liberty is one _____symbol_____ of the United States.

6. The class will _____organize_____ the books so they are easier to find.

7. You can find the _____definition_____ of a word by looking in a dictionary.

Key Vocabulary Review

A. Use these Key Vocabulary words to complete the paragraph.

When the storm caused _____damage_____ to our skate park, my friends and I took action. We began a _____campaign_____ to rebuild it. First, we visited classrooms to beg and _____plead_____ with students for their _____support_____. We wanted the students to be _____informed_____, so we shared the history of the skate park and talked about its advantages. Next, we collected their signatures on a _____petition_____ to rebuild the park. Lastly, we _____volunteered_____ to clean up the site. Thanks to our efforts, it was _____inevitable_____ that the new skate park would be built.

B. Look at each Key Vocabulary word pair. Write a sentence to show how the two words are related.

Word Pairs		Sentences
1. **government**	**democracy**	*Possible response:* The United States government is a democracy.
2. **delegate**	**represents**	*Possible response:* A delegate represents the people who vote him or her into office.
3. **furious**	**complaint**	*Possible response:* If you are furious about something, you may submit a complaint.
4. **debate**	**persuade**	*Possible response:* A person can debate an issue in order to persuade others.
5. **campaign**	**support**	*Possible response:* People can show their support for a candidate by working on his or her campaign.
6. **informed**	**citizen**	*Possible response:* A citizen must be informed on the issues before he or she votes.
7. **plead**	**mercy**	*Possible response:* The suspect will plead for mercy from the jury.

Unit 7 Key Vocabulary

amend	complaint	democracy	inevitable	mercy	relent
argument	damage	furious	informed	persuade	represent
campaign	debate	government	interpret	petition	support
citizen	delegate	independence	justice	plead	volunteer

C. Complete the sentences.

1. If I could **amend** the classroom, I would _____

   Possible response: add a small station with computers so that we could have Internet access

   _____ .

2. The best way to handle an **argument** with a friend is to _____

   Possible response: listen to his or her perspective with an open mind

   _____ .

3. I am a **citizen** of _____

   Possible response: both Burundi and the United States

   _____ .

4. **Independence** is important to me because _____

   Possible response: I have many opinions and I want to be free to share them with others

   _____ .

5. Two people might **interpret** a painting differently because _____

   Possible response: they have different life experiences and perspectives

   _____ .

6. People seek **justice** from a judge because _____

   Possible response: it is a judge's responsibility to uphold the law and decide court cases fairly

   _____ .

7. When someone shows **mercy** to me, I _____

   Possible response: thank them because I feel grateful for their kindness

   _____ .

8. One thing I have wished would **relent** is _____

   Possible response: a storm so that my game would not be canceled

   _____ .

Mind Map

Use the mind map to write your ideas about how to help a community with its problems. Think about different ways to meet the challenge of helping a community.

Answers will vary.

Challenges   **Meeting the Challenges**

Feeding the World — improving farming

_____
_____

Feeding a Community

_____
_____

Feeding a Family

_____
_____

Academic Vocabulary

Think about your community. What are some actions you could take to **benefit** people in need? Use the word **benefit** in your answer.

Answers will vary.

_____
_____
_____
_____

Evaluate Argument

Read the passage. Underline the claim and circle an argument. Then evaluate the author's support for the argument.

> Attention teens! <u>The local market near our school needs to provide healthful snacks.</u> (I need an apple and a banana every day before I go to my job.) The market aisles are full of unhealthful snacks such as candy, cookies, and chips. All of them are high in sugar, fat, and salt. I certainly shouldn't eat these kinds of snacks every day, but the market offers few alternative choices. We cannot stay healthy on snacks like these!
>
> I asked the market manager to sell fruits, yogurt, and granola bars in her store. I stated that it is important for growing teens to have healthful snack choices. "You don't want to be responsible for kids having bad teeth, do you?" I asked. The manager offered to put a few new items on the shelves to test how they sell. Now it's up to you, my friends, to make good choices and buy the healthful snacks!

Write complete sentences to answer the questions.

1. What fact does the author offer to support the argument? _The market offers few alternative choices._

   _____

2. What appeals does the author use? _Appeal to ethics: Now it's up to you, my friends, to make good choices and_ _buy the healthful snacks! Appeal to emotions: We cannot stay healthy on snacks like these!_

   _____

3. List examples of inappropriate argument the author uses. _Unsupported Inferences: All of them are high in_ _sugar, fat, and salt. Fallacious Reasoning: You don't want to be responsible for kids having bad teeth, do you?_

   _____

Academic Vocabulary

Write an **appeal** to a local market. Ask the market to carry more healthful drinks, not just soda.

Answers will vary.

_____

_____

_____

_____

Use Context Clues and References: Specialized Language and Vocabulary

▶ Read the passages. Follow these steps to figure out the meaning of each underlined word or words.

1. Think about the topic of the piece and the subject area it covers.
2. See how the word fits into the sentence. Does the word seem like jargon or a **technical** term?
3. Make a guess about the meaning of the word.
4. Use the context and information about the word in a dictionary to figure out its meaning.

Follow the directions above. Write the meaning of each underlined word or words.

> Electricity is made at a power plant by huge generators. Power plants can use coal, natural gas, water, or wind to create electricity. The electrical current runs through transformers to make it stronger. This helps to move power long distances. Then the electrical charge goes through transmission lines that reach across the country, connecting both small and large communities. These lines are usually strung together above the ground. A smaller line connects to your neighborhood, and then another line brings electricity into your house. These lines can be either above the ground or buried below the ground.

power plant   a building used to make power or electricity

transformers   equipment used to change the power of energy/electricity

charge   current of electricity

transmission lines   wires or cables that carry energy/electricity

Academic Vocabulary

Give a **technical** word you learned in math class and explain what it means.

Possible response: A technical word I learned in math class is *sum*. You get a sum when you add two numbers together

to get a total. *Sum* is another word for total.

_____

_____

Critical Viewing Guide

▶ Take Notes

A. View the video. Take notes on at least three things that you learned.

Answers will vary.

_____

_____

_____

_____

_____

_____

_____

▶ Analyze the Video

B. Review your notes to help answer these questions.

1. Write two sentences to explain what was in the video.

Answers will vary.

_____

_____

2. What was the most interesting thing you learned?

Answers will vary.

_____

_____

3. What did the video tell about the different ways to feed a **community**?

Answers will vary.

_____

_____

_____

_____

Learn Key Vocabulary

Name _____

Feeding the World: Key Vocabulary

A. Study each word. Circle a number to rate how well you know it. Then complete the chart.

▲ **Agricultural** equipment often improves with new **technology**.

Rating Scale	**1** I have never seen this word before.	**2** I am not sure of the word's meaning.	**3** I know this word and can teach the word's meaning to someone else.

Key Words	Check Understanding	Deepen Understanding
❶ **agricultural** (ag-ri-**kul**-chur-ul) *adjective* **Rating:** 1 2 3	☒ related to farming ☐ related to science	Agricultural issues affect us all because _____ *Possible response: we all rely on farm products for* food _____ _____ _____ .
❷ **gene** (**jēn**) *noun* **Rating:** 1 2 3	☐ the outer lining of a cell ☒ the unit that controls what a cell is like	Your genes determine _____ *Possible response: the color of your hair and eyes* _____ _____ _____ .
❸ **mission** (**mish**-un) *noun* **Rating:** 1 2 3	☐ a laboratory that specializes in plant studies ☒ the goal of someone's work	I think a doctor's mission should be _____ *Possible response: to heal all patients to the best of* his or her ability _____ _____ _____ .
❹ **modified** (**mod**-u-fīd) *adjective* **Rating:** 1 2 3	☒ changed ☐ limited	I think modified foods _____ *Possible response: could be unsafe to eat* _____ _____ _____ .

Name _____

People have different **viewpoints** about **modified** foods such as this corn. ▶

Key Words	Check Understanding	Deepen Understanding
❺ technique (tek-**nēk**) *noun* **Rating:** 1 2 3	☒ a skilled way of doing something ☐ a desire to help others through action	A drummer will improve his or her technique if *Possible response:* he or she practices every day _____ _____ _____ .
❻ technology (tek-**nol**-u-jē) *noun* **Rating:** 1 2 3	☐ the separate parts that combine to make a functional machine ☒ a process of using scientific knowledge to improve how something is done	An example of an advance in technology is _____ *Possible response:* the invention and improvement of mobile phones _____ _____ .
❼ viewpoint (vyü-**point**) *noun* **Rating:** 1 2 3	☒ the way a person thinks about things ☐ an argument in favor of optimism	My viewpoint about watching TV on school nights is *Possible response:* that watching one hour or less is okay _____ _____ .
❽ virus (vī-rus) *noun* **Rating:** 1 2 3	☒ something that causes disease ☐ something that causes growth	If I got a virus, I would _____ *Possible response:* go to the doctor to get medicine or some other treatment _____ _____ .

B. Use at least two of the Key Vocabulary words. Write your opinion about modified foods. Explain your viewpoint.

Answers will vary.

_____

_____

_____

Analyze Argument and Support

Complete the Pro Arguments Chart as you read the first part of the selection. Create another chart with "Con Arguments" as the label for the first column. Complete the Con Arguments Chart as you read the second part of the selection. Then compare the two charts to come up with your own viewpoint about the argument.

Pro Arguments Chart

Pro Arguments	Support	Type of Evidence
1. High-tech foods are a safe way to improve farming.	1. Genetically modified corn and soybeans have been used… since 1996 and…no one has suffered.	1. Fact
2. African growers desperately need access to the best management practices and fertilizer. They need better seeds and biotechnology to help improve crop production.	2. Crop production is currently the lowest in the world per unit area of land.	2. Fact
3. The priority of Africa must be to feed its people and to sustain agricultural production and the environment.	3. Traditional agricultural practices continue to produce only low yields and poor people. These practices will not be sufficient to feed the additional millions of people who will live on the continent fifty years from now.	3. Fact; Expert Opinion
4. The people of Africa cannot wait for others to debate the merits of biotechnology. America and other developed nations must act now to allocate technologies that can prevent suffering and starvation.	4. These practices will not be sufficient to feed the additional millions of people who will live on the continent fifty years from now.	4. Expert Opinion

Feeding the World

A. Read the paragraph.
Write a Key Vocabulary word in each blank.
Reread the paragraph to make sure the words make sense.

This article presents two different opinions, or ____viewpoints____ , about altering ____genes____ to grow crops. One view states that plants should not be changed, or ____modified____ , in any way. The ____mission____ of people with this view is to make sure ____agricultural____ products are labeled if scientific ____technology____ has been used to change their chemical makeup. The other view is in favor of using engineering ____techniques____ to make crops that can grow strong to withstand ____viruses____ and to produce many fruits, vegetables, or grains.

B. Write complete sentences to answer these questions about "Feeding the World."

1. How can **technology** be both positive and negative when it comes to **modified** crops?

   Possible response: Technology can improve crops, but there may be hidden health issues that cause problems later.

   _____

   _____

   _____

   _____

   _____

   _____

2. Why do you think it is important to find ways to improve crops?

   Possible response: World hunger is a huge problem that cannot be solved unless plants can be made to grow bigger

   and better.

   _____

   _____

   _____

   _____

   _____

Vocabulary Study

Name _____

Use Context Clues: Technical Vocabulary

▶ Follow the steps below to figure out the meaning of each word.

1. Read each sentence. Study the underlined technical term.
2. Look for context clues to help you understand the meaning of the technical term.
3. Use context clues to write a meaning for each technical term.

1. When you swallow your food, it travels through a tube called the <u>esophagus</u> and ends up in your stomach where it is broken down.

   a tube that transports chewed food to your stomach

2. The company wanted to let everyone in the town know about an event they were having at the shopping mall, so they sent out a <u>press release</u> to the newspapers and the news stations.

   a written statement delivered to the media

3. The lawyer defended his client, but he lost the case. He knows his client is innocent, so he plans to <u>appeal</u> the judge's decision.

   to apply for a new trial or review

4. Miranda was feeling very ill so she visited her doctor. Her doctor gave her a <u>prescription</u> so she could get some medicine.

   a note from a doctor so the patient can get medicine

5. The <u>thorax</u> is the section of an insect's body between the head and the abdomen. The wings and legs attach to the thorax.

   the middle section of an insect's body

6. <u>Proteins</u> are important nutrients in your diet. Proteins help build and repair body tissue and give you energy so you do not feel tired.

   nutrients that give you energy and build and repair body tissue

7. The dancer worked with a <u>choreographer</u> who created special dance movements to go along with the dancer's music.

   a person who develops or creates dance movements

Name _____

Feeding the World: Academic Vocabulary Review

A. Draw a line to match each Academic Vocabulary word with its meaning.

Word	Definition
1. **appeal**	beliefs, proof, facts, or details that support a conclusion
2. **benefit**	a request for a response
3. **evidence**	based on scientific knowledge
4. **propaganda**	something that helps you
5. **technical**	faulty methods used to persuade an audience

B. Read each statement. Circle **Yes** or **No** to answer.

1. A **technical** book is based on opinion and speculation.   Yes   (No)
2. A strong community cannot be a **benefit** to its members.   Yes   (No)
3. Strong **evidence** can help support a conclusion.   (Yes)   No
4. You make an **appeal** when you raise money for a charity.   (Yes)   No
5. When you state simple facts, you use **propaganda**.   Yes   (No)

C. Use each Academic Vocabulary word in a sentence.

1. **benefit**

   Answers will vary.

   _____

   _____

2. **evidence**

   Answers will vary.

   _____

   _____

Critical Viewing Guide

▶ Take Notes

A. View the video. Take notes on at least three things that you learned.

Answers will vary.

_____

_____

_____

_____

_____

_____

_____

▶ Analyze the Video

B. Review your notes to help answer these questions.

1. Write two sentences to explain what was in the video.

Answers will vary.

_____

_____

_____

2. What was the most interesting thing you learned?

Answers will vary.

_____

_____

_____

3. Why is it important to help people in your **community**?

Answers will vary.

_____

_____

_____

_____

Learn Key Vocabulary

Soup for the Soul: Key Vocabulary

A. Study each word. Circle a number to rate how well you know it. Then complete the chart.

Rating Scale	1	2	3
	I have never seen this word before.	I am not sure of the word's meaning.	I know this word and can teach the word's meaning to someone else.

▲ Farmers grow **organic ingredients** without the use of chemicals.

Key Words	Check Understanding	Deepen Understanding
❶ benefit (ben-e-fit) *noun* Rating: 1 2 3	One **benefit** of a good _____ is better health. (diet) donut	Example: _____ *Possible response:* A good education is a benefit of going to school.
❷ career (ku-rear) *noun* Rating: 1 2 3	The _____ has a **career**. (lawyer) teen	Example: _____ *Possible response:* A job as a university professor is a career.
❸ donate (dō-nāt) *verb* Rating: 1 2 3	To **donate** is to _____ time or money. request (give)	Example: _____ *Possible response:* You can donate money to your favorite charity.
❹ founder (fown-der) *noun* Rating: 1 2 3	A **founder** _____ something. (begins) ends	Example: _____ *Possible response:* A person who starts a volunteer program is the program's founder.

Consider a **career** as a chef if you find **inspiration** in cooking for others. ▶

Key Words	Check Understanding	Deepen Understanding
❺ ingredient (in-**grē**-dē-unt) *noun* **Rating:** 1 2 3	**Ingredients** are the _____ we use to make a meal. (**parts**) **pots**	Example: _____ *Possible response:* Noodles, tomato sauce, and parmesan cheese are ingredients for spaghetti. _____ _____
❻ inspiration (in-spu-**rā**-shun) *noun* **Rating:** 1 2 3	**Inspiration** _____ people to act. (**moves**) **prevents**	Example: _____ *Possible response:* A beautiful landscape can be an inspiration for a painter. _____ _____
❼ organic (or-**gan**-ik) *adjective* **Rating:** 1 2 3	**Organic** foods are _____ . (**natural**) **modified**	Example: _____ *Possible response:* Organic tomatoes come from a farm that does not use pesticides. _____ _____
❽ organization (or-gu-nu-**zā**-shun) *noun* **Rating:** 1 2 3	An **organization** is made up of _____ . **animals** (**people**)	Example: _____ *Possible response:* The local PTA is an organization. _____ _____ _____

B. Use at least two of the Key Vocabulary words. Write about someone who inspired you to take action.

Answers will vary.

_____

_____

_____

Compare Writing About the Same Topic

Complete the Venn Diagram to compare the article about First Slice with the "Yes!" and "No!" essays.

Venn Diagram

First Slice   **Both**   **"Yes!" and "No!"**

Information that is provided:

- what inspired Diaz to found First Slice
- the kinds of food First Slice serves
- where ingredients for the food come from
- when First Slice serves soup
- the big lesson Diaz learned
- how Diaz works with volunteers

Topic:

running a restaurant

Information that is provided:

Yes!
- running a restaurant can be creative
- you make other people happy
- you get to be part of a community

No!
- running a restaurant is very tiring
- you have a lot of responsibility
- you may lose your job

Soup for the Soul

Key Vocabulary

benefits	ingredients
career	inspiration
donate	organic
founder	organization

A. Read the paragraph.
Write a Key Vocabulary word in each blank.
Reread the paragraph to make sure the words make sense.

Mary Ellen Diaz is truly an ___inspiration___ to many people. She has made it her job, or ___career___,

to help people who are less fortunate. She is the ___founder___ who started an ___organization___ to feed

the homeless in Chicago. She calls her soup kitchen First Slice because she wants to give the very

best to people who rarely get special treatment. Diaz uses only the freshest, healthiest ___ingredients___

to prepare delicious meals. In fact most of the produce she uses is ___organic___ and grown locally.

I ___donate___ my time by volunteering to help in the kitchen. It's wonderful to see how this innovative

soup kitchen helps others. Also, one of the best ___benefits___ of working at First Slice is getting to

sample the soup!

B. Write complete sentences to answer these questions about "Soup for the Soul."

1. What would be the hardest part of running an **organization** like First Slice?

   Possible response: You would be able to help some people, but you would not be able to feed everyone on the

   street who is hungry. _____

   _____

   _____

   _____

2. Imagine that you are the **founder** of an **organization** that helps people. What **benefit**
   do you provide? Why?

   Answers will vary. _____

   _____

   _____

   _____

Vocabulary Study

Use Context Clues: Jargon

▶ Follow the steps below to figure out the meaning of the underlined words.

1. Read each sentence. Look carefully at the underlined word or phrase.
2. Underline the context that helped you determine the meaning.
3. Use the context to help you write the meaning of the underlined word or words.

1. The teacher asked her class to use manipulatives, such as blocks and tiles, to help them understand the lesson.

   manipulatives _objects that are used during lessons to help students learn_

2. The camper had trouble pitching the tent because it was dark outside and they could not find the instructions.

   pitching the tent _assembling the tent_

3. The waitress found out that French fries were eighty-sixed, so she had to tell the diner to order something else to eat.

   eighty-sixed _to have no more of something_

4. New members of the military go to boot camp to learn basic skills.

   boot camp _a place where the military trains in basic skills_

5. My friend texted me with her new cell phone and I read her message.

   texted _to send a typed message with a cell phone_

6. I wanted to go out to dinner with ten of my friends, but the restaurant manager said that it would cost $20 per head.

   per head _each person_

7. The earthquake in California that measured 6.0 on the Richter Scale was very strong and knocked dishes off the shelf.

   Richter Scale _a way that the strength of an earthquake is measured_

8. Since the hikers were only going to be gone for one day, they brought their lighter day packs.

   day packs _a smaller backpack for a day trip_

Name _____

Soup for the Soul: Academic Vocabulary Review

A. Use your own words to tell what each Academic Vocabulary word means.

Word	Meaning
1. **appeal**	*Possible response:* a request for a response
2. **benefit**	*Possible response:* something that helps you
3. **technical**	*Possible response:* based on scientific knowledge

B. Answer the questions in complete sentences.

1. How could you make an **appeal** to provide a **benefit** for your community?

   Possible response: I could ask people to not litter in the park.

   _____

   _____

   _____

   _____

   _____

2. Who might read a **technical** journal?

   Possible response: A doctor or a scientist might read a technical journal.

   _____

   _____

   _____

   _____

   _____

Name _____

Critical Viewing Guide

▶ Take Notes

A. View the images. Take notes on at least three things that you learned.

Answers will vary.

_____

_____

_____

_____

_____

_____

_____

▶ Analyze the Images

B. Review your notes to help answer these questions.

1. Write two sentences to explain what was in the images.

Answers will vary.

_____

_____

_____

2. What was the most interesting thing you learned?

Answers will vary.

_____

_____

_____

3. Tell about the ways food can connect people in a community.

Answers will vary.

_____

_____

_____

_____

Learn Key Vocabulary

Name _____

The Girl and the Chenoo: Key Vocabulary

A. Study each word. Circle a number to rate how well you know it. Then complete the chart.

Rating Scale	**1** I have never seen this word before.	**2** I am not sure of the word's meaning.	**3** I know this word and can teach the word's meaning to someone else.

▲ A restaurant can provide a space for **relatives** to enjoy a meal and **engage** in lively conversation.

Key Words	Check Understanding	Deepen Understanding
❶ **brag** (brag) *verb* **Rating:** 1 2 3	Circle the synonym for **brag**. (**show off**) rest	Example: _____ *Possible response:* to tell everyone how great you are _____ _____ _____
❷ **confident** (kon-fi-dent) *adjective* **Rating:** 1 2 3	Circle the synonym for **confident**. unsure (**secure**)	Example: _____ *Possible response:* to believe in yourself _____ _____ _____
❸ **engage** (en-gāj) *verb* **Rating:** 1 2 3	Circle the synonym for **engage**. (**participate**) disguise	Example: _____ *Possible response:* to take part in an activity _____ _____ _____
❹ **hesitant** (hez-i-tent) *adjective* **Rating:** 1 2 3	Circle the synonym for **hesitant**. excited (**uncertain**)	Example: _____ *Possible response:* feeling or acting unsure _____ _____ _____

Name _____

> **Did You Know?**
> Confucius, a Chinese philosopher, once said, "A superior man is **modest** in his speech, but exceeds in his actions." Do you agree?

Key Words	Check Understanding	Deepen Understanding
❺ modest (**mod**-ist) *adjective* **Rating:** 1 2 3	Circle the synonym for **modest**. rich (**shy**)	Example: _____ *Possible response:* not bringing attention to yourself
❻ react (**rē**-akt) *verb* **Rating:** 1 2 3	Circle the synonym for **react**. (**respond**) improve	Example: _____ *Possible response:* to show your feelings
❼ relative (**rel**-u-tiv) *noun* **Rating:** 1 2 3	Circle the synonym for **relative**. neighbor (**family member**)	Example: _____ *Possible response:* a person in your family
❽ talented (**tal**-en-tid) *adjective* **Rating:** 1 2 3	Circle the synonym for **talented**. (**gifted**) prepared	Example: _____ *Possible response:* to be naturally skilled at something

B. Use at least two of the Key Vocabulary words. Write about a time you acted with confidence.

Answers will vary.

_____

_____

Analyze Drama

As you read the play, analyze what the dialogue tells you about the events. Study the dialogue in the left column. In the right column, record what the dialogue reveals about events.

Dialogue and Events Chart

Dialogue	Events the Dialogue Reveal
LITTLE LISTENER. No, uncle. My brothers have not yet returned…	The nephews have gone on a hunt but have not returned.
SECOND BROTHER. …two mountain lions… grabbed my two deer and carried them off… I did bring this. This very fat rabbit.	The brothers brought back from their hunt only one rabbit.
LITTLE LISTENER. I can see that you are all brave, so I'll tell you. A Chenoo is a huge monster whose hunger is never satisfied…	Little Listener tells the children about a scary creature called the Chenoo.
LITTLE LISTENER. I, too, have seen those tracks… And I know that those were not bear tracks… But I mustn't speak the name out loud… I will remain quiet, but I must make a plan.	Little Listener will make a plan to deal with the Chenoo.
LITTLE LISTENER. I think this may be enough food… And I have spread out all of our blankets to make a resting place back here. Yes, I think everything is ready.	Little Listener's plan is to attract the Chenoo with food and a place to rest.

The Girl and the Chenoo

A. Read the paragraph.
Write a Key Vocabulary word in each blank.
Reread the paragraph to make sure the words make sense.

My granddaughter, Little Listener, is a very clever and ____talented____ person. She is very ____confident____ and sure of herself, but is also quite ____modest____ . She never boasts or ____brags____ about things she has done. She never ____engages____ in any of the silly games her brothers play. However, I am a bit ____hesitant____ to say that Little Listener is my favorite ____relative____ . How would my grandsons ____react____ if I stated my preference? They might actually agree with me!

B. Write complete sentences to answer these questions about "The Girl and the Chenoo."

1. How do Little Listener's responsibilities help her?

Possible response: Little Listener does all the work keeping the camp running, feeding the people, and taking care of the

children. These duties give her experience, so that she knows how to handle the Chenoo when he comes around.

_____

_____

_____

_____

_____

2. If you were Little Listener, would you also agree to go on the hunting trip with your brothers? Explain.

Possible response: Yes, I would go on the hunting trip because my brothers would be helpless without me. They would

need me to take care of them.

_____

_____

_____

_____

_____

Use Context Clues: Specialized Language

▶ Follow the steps below to figure out the meaning of each underlined word.

1. Read each sentence. Study the underlined word.
2. Use context to help you figure out the specialized language.
3. Write the meaning of each underlined word.

1. My math teacher asked us to plot <u>integers</u>, which are negative numbers, whole numbers, and zero, on a line.

   integers _negative numbers, whole numbers, and zero_

2. Some spas offer a hot, dry <u>sauna</u> where people can sit and refresh their skin.

   sauna _a hot and dry room where people sit_

3. My friend's little sister showed us how to spin her toy <u>dreidel</u> like a top during Hanukkah.

   dreidel _a toy that is shaped like a top and spins_

4. Native Americans sometimes wear <u>moccasins</u> that are made from animal skin on their feet.

   moccasins _shoes that are made from animal skin_

5. The Japanese woman wore a beautiful <u>kimono</u> that reached the ground and was decorated with bright flowers.

   kimono _a long, decorated article of clothing_

6. The woman put her baby in the <u>cradleboard</u> and lifted it onto her back so she could work.

   cradleboard _a baby carrier that is worn on the back_

7. Some Native American men wore feathered <u>headdresses</u> that symbolized their power.

   headdresses _a feathered ornament worn on the head_

8. When you go skiing, you can wait in the <u>lodge</u> and have a cup of hot chocolate to warm up.

   lodge _a warm place near to where people go skiing_

9. The airplane's engine was so loud it must have measured over 120 <u>decibels</u>.

   decibels _a unit of measurement for the loudness of a sound_

The Girl and the Chenoo: Academic Vocabulary Review

A. Draw a line to connect the beginning and ending of each sentence.

Beginning of Sentence	Ending of Sentence
1. Those songs **appeal** to	my sense of rhythm.
2. We built a garden as a **benefit** for the	some **technical** information on genes.
3. A forward slant	community to share.
4. This science journal includes	is **characteristic** of Betsy's handwriting.

B. Use your own words to tell what each Academic Vocabulary word means.

1. **appeal** _Answers will vary._

2. **characteristic** _Answers will vary._

3. **technical** _Answers will vary._

C. Describe a **characteristic** of the foods that **appeal** to you.

Answers will vary.

_____

_____

from The Omnivore's Dilemma

by Michael Pollan

VIEWPOINT #1

There Goes the Sun

1   Like most factories, **the industrial farm** is powered with fossil fuels. There's the natural gas in the fertilizer and the fossil fuel energy it takes to make the **pesticides**, the diesel used by the tractors, and the fuel needed to harvest, dry, and transport the corn. Add it all up and you find that every bushel of corn from an industrial farm requires about half a gallon of oil to grow. That's around seventy-five gallons of oil per acre of corn.

E.2

2   Here's another way to look at it. Calories, like the calories in food, are units of energy. On the industrial farm, it takes about ten calories of fossil fuel energy to produce one calorie of food energy. That means the industrial farm is using up more energy than it is producing. This is the opposite of what happened before chemical fertilizers. Back then, the Naylor

E.2

farm produced more than two calories of food energy for every calorie of fossil fuel energy invested. In terms of energy, the modern farm is a **losing proposition.** It's too bad we can't simply drink the **petroleum** directly—it would be more efficient.

3   The factory farm produces more food much faster than the old solar-based farm. But the system only works as long as fossil fuel energy is cheap.

Eating Oil

4   My industrial **organic** meal is nearly as drenched in fossil fuel as a non-organic meal. Asparagus traveling in a **747** from Argentina; blackberries trucked up from Mexico; a salad chilled to thirty-six degrees from the moment it was picked to the moment I walk it out the doors of my supermarket. That takes a lot of energy and a lot of fossil fuel. Organic farmers

---

Key Vocabulary
- **viewpoint** *n.*, a way of thinking about something
- **organic** *adj.*, naturally grown

In Other Words
the industrial farm a farm that is run with machinery and technology
pesticides chemicals that kill unwanted plants and animals
losing proposition plan that won't work
petroleum fuel
747 jet plane

generally use less fuel to grow their crops. Yet most of the fuel burned by the food industry isn't used to grow food. Almost 80 percent of the fuel burned is used to process food and move it around. This is just as true for an organic bag of lettuce as a non-organic one.

F.1

5 The original organic food movement thought organic farming should be sustainable. That means it should be, as much as possible, a closed loop, recycling fertility and using renewable energy. The industrial organic food chain is anything but a closed, renewable loop. The food in our organic meal had floated to us on a sea of petroleum just as surely as the corn-based meal we'd had from McDonald's.

6 Well, at least we didn't eat it in the car.

"...the industrial farm is using up more energy than it is producing."

Food Miles and Jet-Setting Carrots

7 The term "food miles" tells you how far your food has traveled from where it was originally grown to your supermarket. In the U.S., that's usually about 1,500 miles—or 27 times farther than it would travel to a local market. For example, while carrots at the farmers' market are likely grown within 50 miles of your house, the carrots you find at the grocery store traveled around 1,800 miles (or about the distance between New York City and Denver). Many of our fruits, vegetables, and meat also come from foreign countries—and in a typical TV dinner, at least five of the **ingredients** are shipped in from abroad.

Key Vocabulary
- **ingredient** *n.*, a part of a mixture

Math for Locavores

by Stephen Budiansky

VIEWPOINT #2

1   The local food movement now threatens to devolve into another one of those self-indulgent—and self-defeating—do-gooder **dogmas**. Words like "sustainability" and "food miles" are thrown around without any clear understanding of the larger picture of energy and land use. For instance, it is sinful in New York City to buy a tomato grown in a California field because of the energy spent to truck it across the country; it is virtuous to buy one grown in a lavishly heated greenhouse in, say, **the Hudson Valley**.

2   One popular and oft-repeated statistic is that is takes 36 (sometimes it's 97) calories of fossil fuel energy to bring one calorie of iceberg lettuce from California to the East Coast. That's an **apples and oranges** comparison to begin with, because you can't eat petroleum or burn iceberg lettuce.

3   It is also an almost complete misrepresentation of reality, as those numbers reflect the entire energy cost of producing lettuce from seed to dinner table, not just transportation. Studies have shown that whether it's grown in California or Maine, or whether it's organic or conventional, about 5,000 calories of energy go into one pound of lettuce. Given how efficient trains and tractor-trailers are, shipping a head of lettuce across the country actually adds next to nothing to the total energy bill. Overall, transportation accounts for about 14 percent of the total energy consumed by the American food system.

4   Other favorite targets of **sustainability advocates** include the fertilizers and chemicals used in modern farming. But their share of the food system's energy use is even lower, about 8 percent.

Key Vocabulary
- **viewpoint** *n.*, a way of thinking about something

In Other Words
dogmas beliefs
the Hudson Valley a place about an hour from New York City
apples and oranges unequal
sustainability advocates people who encourage farming practices that don't destroy resources

5 The real energy hog, it turns out, is not industrial agriculture at all, but you and me. Home preparation and storage account for 32 percent of all energy use in our food system, the largest component by far.

6 A single 10-mile round-trip by car to the grocery store or the farmers' market will easily eat up about 14,000 calories of fossil fuel energy. Just running your refrigerator for a week consumes 9,000 calories of energy. That assumes it's one of the latest high-efficiency models; otherwise, you can double that figure. Cooking and running dishwashers, freezers, and second or third refrigerators (more than 25 percent of American households have more than one) all add major hits. Indeed, households make up for 22 percent of all the energy **expenditures** in the United States.

"The real energy hog . . . is you and me."

7 Agriculture, on the other hand, accounts for just 2 percent of our nation's energy usage; that energy is mainly devoted to running farm machinery and manufacturing fertilizer. In return for that quite modest energy investment, we have fed hundreds of millions of people, liberated tens of millions from backbreaking **manual labor** and spared hundreds of millions of acres for nature preserve forests and parks that otherwise would have come under the plow.

8 Eating locally grown produce is a fine thing in many ways. But it is not an end in itself, nor is it a virtue in itself. The **relative pittance** of our energy budget that we spend on modern farming is one of the wisest energy investments we can make, when we honestly look at what it returns to our land, our economy, our environment and our well-being.

In Other Words
expenditures spending
manual labor work done by hand
relative pittance very small amount in comparison to another amount

▶ Read for Understanding

A. From what kind of text is this passage taken? How do you know?

Possible response: persuasive essays; The essays have labels that say "Viewpoint #1" and "Viewpoint #2."

B. Write a sentence that tells the topic of the selection.

Possible response: This text is mostly about the energy it takes to transport food from farm to table and whether that energy

usage is unsustainable.

▶ Reread and Summarize

C. On **Practice Book** pages 260–263, circle the 3–5 most important words in each section. Make notes about why you chose each word. Why is the word important in the section?

1. Passage 1, Section 1: (paragraphs 1–3)

Answers will vary.

2. Passage 1, Section 2: (paragraphs 4–7)

Answers will vary.

3. Passage 2, Section 1: (paragraphs 1–5)

Answers will vary.

4. Passage 2, Section 2: (paragraphs 6–8)

Answers will vary.

D. Use your topic sentence from above and your notes to write a summary of the selection.

Possible response: Producing and transporting food from farm to table uses up a lot of energy. Pollan argues that this energy

usage is wasteful and unsustainable. Budiansky argues that transportation is only a small part of food production. He believes

the benefits of locally grown food are not as significant as the benefits of modern farming.

⏵ Reread and Analyze

E. Analyze the speaker's viewpoint.

1. Reread paragraphs 1–3 in "The Omnivore's Dilemma" on **Practice Book** page 260. What is the issue? What is the author's position on the issue? What evidence does he use to support his position?

   Possible responses: The issue is the amount of energy it takes to produce and transport food from farm to consumer. The

   author believes that the energy used by the "factory farm" system is wasteful. He uses statistics about gallons of oil and

   calories of fossil fuel to support his position.

2. Underline phrases and sentences on **Practice Book** pages 260–263 that help support the author's argument. What evidence does he give to support his position?

   Possible responses: He tells how much oil a bushel of corn needs to get from farm to table. He compares the amount

   of energy used to produce food to the amount of energy the food provides the consumer, in an old-fashioned farm and a

   modern farm.

F. Analyze the facts and emotions used to support an argument.

1. Reread paragraphs 4–6 in "The Omnivore's Dilemma" on **Practice Book** pages 260–261. What are some facts presented by the author? Underline those facts.

   Answers will vary. Possible response: "Almost 80 percent of the fuel burned is used to process food and move it around."

2. How does the author use emotion to convince readers of the argument? Give one example.

   Answers will vary. Possible response: "The food in our organic meal had floated to us on a sea of petroleum just as surely as

   the corn-based meal we'd had from McDonald's."

▶ Reread and Analyze

G. Identify facts that support the author's argument.

1. Reread paragraphs 2–6 in "Math for Locavores" **Practice Book** pages 262–263. What are three facts Budiansky uses to support his argument? How are those facts different from the facts Michael Pollan uses in "The Omnivore's Dilemma"?

   Possible responses: Facts: 5,000 calories of energy go into one pound of lettuce; transportation is 14 percent of the

   energy consumed by the American food system; home preparation and storage account for the largest portions. Budiansky

   uses facts that show that the biggest energy consumption is not machines or transportation.

2. Underline the facts in paragraphs 2–6 that you find best support Budiansky's argument. Explain why.

   Answers will vary.

   _____

   _____

H. Analyze opposing arguments.

1. Reread paragraph 8 on **Practice Book** page 263. How does the author sum up his argument?

   Possible response: The amount of energy used to transport food is too small a factor to be a real problem. The benefits of

   modern farming outweigh the drawbacks.

   _____

2. How does Budiansky's argument compare with Pollan's argument? Which argument do you find more convincing, and why?

   Answers will vary.

   _____

   _____

   _____

   _____

⏵ Discuss and Write

I. Synthesize your ideas about analyzing arguments.

1. With the class, discuss how Pollan and Budiansky used evidence to support their viewpoints. List three facts or other pieces of evidence used by each author.

Answers will vary. Possible response: Pollan: Amount of oil used for corn; ratio of food produced to oil used; how much

fossil fuel is used to transport instead of to produce food. Budiansky: calories of energy that go into one pound of lettuce;

percentage of energy used for transportation vs. storage; how much energy agriculture uses

2. Choose one author's viewpoint. Write a paragraph about how the author developed his argument. Use the questions below to organize your thoughts.

- What is the topic? What is the author's argument about the topic?
- What facts does the author use as evidence?
- What language does the author use to convince the reader?
- How does this argument help you see the author's viewpoint?

Answers will vary.

_____

_____

_____

_____

⏵ Connect with 🄠 GUIDING QUESTION

J. Discuss the Guiding Question: How can we provide for our communities?

1. What is each author's opinion on how food production and transportation affect communities?

Possible response: Pollan thinks that food produced and transported from far away is wasteful. Budiansky thinks that

modern farming is a smart energy investment.

_____

2. With which viewpoint do you most agree? Which viewpoint do you think would most benefit your community? Why?

Answers will vary.

Name _____

Academic Vocabulary Review

Academic Vocabulary	
appeal	evaluate
benefit	evidence
characteristic	propaganda
convince	technical

A. Circle the Academic Vocabulary word that best fits into each sentence.

1. Nicki tried to (**convince** / **evaluate**) me to try a new food.

2. Television commercials often contain (**benefits** / **propaganda**) that makes unsupported claims.

B. Read each statement. Circle **Yes** or **No** to answer.

1. A poem is a type of **technical** writing.   Yes   **No**

2. When you answer someone, you make an **appeal**.   Yes   **No**

C. Respond in complete sentences.

1. Describe one **characteristic** of your community that provides a **benefit** for many people.

   Answers will vary.

   _____

2. List two kinds of **evidence** police might use to solve a crime.

   Answers will vary.

   _____

3. Describe a kind of **propaganda** that you have read, heard, or seen.

   Answers will vary.

   _____

4. How would you **evaluate** the last movie you saw?

   Answers will vary.

   _____

Key Vocabulary Review

A. Read each sentence. Circle the Key Vocabulary word that best fits into each sentence.

1. A teacher's (**mission** / **organization**) is to educate others.

2. Farmers are most interested in (**technology** / **agricultural**) issues.

3. I have many (**relatives** / **viewpoints**) from my mother's side of the family.

4. A (**virus** / **gene**) controls what a living cell is like.

5. The (**founder** / **inspiration**) of the company was also the president.

6. (**Organic** / **Modified**) foods are grown without chemicals.

7. A (**virus** / **gene**) causes disease in plants and animals.

8. When you practice a sport, you improve your (**benefit** / **technique**).

B. Write the synonym and antonym for each word.

Word	Choose from These Words		Synonym	Antonym
1. **benefit**	loss	gain	gain	loss
2. **career**	hobby	job	job	hobby
3. **confident**	certain	insecure	certain	insecure
4. **donate**	give	take	give	take
5. **hesitant**	bold	unsure	unsure	bold
6. **modest**	showy	shy	shy	showy
7. **modified**	changed	unchanged	changed	unchanged
8. **talented**	gifted	unskilled	gifted	unskilled

Unit 8 Key Vocabulary

agricultural	confident	gene	mission	organization	technique
benefit	donate	hesitant	modest	react	technology
brag	engage	ingredient	modified	relative	viewpoint
career	founder	inspiration	organic	talented	virus

C. Answer the questions in complete sentences.

1. Why is it annoying to hear people **brag** ?

   Possible response: It is annoying to hear people brag because they sound self-centered and

   act superior to everyone else.

2. What kinds of activities do you **engage** in after school?

   Possible response: I take guitar lessons, ride my bike, or play basketball with my friends.

3. What **ingredients** go in your favorite meal?

   Possible response: The ingredients in my favorite meal are pizza dough, tomato sauce,

   mozzarella cheese, sausage, and green peppers.

4. Who is a source of **inspiration** for you? Explain.

   Possible response: My dance instructor is a source of inspiration for me because he can express powerful

   emotions without words.

5. What **organization** would you like to help? Explain.

   Possible response: I would like to help a volunteer organization that works with rescue and guide dogs.

6. How would you **react** if you saw someone steal your backpack?

   Possible response: I would confront the person right away and demand that he or she return the backpack.

7. How has **technology** improved travel?

   Possible response: We can travel faster and go to new places with technological advances in cars, trains,

   planes, and space shuttles.

8. What is your **viewpoint** on cell phones at school?

   Possible response: I think cell phones should be allowed, but students shouldn't use them in class.

Grammar Practice

1 What Do You Need for a Sentence?

A Subject and a Predicate

A complete sentence has two parts: the **subject** and the **predicate**.

subject   predicate

Paula goes to school with Brett.

To find the parts, in most sentences, ask yourself:

1. Whom or what is the sentence about? The answer is the **subject**.

2. What does the subject do? The answer is the **predicate**.

Sentence	Whom or What?	What Does the Subject Do?
Brett needs help in science.	Brett	needs help in science
Paula helps him.	Paula	helps him

Try It

A. Draw a line from each subject to a predicate to make a sentence. Possible responses:

1. Rosa   finds the backpack under a tree.

2. Her backpack   looks for her backpack.

3. Rico   has her books, homework, and keys in it.

4. He   helps Rosa look for her backpack.

B. Complete each sentence with a subject or a predicate. Possible responses:

5. _____ The coach _____ teaches me to play basketball.

6. Craig _____ works at the toy store _____.

7. _____ Martha _____ shares her lunch with me.

8. The new girl _____ makes friends at school _____.

C. Answer the questions about people who are your friends. Circle the subjects in your answers. Underline the predicates.

9. Who is one of your friends? _____ is one of my friends.

10. What do you and your friend do together? We _____.

11. How does your friend help you? _____

_____

12. How do you help your friend? _____

_____

D. (13–16) What makes someone a good friend? Write at least four complete sentences. Circle the subjects. Underline the predicates.

_____

_____

_____

_____

_____

Edit It

E. (17–20) Edit this journal entry. Fill in the five missing subjects or predicates. The first one is done for you.   Possible responses:

May 23

Celia has lived next door to me for two years.
I
ᴧNever knew her before. I locked myself out of my
                                            were closed
house today. The windows and doors. Celia invited
                              ᴧ played board games
me in. I Stayed with her until Mom got home. We.
        ᴧ   ᴧ
Now I have a new friend. I Am glad.
                           ᴧ

Proofreader's Marks
Add text:
She gave me lunch.
Do not capitalize:
We had Fun.
See all Proofreader's Marks on page xi.

❷ What Is a Fragment?

It's an Incomplete Sentence.

A **fragment** is a group of words that begins with a capital letter and ends with a period. It looks like a sentence, but it is not complete. A subject or a verb may be missing.

Fragments	Sentences
1. Is a big city school.	My school is a big city school.
2. Has hundreds of kids in it.	It has hundreds of kids in it.
3. Many of the students.	Many of the students hang out together.
4. My friends members of one group.	My friends are members of one group.

Try It

A. Write whether each group of words is a fragment or a sentence. If it is a fragment, add a subject or a verb. Write the complete sentence. Possible responses:

1. Some groups of students athletes. __fragment; Some groups of students are athletes.__

   _____

2. Hang out together. __fragment; The athletes hang out together.__

3. Another group likes math, music, and computers. __sentence__

4. People that group is really smart. __fragment; People think that group is really smart.__

   _____

B. Fix the fragments. Add a subject or a verb. Possible responses:

5. My friends and I ⌃are friendly with all the groups.

6. ⌃We Play sports.

7. I ⌃compete on the math team, too.

8. All of the groups ⌃have interesting kids in them.

Proofreader's Marks
Add text:
The math team ⌃meets on Fridays.
Do not capitalize:
I like Football.
See all Proofreader's Marks on page xi.

C. Answer the questions about groups in your school. Use complete sentences.

9. What groups exist in your school? _____

_____

10. What groups are you part of? _____

_____

11. How do the groups get along with one another? _____

_____

D. (12–15) Write at least four sentences about different school groups. Then read your sentences aloud. Fix any fragments that you hear.

_____

_____

_____

_____

_____

Edit It

E. (16–20) Edit the journal entry. Fix the five fragments.   Possible responses:

September 29

I am a new kid in this school. At first, ^I was

really worried. My old school had a lot of groups.

^It Was hard to make friends there. Everyone in this

school ^gets along, though. All the kids ^are friendly. I have many

new friends. Some of them ^play sports. Others are

in the drama club. The kids are all nice to each

other.

Proofreader's Marks

Add text:
                    edits
Manny ^the student
newspaper.

Do not capitalize:
I attend a $\cancel{S}$chool in the
city.

See all Proofreader's Marks
on page xi.

3 How Can You Fix Some Fragments?

Combine Neighboring Sentences.

Writers may create a fragment by starting a new sentence when they shouldn't. These fragments are easy to fix. Just combine the fragment with the sentence before it.

1. ⌐————— sentence —————⌐ ⌐————— fragment —————⌐
   I live in a neighborhood. That is multicultural.
   I live in a neighborhood that is multicultural.

2. ⌐————— sentence —————⌐ ⌐————— fragment —————⌐
   I enjoy my neighborhood. And all the people in it.
   I enjoy my neighborhood and all the people in it.

Try It

A. Combine each fragment with the neighboring sentence. Write the new sentence.

1. My parents left Italy. When I was a baby. _My parents left Italy when I was a baby._

2. We have many neighbors. Who come from different countries. _We have many neighbors who come from different countries._

3. I met a boy from Greece. When I started school. _I met a boy from Greece when I started school._

4. I like to eat at his house. Because his mom is a great cook. _I like to eat at his house because his mom is a great cook._

5. All the neighbors get together. And have a big dinner. _All the neighbors get together and have a big dinner._

6. I love these dinners. Because all the food is delicious. _I love these dinners because all the food is delicious._

B. Combine the fragments with the sentences to make new sentences. You can use sentences and fragments more than once. Possible responses:

Sentences	Fragments
I like my neighborhood. My neighbors have different backgrounds. We all get along well.	And speak many languages. Even though we come from different countries. Because of all the different people.

7. I like my neighborhood because of all the different people.

8. My neighbors have different backgrounds and speak many languages.

9. We all get along well even though we come from different countries.

Write It

C. Fix each fragment by combining it with a sentence. Write new sentences about living with people from different countries.

10. Because the students come from many countries.

11. My friend from India.

12. Before I tasted Chinese food.

D. (13–15) Would you like to live in a neighborhood with people from many countries? Write at least three sentences to explain your reasons. Read your sentences aloud. Fix any fragments.

4 What Is a Sentence About?

The Subject

The **complete subject** can be one word or several words. Zoom in on the most important word. Is it a noun? A **noun** is the name of a person, place, thing, or idea.

Nouns in the Subject	
Person	Joshua player
Place	room
Thing	ball ambulance
Idea	pain

1. **Joshua** played soccer yesterday.
2. A **player** kicked the ball hard.
3. The **ball** flew into Joshua's leg.
4. The **pain** was serious.
5. An **ambulance** took him to the hospital.
6. The emergency **room** was quite busy.

Try It

A. Write a noun to complete the subject of each sentence about Joshua.   Possible responses:

1. The _____doctor_____ took x-rays.

2. Joshua's _____leg_____ was broken.

3. Now the unhappy _____boy_____ has a cast and crutches.

4. His _____friends_____ signed the cast and drew pictures on it.

5. The colorful _____cast_____ has to stay on for six weeks.

B. (6–10) Complete the paragraph. Write nouns to complete the subjects.   Possible responses:

   Joshua's soccer _____team_____ felt bad for Joshua. The _____players_____ decided to cheer him up with a dinner. The big _____dinner_____ was delicious. Joshua's _____kitchen_____ was full of all kinds of food. His friends' _____kindness_____ made Joshua feel a lot happier.

C. Suppose you broke your leg. Answer the questions about how life would be different. Circle the most important noun in the complete subject.

11. Who would help you carry your books at school? _____ would help me

_____.

12. How would you get up and down stairs? I would _____.

13. What activities would have to change? I wouldn't be able to _____.

14. What kinds of people would help you get better? _____

_____.

D. (15–18) How can you help friends or family who are sick? Write at least four sentences telling what you could do to help out. Use a different subject in each sentence.

_____

_____

_____

_____

_____

E. (19–25) Edit the letter. Fix the seven mistakes by adding subjects. Possible responses:

Dear Grandpa,

    I want to thank you for your visit today. The pretty ^flowers really brighten my hospital room. This broken ^leg is a problem for me. The ^crutches make it hard to get around. The ^nurses praised my effort, though. My ^doctor just stopped by. I can go home soon. This ^hospital is nice. Home is better, though. My ^mama will take good care of me there.

               Love,

               Joshua

Proofreader's Marks

Add text:
Grandpa
^visited Joshua at the hospital.

See all Proofreader's Marks on page xi.

5 What's a Plural Noun?

A Word That Names More Than One Thing

One	More Than One
A **singular noun** names one thing.	A **plural noun** names more than one thing.

Use these spelling rules for forming plural nouns.

1. To make most nouns plural, just add -s.

2. If the noun ends in **s, z, sh, ch,** or **x**, add -es.

3. If the noun ends in **y** after the consonant, change the **y** to i and add -es.

4. If the noun ends in **y** after a vowel, just add -s.

5. Some nouns have special plural forms.

One	More Than One
hope	hopes
dish	dishes
memory	memories
valley	valleys
child	children
woman	women

Try It

A. (1–4) Read these nouns: **children, dream, family, wishes.** Which nouns are singular and which are plural? Put each noun in the correct column. Then add its other form.

Singular Nouns (one)		Plural Nouns (more than one)	
child	dream	children	dreams
family	wish	families	wishes

B. (5–10) Write nouns from the chart to complete the paragraph. Possible responses:

My _____family_____ lives in the same building as two other

_____families_____. All of the _____children_____ are

good friends. We share a lot of the same _____wishes/dreams_____ and

_____dreams/wishes_____. One _____dream/wish_____ we all have is to

go to college. I hope it comes true for all of us.

C. How can you get to know someone well? Circle the singular noun in each question you might ask someone. Then use its plural form to answer the question.

11. What (city) do you like to visit? *Cities I like to visit are* _____ .

12. What is your favorite (movie)? _____

13. What (country) would you like to visit? _____

14. Do you like the (beach)? _____

D. (15–18) Write at least four sentences about people you know well. Use at least two singular nouns and two plural nouns in your response.

_____

_____

_____

_____

_____

Edit It

E. (19–25) Edit the journal entry. Fix the seven mistakes with nouns.

November 4

I thought I knew my mother really well. Then
she surprised me. She told me many ~~story~~ stories about
her youth. Mom had a lot of ~~hobby~~ hobbies. She had two
~~bicycle~~ bicycles. She was on a cycling team with four
other ~~woman~~ women. She took many ~~journey~~ journeys to other
~~country~~ countries. My mother would like to cycle around
the world. One of my ~~wish~~ wishes is to go with her.

Proofreader's Marks

Change text:
My parents were ~~childs~~ children
once.

See all Proofreader's Marks on page xi.

6 How Do I Show Possession?

One Way Is to Use a Possessive Noun.

Use a **possessive noun** to show that someone owns, or possesses, something. Add **'s** if the possessive noun names one owner.

My mother left a note for us. My **mother's** note was on the refrigerator.

My brother writes notes on our calendar. My **brother's** notes help us know where he is.

My older sister is busy, too. My **sister's** calendar is on the bulletin board in the kitchen.

A possessive noun can name more than one owner. Follow these rules:

1. Add only an apostrophe if the plural noun ends in **-s**.

I read my **sisters'** notes to find them today.

2. Add **'s** if the plural noun does not end in **-s**.

Children's lives can be very busy!

Try It

A. Rewrite each sentence about a family's communication. Turn the underlined words into a possessive noun.

1. The top goal of my family is keeping in touch. _____My family's top goal is keeping in touch._____

2. The cell phone number of each family member is on the bulletin board. _____Each family member's cell phone number is on the bulletin board._____

3. A note from my parents said they will be home later than usual. _____My parents' note said they will be home later than usual._____

4. Messages from my brother are usually taped to the refrigerator. _____My brother's messages are usually taped to the refrigerator._____

B. (5–9) Complete each sentence with the possessive form of the noun in parentheses.

Text messages and e-mail are my _____friends'_____ (friends) favorite kinds of communication. _____Paul's_____ (Paul) messages are short and funny. _____Olya's_____ (Olya) messages are longer and full of questions. In _____Oscar's_____ (Oscar) opinion, e-mail is the best way to send messages. I like getting all my _____friends'_____ (friends) notes, whether by e-mail or text message.

Write It

C. Answer the questions about communication. Use possessive nouns in your responses.

10. In what ways does your family communicate with you? _____

11. What are ways your friends communicate with you? _____

D. (12–15) Write at least four more sentences about your communication with family and friends. Use possessive nouns.

_____

_____

_____

_____

Edit It

E. (16–20) Edit the journal entry. Fix the five mistakes with possessives.

May 15

My uncle's house is right next door. My aunts house is far away, beside my grandparents house. My relatives letters keep us in touch. My familys distance does not stop us from communicating. My mothers wish is that we stay in close contact.

Proofreader's Marks

Add an apostrophe:

My fathers note said he would be back in five minutes.

Transpose:

My sisters cell phone is off.

See all Proofreader's Marks on page xi.

7 What Adds Action to a Sentence?

An Action Verb

- An **action verb** tells what the subject does. Some action verbs tell about an action that you cannot see.

    Minh **enjoys** trips with his family.

    His father **likes** the mountains.

- Make sure the action verb agrees with its subject. Add **-s** if the subject tells about one place, one thing, or one other person.

    Minh buys a new pair of hiking boots.

    His **family camps** at the base of the mountain.

    He looks at the trail map.

    At night, **they plan** the trip to the top.

Try It

A. Write an action verb to complete each sentence. Possible responses:

1. Minh _____packs_____ his things in his backpack.

2. Minh and his parents _____cross_____ a river in the morning.

3. Minh _____drinks_____ a lot of water on the hike.

B. Complete each sentence about the hiking challenge. Write the correct action verb.

4. Minh's parents _____check_____ Minh's boots.
   check/checks

5. Minh _____needs_____ energy on this steep mountain.
   need/needs

6. He _____climbs_____ up the mountain.
   climb/climbs

7. Minh _____avoids_____ sharp rocks.
   avoid/avoids

8. Minh and his parents _____celebrate_____ their success!
   celebrate/celebrates

C. You plan a camping trip with your friend's family. This is your first hike. How do you meet this challenge? Use action verbs.

9. What do you do to prepare for the trip? I _____.

10. How do you make it over the rough trail? I _____.

11. How does another person guide you? _____

_____

12. What does your group do when you reach the top? We _____

_____.

D. (13–15) Write at least three sentences about your success with a great challenge. Use action verbs.

_____

_____

_____

_____

E. (16–20) Edit the postcard. Fix the five mistakes in verbs.

Dear Mom and Dad,

    We are on our way to base camp. Sarah pack, the food. Her dad organize, the tents. We help with the maps. I like the mountains. They are so beautiful. The sun shine, brightly. I needs a lot of water here. On Wednesday, we makes the summit.

                     Love,

                     Brisa

Proofreader's Marks
Add text:
This hike challenge me.
Delete:
I stops to drink water.
See all Proofreader's Marks on page xi.

8 Which Action Verbs End in *-s*?

The Ones That Go with *He*, *She*, or *It*

- An **action verb** tells what someone or something does.
- Add **-s** to the action verb if the subject tells about one place, one thing, or one other person.

    Yuri **likes** soccer. He **works** hard at practice.

- If the verb ends in **sh**, **ch**, **ss**, **s**, **x**, or **z**, add **-es**.

    Time **passes**. He **reaches** for a new challenge.

- Do not add **-s** to the action verb if the subject is **I**, **you**, **we**, **they**, or a plural noun.

    They **need** help at the camp. You **call** Yuri. You **tell** him about a volunteer job.

Try It

A. Write the correct action verb to complete each sentence.

1. Yuri _____practices_____ playing soccer.
     practice/practices

2. Mr. Ruiz _____coaches_____ him every Tuesday.
     coach/coaches

3. Yuri's parents _____watch_____ his games.
     watch/watches

4. Sometimes rain _____delays_____ the game.
     delay/delays

B. Write the correct form of the action verb in parentheses.

5. Yuri _____kicks_____ the ball down the field. **(kick)**

6. The ball _____slams_____ into the net. **(slam)**

7. Yuri's teammates _____leap_____ in the air. **(leap)**

8. The coach _____gives_____ Yuri a high five. **(give)**

C. Answer the questions about your favorite activity. Use action verbs.

9. What activity interests you? _____

_____ .

10. What do you do to prepare for this activity? To _____ , I _____

_____ .

11. How do your friends encourage you in this activity? _____

_____

12. How does your family help you succeed in this activity? _____

_____

D. (13–15) Write at least three sentences about what you can do to stand out in your favorite activity. Use action verbs.

_____

_____

_____

_____

Edit It

E. (16–20) Edit the letter. Fix the five mistakes in verbs.

Dear Camp Director,

    I read your ad for assistant counselors. I think I can do this work. I plays on a soccer team at school. We practices three times a week. I babysits for four young kids on my street. They learns to play soccer with me. This work prepare me for a job as counselor.

                           Sincerely,

                           David Brenner

Proofreader's Marks

Add text:

Mr. Brennar call me for the job.
Haas   s

Delete:

I starts on Tuesday.

See all Proofreader's Marks on page xi.

9 What Kinds of Verbs Are *Can, Could, May,* and *Might*?

They Are Helping Verbs.

- An action verb can have two parts: a **helping verb** and a **main verb**. The main verb shows the action.

  Today, Charles **walks** with a guide dog. He **may walk** into the city.

- Some helping verbs change the meaning of the action verb.

  1. Use **can** or **could** to tell about an ability.

  Charles **can walk** to many places.

  He **could walk** around in his building last month.

  2. Use **may**, **might**, or **could** to tell about a possibility.

  Charles **may walk** to the store. He **might visit** the museum, too.

  Charles **could walk** to the park if he has time.

- **Can**, **could**, **may**, and **might** stay the same with all subjects. Do not add **-s**.

  His dog **knows** what to do. She **can sense** danger. Charles **might enjoy** many new things with his guide dog.

Try It

A. Complete each sentence with can, could, may, or might. More than one answer is possible. Possible responses:

1. Charles always thought he _____could_____ take care of a guide dog.

2. With the guide dog, he believes he _____can_____ do anything.

3. Yesterday, they walked one half mile. Tomorrow, they _____may/might_____ walk a mile.

4. Charles _____may/might_____ let the dog rest this afternoon.

5. His dog's name is Sally. She _____can_____ help Charles get around the city.

6. Tomorrow, they _____may/might_____ go to the beach.

B. **Complete each sentence with a helping verb.** Possible responses:

7. Sally is a guide dog. She _____ can _____ help Charles cross streets.
   can/might

8. Charles takes care of her. He _____ may _____ brush her on Tuesday.
   could/may

9. Sally _____ might _____ change Charles's life.
   could/might

10. Sally knows how to help Charles on the bus. She _____ can _____ help him
    can/might
    get on the bus.

11. Sally helps Charles near stairways. She _____ may _____ stop him at the
    could/may
    bottom of stairs.

12. Charles gives Sally commands. He _____ can _____ tell Sally where to go.
    can/could

13. Sally makes some decisions herself. She _____ may _____ decide to stop
    can/may
    without a command.

Write It

C. **Answer the questions about a pet as a companion. Use the helping verbs can, could, may, or might.**

14. Have you ever had a pet or known a friend's pet? What can pets do? A pet _____
    _____ .

15. What might a dog do to comfort you? _____

16. What could you teach a pet to do? _____

D. **(17–20) Write at least four sentences about a pet you have or a friend has. Use can, could, may, and might.**

_____

_____

_____

_____

_____

_____

10 Fix Sentence Fragments

Remember: You can fix a fragment by adding a subject or a predicate that includes a verb. Or, you can combine the fragment with another sentence.

Fragment:	Want to make new friends.
Sentence:	I want to make new friends.
Fragment:	Friends their thoughts and feelings.
Sentence:	Friends share their thoughts and feelings.
Fragment:	Won't judge people. I about them.
Sentence:	I won't judge people before I learn about them.

Grammar at Work

A. Fix the fragments. Write the new sentences.

1. Ava always purple socks. _Ava always wears purple socks._____

2. I think she is odd. Because of her appearance. _I think she is odd because of her appearance.___

   _____

3. Then bump into Ava at the basketball court. _Then I bump into Ava at the basketball court._____

   _____

4. She is athletic. And really funny, too. _She is athletic and really funny, too._____

   _____

B. Change each fragment into a sentence about getting to know Ava. Write your sentences.

Possible responses:

5. Ava and I. _Ava and I become friends._____

6. Learn not to judge people. _I learn not to judge people._____

   _____

7. Because Ava is a lot like me. _We become friends because Ava is a lot like me._____

   _____

C. Answer the questions about getting to know people. Make sure you use complete sentences.

8. Why is it important to get to know people? It is important to get to know people because _____

_____.

9. Why should you learn about people before you judge them? You should _____

_____.

10. What is the best way to get to know someone? The best way to get to know someone is _____

_____.

D. (11–15) Write at least five sentences about getting to know a new friend. Then read your sentences aloud. Fix any fragments.

_____

_____

_____

_____

_____

Grammar at Work

E. (16–20) Edit the paragraph. Fix the <u>five</u> fragments.   Possible responses:

All around the world, people are different from one another. We should not judge those people. Until we meet them. It takes time to know new people. We can share our ideas. And our feelings with new people. Then they get to know us. We get to know them, too. In this way, we look beyond our first impressions.

Proofreader's Marks

Delete:

I made a new friend.
~~today.~~

Add text:
                    is
Her name ʌ Jen.

Do not capitalize:
We are in /Band together.

See all Proofreader's Marks on page xi.

11 Subject-Verb Agreement

Remember: A verb must agree with its subject.

- Subjects **I**, **you**, **we**, **they**, or **plural nouns** do not add **-s** on the **action verb**. Subjects that tell about one place, one thing, or one other person take **-s**.

I **dream** about a goal.	Natalya **dreams** about the Olympics.
You **believe** in her goals.	She **believes** in herself.
We **inspire** each other.	The competition **inspires** people.
They **ask** for help.	Jared **asks** Natalya about her goals.

- These verbs don't change. Do you know why?

A coach **may help** Natalya.	She **might learn** new skills.
He **can inspire** her.	She **could become** a champion.

Try It

A. Choose the verb to complete each sentence.

1. Natalya _____ dreams _____ about a medal.
   dream / dreams

2. Jared dreams that he _____ may play _____ in the major league.
   may play / may plays

3. The players _____ work _____ for their goals.
   work / works

4. Their goals _____ may lead _____ to success.
   may lead / mays lead

B. Write the correct form of the verb in parentheses.

5. Natalya _____ wants _____ a medal. **(want)**

6. Her injury _____ causes _____ sadness. **(cause)**

7. She _____ trains _____ again. **(train)**

8. Natalya _____ learns _____ the results of hard work. **(learn)**

9. Her medals _____ hang _____ in her room. **(hang)**

C. Answer the questions about someone who doesn't give up on a dream. Use the correct form of verbs.

10. Whom do you know who doesn't give up, even after failure? I _____

_____.

11. What can this person do that is special? This person _____

_____.

12. What might this person do in the future? _____

_____

D. (13–15) Write at least three sentences about someone who worked hard and became a success. Use some verbs in your response.

_____

_____

_____

_____

_____

Grammar at Work

E. (16–20) Edit the postcard. Fix <u>four</u> mistakes in subject-verb agreement. Fix <u>one</u> fragment.

Dear Natalya,

    Tomorrow is the big tennis match! I look forward to watching you compete.

    My family like(s) to watch you, too. They can comes with me. We are not sure, but we (may) bring the video camera. Your dream inspire(s) me. (I) Know you can make it to the Olympics!

                        Love,

                        Katie

Proofreader's Marks

Delete:

  I likes tennis.

Add text:
             s
  She believe in herself.

See all Proofreader's Marks on page xi.

12 Is the Subject of a Sentence Always a Noun?

No, It Can Be a Pronoun.

- Use **I** when you talk about yourself.
  I want to start a club at school.

- Use **you** when you talk to another person.
  Do **you** want to join?

- Use **he** when you talk about one man or one boy.
  Use **she** when you talk about one woman or one girl.
  Mr. Bai will help us.
  He speaks Chinese.

- Use **it** when you talk about one place, thing, or idea.
  The club meets on Mondays. **It** is a Chinese language club.

Subject Pronouns
Singular
I
you
he, she, it

Try It

A. Complete each sentence. Use the subject pronouns I, you, he, she, or it.

1. Mr. Bai describes the new Chinese club. _____He_____ invites students to join.

2. Mr. Bai says, "_____You_____ will like the club."

3. I am excited. _____I_____ ask some questions.

4. The club will be fun. _____It_____ will be interesting to learn Chinese.

B. (5–8) Write the correct pronoun to complete the sentence.

My mom is surprised about the new language club. _____She_____ asks about this new interest. Mr. Bai describes the club. _____He_____ describes the beauty of Chinese. I want to learn this language. _____I_____ will need to work very hard. Mr. Bai says, " _____You_____ must study every night."

C. Answer the questions about a new interest. Use subject pronouns.

9. In the past year, what new interest or hobby have you discovered? In the past year,
_____ have discovered _____.

10. How did you discover this interest? _____
_____

11. Who was surprised by your new interest? Why? _____
_____

D. (12–14) Write at least three sentences that tell more about this interest you
discovered. Use subject pronouns.

_____

_____

_____

_____

_____

Edit It

E. (15–20) Edit the letter. Fix the six mistakes in subject pronouns.

Dear Marissa,

Today I joined the Chinese club. She love it! Mrs. Cramer joined
too. He is excited about Chinese. Mr. Bai is nice. She is also
smart. Mr. Bai showed pictures of China. He is a beautiful place.
Mr. Bai asked, "Would it like to visit China?" I replied, "She
would love to visit China."

Your friend,

Ella

Proofreader's Marks

Change text:

She is helpful.

Add text:

told me what to study.

See all Proofreader's Marks
on page xi.

13 Can a Pronoun Show "More Than One"?

Yes, It Can.

- Use **we** to talk about yourself and another person.

  Omar and I talk about our writing.
  We talk about my story.

- Use **you** to talk to one or more persons.

  You are talented, Omar.
  You are all talented writers.

- Use **they** to talk about more than one person or thing.

  The students listen to my story. **They** laugh and clap.

Subject Pronouns	
Singular	**Plural**
I	we
you	you
he, she, it	they

Try It

A. Read the first sentence. Complete the second sentence with **we**, **you**, or **they**.

1. Ms. Stone leads the writing club. _____We_____ meet every Wednesday.

2. Ms. Stone reads my work. She says, "_____You_____ are a very good writer."

3. We write one story a month. _____We_____ sometimes read the stories aloud.

4. The students listen to my story. _____They_____ like the characters a lot.

5. After the meeting, Ms. Stone and I talk. She says, " _____You_____ should publish this story."

6. We talk about magazines that publish short stories. _____We_____ make a plan to send the story to the magazines.

7. The other students like this plan. _____They_____ want to be published, too.

B. Choose words from each column to write five sentences. You may use words more than once.

We	give	the magazine will publish it.
You	suggest	send in your story.
They	should	ways to improve it.
	think	the magazines we like to read.
	choose	me hope.

Possible responses:

8. The students give comments about each story. ___They suggest ways to improve it.___

9. We look at magazines. ___We choose the magazines we like to read.___

10. One student says, "You should take a chance." ___You should send in your story.___

11. All of the students are encouraging. ___They give me hope.___

12. My teacher and I decide to send the story to a magazine. ___We think the magazine will publish it.___

Write It

C. Answer the questions about a group that takes a chance, based on their abilities. Use **we**, **you**, or **they**.

13. What sports team or other group do you know that succeeded at something difficult?
_____ succeeded because _____.

14. How did this group take a chance? _____

15. Who thought the group might fail? _____ thought the group might not succeed, but _____.

D. (16–20) Write at least five sentences that tell more about when this group took a chance. Use plural subject pronouns.

_____

_____

_____

_____

_____

14 How Do You Avoid Confusion with Pronouns?

Match the Pronoun to the Noun.

If you're not sure which **pronoun** to use, first find the **noun** it goes with. Then ask yourself:

- Is the noun a man or a woman?
  Use **he** for a man and **she** for a woman.

- Is the noun singular or plural? If plural, use **they**.

If a pronoun does not refer correctly to a noun, change the pronoun.

Incorrect: **Jesse** waits for the answer. **It** feels nervous.

Correct: **Jesse** waits for the answer. **He** feels nervous.

The pronouns in these sentences are correct. Do you know why?

1. **Teachers** think Jesse is lazy. **They** remember him in class.

2. **Jesse** makes changes. **He** also writes an essay about his goals.

Try It

A. Read the first sentence. Complete the second sentence with the correct pronoun.

1. Jesse wants to run for class president. _____He_____ takes the race very seriously.

2. The teachers are not sure about Jesse's ability. _____They_____ think he doesn't work hard in class.

3. Ms. Browne wants to give Jesse another chance. _____She_____ asks Jesse to write an essay about his goals.

4. Ms. Browne and the other teachers will read the essay. _____They_____ will read the essay next week.

5. Mr. Shepard is the first teacher to read Jesse's work. _____He_____ thinks Jesse has a lot of talent.

6. The essay is good. _____It_____ proves that Jesse can work hard.

B. Draw lines to connect the words in the first column with the ones that make sense in the second column.

7. All of the teachers say — They want to help Jesse succeed.

8. Ms. Browne and Mr. Santoro find a tutor for Jesse. — they think Jesse is a good writer.

9. Mr. Shepard talks to the other teachers. — He says Jesse can win the election.

10. Maria will tutor Jesse. — She will meet with Jesse on Fridays.

Write It

C. Answer the questions about someone who did well. Make sure the pronouns refer correctly to their nouns.

11. Whom do you know who worked hard to meet a goal? _____

12. What did this person do to meet the goal? He/She _____.

13. Who thought this person might fail, and what did they say? _____

_____

D. (14–16) Write at least three sentences that tell more about someone who did very well. Make sure pronouns refer correctly to nouns.

_____

_____

_____

Edit It

E. (17–20) Edit the election poster. Fix the four mistakes in pronouns.

Vote for Jesse. He is a winner!
Students believe ~~it~~ he is a good leader. ~~believe~~ They believe in Jesse! This school needs change. ~~They~~ It can be better! Jesse will work for all students. ~~It~~ He is a real leader.

© National Geographic Learning, a part of Cengage Learning, Inc.

15 How Do You Know What Verb to Use?

Match It to the Subject.

- Use **I** with **am**.
  I **am** a volunteer.

- Use **he**, **she**, or **it** with **is**.
  It **is** a great experience!
  My job **is** to read to a child.
  He **is** happy to see me.

- Use **we**, **you**, or **they** with **are**.
  My friends **are** volunteers, too.
  They **are** volunteers at the same community center.
  We **are** happy to help out. **Are** you?

Forms of *Be*
I **am**
he, she, or it **is**
we, you, or they **are**

Try It

A. (1–6) Write **am**, **is**, or **are** to complete the paragraph.

I _____am_____ a volunteer at the neighborhood community center. My friend

Annie _____is_____, too. She _____is_____ quiet about her volunteer

work, though. People _____are_____ surprised when they learn that she is so

involved. I _____am_____ happy to share the time with her. It _____is_____

good to feel that we are helping out.

B. (7–12) Write **am**, **is**, or **are** to complete the interview with Annie.

Reporter: What _____are_____ your favorite activities?

Annie: Well, I _____am_____ always busy. Soccer _____is_____ my
favorite sport.

Reporter: When _____are_____ the practices for soccer?

Annie: They _____are_____ every day after school. My volunteer work
_____is_____ rewarding, too.

C. Complete the sentences about your after-school activities.
Use **am**, **is**, or **are** in each sentence.

13. I _____ busy because _____

_____.

14. My favorite activity _____.

15. After-school activities _____ important because _____

_____.

D. (16–19) Tell how two of your friends spend their time after school. Use **am**,
is, and **are**. Write at least four sentences.

_____

_____

_____

_____

_____

Edit It

E. (20–25) Edit the letter. Fix the six mistakes with verbs.

Dear Uncle Ted,

    I am very busy these days. I have many after-school
activities. My theater group keeps me really busy. It ~~are~~ ^{is}
my favorite activity. The play ~~are~~ ^{is} next weekend. We ~~is~~ ^{are} in
rehearsals every day. I ^{am} also a volunteer at the community
center. I read to the children. I ~~is~~ ^{am} there only a few hours a week.
I hope to do more next year. How busy I ~~are~~ ^{am} these days!

                Your favorite nephew,

                Michael

Proofreader's Marks

Add text:
We ∧ busy.
    are

Change text:
Drama ~~am~~ fun.
         is

See all Proofreader's Marks
on page xi.

16 How Do You Know What Verb to Use?

Match It to the Subject.

- Use **I** with <u>**have**</u>.
  I **have** great news!

- Use **he**, **she**, or **it** with <u>**has**</u>.
  There's a new store at the mall. It **has** all the best designers.
  Felicia is the manager. She **has** good ideas for the store.

- Use **we**, **you**, or **they** with <u>**have**</u>.
  We **have** some extra money.
  You **have** time to shop!
  We can meet Felicia's helpers. They **have** great ideas, too.

Forms of *Have*
I **have**
he, she, or it **has**
we, you, or they **have**

Try It

A. Complete each sentence with the correct form of **have**.

1. Felicia _____ has _____ every issue of this fashion magazine.
   have / has

2. Do you _____ have _____ a copy of the September issue?
   have / has

3. Jan _____ has _____ a copy in her bag.
   have / has

4. Now we _____ have _____ ideas for new winter dresses!
   have / has

B. Complete each sentence with **have** or **has**.

5. I also _____ have _____ an idea for the winter dance.

6. Jan _____ has _____ the picture from the magazine.

7. We _____ have _____ a plan to decorate the gym.

8. We _____ have _____ lots of people to help us.

C. Answer the questions about reaching a goal. Use the correct forms of **have**.

9. What school club or activity interests you? _____

_____

10. Why does the club or activity interest you? _____

_____

11. What does the club or activity teach you? _____

_____

12. Imagine that a friend joins the club or activity. What advice will you give the friend? _____

_____

D. (13–16) Who helps you in your club or activity? Write four sentences about this person. Use forms of **have** in some of your sentences.

_____

_____

_____

_____

_____

Edit It

E. (17–20) Edit the letter. Fix the four errors with **have** and **has**.

Dear Uncle Martin,

Mom has pictures of you. She ~~have~~ *has* several pictures of you at
the top of mountains. She ~~have~~ *has* pride in your skills as a mountain
climber. You ⌃*have* a lot of courage to climb those peaks. Thanks to
you, I have an idea. I will join the climbers' club at school. I ~~has~~ *have* a
dream to become a climber, too.

Andrew

Proofreader's Marks

Add text:
have
You ⌃ a goal to rock climb.

Change text:
has
Pedro ~~have~~ the right
gear for you.

See all Proofreader's Marks
on page xi.

17 How Do You Know What Verb to Use?

Match It to the Subject.

- Use the form of **do** that matches the subject. You can use **do** as a **main verb** or as a **helping verb**.

  Jorge **does** three sports during the week.
  We **do admire** him.
  Our workouts **do help** us.
  They **do prepare** our bodies for the competition.
  We always **do** our best.

- The short form of **does not** is **doesn't**.

- The short form of **do not** is **don't**.

Forms of *Do*
I **do**
he, she, or it **does**
we, you, or they **do**

1. He **does not** accept failure.

   He **doesn't** accept failure.

2. They **do not** expect him to win.

   They **don't** expect him to win.

Try It

A. Complete the sentence with the correct form of do.

1. Jorge _____does_____ a workout three times a week.
   do / does

2. His friends _____do_____ some of the exercises with him.
   do / does

3. They _____don't_____ like the workouts.
   doesn't / don't

4. Jorge _____doesn't_____ complain.
   doesn't / don't

5. We _____do_____ admire his effort.
   do / does

6. Jorge _____does_____ enjoy a new challenge.
   do / does

7. The training is hard, but it _____doesn't_____ bother him.
   doesn't / don't

B. Complete the sentence with **do**, **does**, **don't**, or **doesn't**.

8. Jorge _____ does _____ twenty push-ups every morning.

9. He _____ does _____ his strength training on Saturdays.

10. Biking to school _____ does _____ help Jorge train, too.

11. Jorge _____ doesn't _____ swim now, but he will next year.

12. Jorge's coach _____ doesn't _____ want him to hurt himself.

13. Now Jorge's parents _____ don't _____ have as many worries.

14. Jorge _____ does _____ enjoy his new workout plan.

15. We _____ do _____ know he works hard.

Write It

C. Answer the questions about hard work. Use **do** and **does** in some of your sentences.

16. What do you do to help yourself work hard? I _____
_____.

17. What do you do to get ready to work hard? _____
_____

18. How do other people help you? _____
_____

D. (19–20) Write at least two sentences about how you test your abilities and push yourself to succeed. Use forms of **do**.

_____
_____
_____
_____

18 When Do You Use an Indefinite Pronoun?

When You Can't Be Specific

- When you are not naming a specific person or thing, you can use an **indefinite pronoun**.

  Everything is ready for our trip.

- Some indefinite pronouns are always singular, so they need a **singular verb** that ends in **-s**.

  Nothing feel<u>s</u> nicer than visiting family.

Singular Indefinite Pronouns

another	each	everything	nothing
anybody	either	neither	somebody
anyone	everybody	nobody	someone
anything	everyone	no one	something

Try It

A. Complete each sentence. Choose the correct verb to go with the indefinite pronoun.

1. Nobody _____ believes _____ that most of my family lives in Argentina.
      believe / believes

2. Everyone in my family here _____ understands _____ English.
      understand / understands

3. When someone _____ speaks _____ Spanish, we understand him or her perfectly.
      speak / speaks

B. (4–7) Complete each sentence about a student's first day at school. Use someone, everyone, neither, no one, or something. Possible responses:

It is my first day of school. It seems that _____ everyone _____ speaks English

well except me. _____ No one _____ wants to sit alone in the cafeteria. Then,

_____ something _____ makes me feel better. I hear two girls speaking Mandarin.

_____ Neither _____ of them knows me yet, but I will say hello.

C. Answer the questions about learning a language. Use indefinite pronouns.

8. Why might someone want to learn a new language? _____

9. Does each person in your family speak the same language? Explain.

_____

10. Can anyone learn a new language? Explain. _____

_____

D. (11–15) Write at least five more sentences about learning languages. Use indefinite pronouns.

_____

_____

_____

_____

_____

Edit It

E. (16–20) Edit the journal entry. Fix the five mistakes in indefinite pronouns or verbs.

November 20

My friend Sasha is from Russia. He does not speak

much Russian in the U.S. ^He feels homesick when ^somebody

speaks his language on television. No#one in our

class speaks Russian except Sasha. Each of his

friends ^knows a few words in Russian from Sasha. But

~~anybody~~ ^nobody has time to learn more.

Proofreader's Marks
Add text: Someone   ^talked to me in my language!
Change text: anybody   I didn't know ~~somebody~~.
Add a space: #   No^one likes to feel left out.
See all Proofreader's Marks on page xi.

19 Which Indefinite Pronouns Are Plural?

Both, Few, Many and *Several*

- Use an **indefinite pronoun** when you are not naming a specific person or thing.

  Both of my parents know sign language.

  Several of their friends use it as well.

- Some **indefinite pronouns** are always plural, so they need a **plural verb**.

  Many in the world **communicate** through sign language.

  A **few** of the teachers in my school **use** international sign language.

Plural Indefinite Pronouns	
both	many
few	several

Try It

A. Complete each sentence about communicating through sign language. Write the correct form of the verb.

1. My parents cannot hear. Both of them _____ use _____ sign language
   use / uses
   to communicate.

2. Several of their friends _____ know _____ this language, too.
   know / knows

3. Many of my hearing relatives _____ use _____ sign language at our house.
   use / uses

4. A few of these people _____ communicate _____ with my parents through letters
   communicate / communicates
   because they do not know sign language.

5. Both of my brothers _____ use _____ sign language at their jobs as
   use / uses
   translators.

6. Many of my classmates at school _____ take _____ the sign language class.
   take / takes

7. Several of us _____ hope _____ to use sign language in future jobs.
   hope / hopes

B. Complete the sentences about a sign language class. Use the correct form of the verb in parentheses.

8. A few of our classmates _____use_____ sign language to communicate with relatives. **(use)**

9. Several of my friends _____study_____ after school. **(study)**

10. Both of my best friends _____know_____ sign language and use it often. **(know)**

Write It

C. Answer the questions about using sign language. Use plural indefinite pronouns.

11. Have you seen people communicate in sign language? _____
_____

12. When have you seen people communicate in sign language? _____
_____

13. How is sign language the same as other languages? How is it different? _____
_____

14. What are reasons that people learn sign language? _____
_____

15. Why is it good to know sign language? _____
_____

D. (16–20) Tell more about communication with sign language. Write at least five sentences. Use plural indefinite pronouns.

_____
_____
_____
_____
_____
_____
_____

20 Which Indefinite Pronouns Are Tricky?

The Ones That Can Be Singular or Plural

- The **indefinite pronouns** in the chart can be either singular or plural.
- The prepositional phrase after the pronoun shows whether the sentence talks about one thing or more than one thing. Use the correct **verb**.

Singular or Plural Indefinite Pronouns	
all	none
any	some
most	

Singular: I volunteer at an animal rescue organization. **Most** of the organization **loves** pets.

Plural: **Most** of the people **have** cats.

Singular: **Some** of my family **loves** dogs.

Plural: **Some** of my relatives **love** dogs.

Try It

A. Complete the sentences about communicating with animals. Use the correct verb form.

1. We have a pet cat. None of my friends ___understand___ the cat.
   understand / understands

2. All of my family ___knows___ how well I understand my cat.
   know / knows

3. My cat gives me hints. Most of the hints ___are___ clear to me.
   is / are

4. Some of the world ___believes___ that cats do not have feelings.
   believe / believes

5. All of my cat's feelings ___are___ easy for me to see and hear.
   is / are

6. My cat is a picky eater. Sometimes none of the food ___tastes___ good.
   taste / tastes

7. Any of her favorite foods ___disappear___ fast.
   disappear / disappears

8. None of my cat's behavior ___surprises___ me.
   surprise / surprises

B. Write sentences about people and pets. Choose words from each box.

All	of my classmates	ask me how to train a dog.
Most	of my family	has pets.
None	of my friends	have a dog.
Some	of our neighborhood	understands how to train dogs.

Possible responses:

9. All of our neighborhood has pets.

10. None of my friends have a dog.

11. Some of my family understands how to train dogs.

12. Most of my classmates ask me how to train a dog.

Write It

C. Answer the questions about people and pets. Use singular or plural indefinite pronouns.

13. How many people do you know who understand animals? _____

_____

14. Do you think most pets behave well? _____

_____

15. Do most most pets love their owners? Why do you think so?

_____

_____

D. (16–20) Write at least five more sentences about people and pets.
Use singular or plural indefinite pronouns.

_____

_____

_____

_____

_____

_____

Name _____

21 Subject Pronouns

Remember: The subject of a sentence can be a pronoun. A **subject pronoun** can be singular or plural.

- Use **I** when you talk about yourself.
- Use **you** to talk to one or more persons.
- Use **we** to talk about another person and yourself.
- Use **he**, **she**, **it**, and **they** to talk about other people or things.

  How do you know which pronoun to use? Look at the noun it goes with.
  1. If the noun is a man or boy, use **he**. If it is a woman or girl, use **she**.
  2. If the noun is a place or thing, use **it**. If the noun is plural, use **they**.

Try It

A. Complete each sentence with the correct subject pronoun.

1. Marisol plans a bake sale. _____She_____ thinks we can make a lot of money.
   They / She

2. We want to earn money for sports equipment. _____We_____ will sell food
   We / They
   and drinks.

3. Mr. Banderas will set up our booth. _____He_____ will help sell food.
   He / It

4. The other coaches think it is too hard to make this money. _____They_____ say
   We / They
   equipment is very expensive.

B. Complete each sentence with the correct pronoun from the box.

he	it	she	they

5. All of the teams need equipment. _____They_____ need uniforms, too.

6. Jeff sells juice and water at the bake sale. _____He_____ raises a lot of money.

7. Victoria helps at the booth. _____She_____ takes the money.

8. The bake sale is a success. _____It_____ brings many people to the school.

Write It

C. Answer the questions about a successful contest or competition. Use subject pronouns.

9. What was the contest or competition? _____

10. Who organized the effort, and how? _____

11. What was the best part of this group's or team's story? _____

_____

D. (12–14) Write at least three sentences about a group whose efforts were more successful than expected. Use subject pronouns correctly.

_____

_____

_____

_____

Grammar at Work

E. (15–20) Fix the <u>four</u> mistakes in subject pronouns. Fix the <u>two</u> mistakes in subject-verb agreement.

Dear Marisol:

You and your team did a great job. The school has money for equipment for next year. ~~They~~ ^{It} can buy helmets and other equipment. Mr. Banderas, Ms. Smith, and I is ^{are} amazed at your efforts. ~~They~~ ^{We} think you did a great job. The teams is ^{are} very happy. ^{They} can play safely next year. He ^I am very proud of you.

Sincerely,

Principal Johnson

Proofreader's Marks

Change text:
~~It~~ ^{He} liked the fundraiser.

Add text:
^{She} sold pizzas.

See all Proofreader's Marks on page xi.

22 Use the Verbs *Be*, *Have*, and *Do*

Remember: The verbs **be**, **have**, and **do** each have more than one form in the present. Use the form that goes with the subject.

Forms of *Be*	Forms of *Have*	Forms of *Do*
I **am**	I **have**	I **do**
he, she, or it **is**	he, she, or it **has**	he, she, or it **does**
we, you, or they **are**	we, you, or they **have**	we, you, or they **do**

Try It

A. Complete the sentence. Write the correct form of the verb.

1. I _____ am _____ interested in explorers.
   am / is

2. This book _____ is _____ about an explorer who went to Antarctica.
   are / is

3. The explorer and his crew _____ have _____ many adventures.
   have / has

4. I _____ have _____ a dream to become an explorer, too.
   have / has

B. Complete each sentence with the correct form of the verb in parentheses.

5. I _____ do _____ like to travel to unusual places. **(do)**

6. An explorer _____ has _____ a life of adventure. **(have)**

7. In the book, the crew _____ has _____ an accident. **(have)**

8. I _____ do _____ understand that a journey can be dangerous. **(do)**

9. We _____ have _____ a lot to learn from modern explorers. **(have)**

C. Write about a person you admire. Use forms of **be**, **have**, and **do** in some of your sentences.

10. Who is a person you admire? _____

_____

11. What makes this person special? _____

_____

12. What did this person say or do? _____

_____

D. (13–15) Write at least three sentences about someone you admire. Use forms of **be**, **have**, or **do** in some of your sentences.

_____

_____

_____

_____

Grammar at Work

E. (16–20) Fix the <u>four</u> mistakes with the verbs **be**, **have**, and **do**. Fix <u>one</u> problem with a <u>subject pronoun</u>.

Dear Natalie,

    I am eager to meet the explorer at the book signing. His
writings is⁀ an inspiration to me. He do⁀ not let fear get in his
                 _{are}   _{does}
way. I already has⁀ a copy of his new book. I know that you
has⁀ great respect for this man, too. Me will meet you at the
bookstore.

                       See you soon,

                       Brigitte

Proofreader's Marks

Change text:
have
   I has⁀ a new book.

See all Proofreader's Marks on page xi.

23 How Do You Know When an Action Happens?

Look at the Verb.

An **action verb** tells what the subject does. The tense of a verb tells when the action happens.

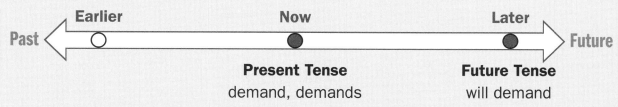

Earlier	Now	Later
	Present Tense	**Future Tense**
	demand, demands	will demand

Past ← → Future

Use the **present tense** to talk about actions that happen now or often.

Mr. and Mrs. Bates **demand** a clean neighborhood.

Carlos **tells** them about a meeting.

The **future tense** tells about an action that will happen later.

All the neighbors **will meet** next Monday.

Try It

A. Underline the verb in the first sentence. Rewrite the sentence, using a different verb. Possible responses:

1. Carlos <u>will speak</u> to people in his neighborhood _Carlos will talk to people in his neighborhood._

_____

2. The neighbors <u>will learn</u> recycling skills. _The neighbors will study recycling skills._

3. Mr. Bates and Carlos <u>explain</u> recycling rules. _Mr. Bates and Carlos describe recycling rules._

4. Mr. Bates <u>gives</u> sorting tips. _Mr. Bates offers sorting tips._

_____

5. The neighbors <u>will practice</u> the rules and tips. _The neighbors will follow the rules and tips._

_____

6. They <u>understand</u> the importance of the lessons. _They know the importance of the lessons._

_____

B. Complete each sentence with a verb from the box. Use the correct verb tense and form.

write	place	gather	fill	receive	work	make	visit

7. Today, my neighbors _____make_____ a plan for Recycling Day.

8. Mr. Chan _____gathers_____ recycling bins.

9. Later on, I _____will write_____ labels for the bins.

10. Joe _____will place_____ the bins on each corner tomorrow.

11. Now we _____fill_____ the bins with glass, cans, and paper.

12. Everyone _____works_____ together to improve the area.

13. City leaders _____will visit_____ the neighborhood next week.

14. Maybe we _____will receive_____ an award for our improvements.

Write It

C. Citizens in your neighborhood want your help to improve the area. You know how to build, plant, and complete home improvement projects. How do you offer to help your neighborhood? Use present and future tense action verbs.

15. What do you do now to help your neighborhood? I _____.

16. How do people in your neighborhood work together? They _____

_____.

17. Describe one way you will work to improve your home or neighborhood in the future. _____

_____

D. (18–20) Write three sentences about ways that people improve their neighborhoods now and what they can do in the future. Use present and future tense action verbs.

_____

_____

_____

24 How Do You Show That an Action Already Happened?

Add -ed to the Verb.

The **tense** of a verb shows when an action happens.

- Action in the **present tense** happens now or on a regular basis.
- Action in the **past tense** happened earlier.

Past Tense
played

Present Tense
play, plays

Add **-ed** to most verbs when you talk about a past action.

1. Linh and Jess **play** music together. They **played** in a concert yesterday.

2. They often **learn** new songs. They **learned** one last week.

Try It

A. Complete each sentence. Write the past tense of the verb in parentheses.

1. The director of the youth orchestra _____displayed_____ a poster. **(display)**

2. The orchestra _____needed_____ new members. **(need)**

3. The director _____wanted_____ musicians to try out. **(want)**

4. Linh and Jess both _____looked_____ at the poster. **(look)**

5. They _____discussed_____ the tryout. **(discuss)**

B. Complete each sentence correctly. Write the present tense or past tense of the verb in parentheses.

6. Earlier this morning, Linh and Jess _____walked_____ to the tryouts. **(walk)**

7. A few hours ago, they both _____played_____ well for the director. **(play)**

8. Now they _____perform_____ with confidence. **(perform)**

C. Imagine that two friends competed against one another to play the drums in an orchestra. Write sentences about what happened after the audition. Use the past tense of each verb in parentheses.

9. **(talk)** They probably _____.

10. **(learn)** They _____.

11. **(remain)** They _____.

D. (12–16) Write five sentences about times when you and a friend worked together and when you worked against each other. Use past tense verbs that end in -ed.

_____

_____

_____

_____

_____

Edit It

E. (17–20) Edit the journal entry. Fix the four mistakes with verbs.

May 10

Right now, I need to practice my song for

the musical. Yesterday, I ~~talk~~ *talked* to my best

friend. I ~~learn~~ *learned* about her plans. She will try

out, too. Last year I ~~play~~ *played* the lead in the

musical. She really ~~want~~ *wanted* that part. One of

us will get the part this year. Either way,

we'll be friends.

Proofreader's Marks

Change text:
I ~~play~~ *played* the lead.

See all Proofreader's Marks on page xi.

25 Can You Just Add -*ed* to Form a Verb in the Past?

Not Always

Most verbs end with **-ed** to show the past tense. Sometimes you have to change the spelling of the verb before you add **-ed**.

1. If a verb ends in silent **e**, drop the **e**. Then add **-ed**.

Josh decid**ed** to play for the Blazers. **(decide)**

Scott's team compet**ed** against the Blazers. **(compete)**

2. Some one-syllable verbs end in one vowel and one consonant. Double the consonant before you add **-ed**.

Josh and Scott jogg**ed** together. **(jog)**

Then they batt**ed** the ball around. **(bat)**

3. If a verb ends in **y**, look at the letter before it. If it is a vowel, just add **-ed**. If it is a consonant, change the **y** to **i** and then add **-ed**.

Josh play**ed** first base. **(play)**

Scott tri**ed** to catch a fly ball. **(try)**

Try It

A. Complete each sentence. Write the past tense of the verb in parentheses.

1. Each boy _____hoped_____ his team would win. **(hope)**

2. They _____patted_____ each other on the back. **(pat)**

3. Then they _____carried_____ their bats onto the field. **(carry)**

B. (4–7) Complete each sentence. Choose a verb from the box and use its past tense form.

slug	enjoy	hurry	raise

Josh walked to the plate. He _____raised_____ his bat. Then he _____slugged_____ the ball. Scott _____hurried_____ to catch it. Both boys _____enjoyed_____ the game.

C. Answer each question about competing against a friend. Use the past tense.

8. When did you compete against a friend? I _____.

9. How did the competition end? _____

10. Did you like the competition? _____

D. (11–13) Imagine that two friends played against each other in a game of basketball. Write three sentences about the game. Use the past tense of these verbs: **dribble, drop, try.**

_____

_____

_____

_____

_____

E. (14–20) Edit the letter. Fix the seven mistakes with verbs.

Dear Scott,

    Do you remember the first game we playd [played] last season? I enjoied [enjoyed] that game so much! You smack [smacked] the ball to me. I remember that Ross cryed [cried] out, "Catch that ball!" I race [raced] for the ball. I tryed [tried], but I droped [dropped] it. We had a lot of fun. I miss those days. It's too bad that I moved away.

                        Your friend,

                        Josh

Proofreader's Marks
Change text:
We ~~playied~~ played our best.
See all Proofreader's Marks on page xi.

26 When Do You Use *Was* and *Were*?

When You Tell About the Past

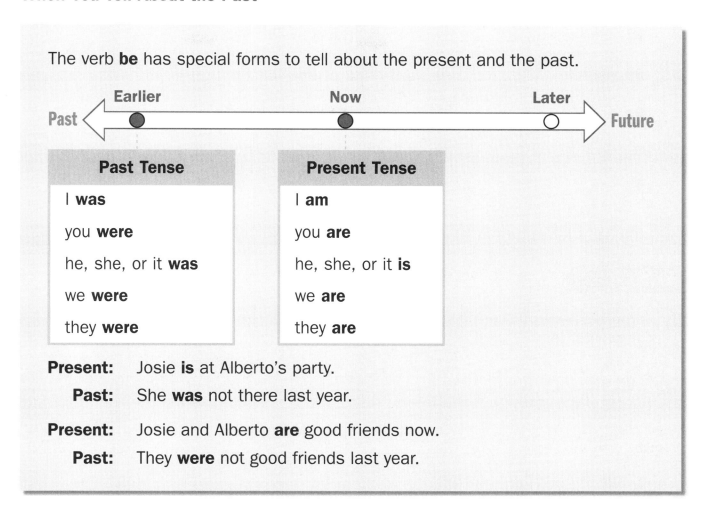

The verb **be** has special forms to tell about the present and the past.

Earlier   Now   Later

Past ◄─────●───────────●──────────○─────► Future

Past Tense	Present Tense
I **was**	I **am**
you **were**	you **are**
he, she, or it **was**	he, she, or it **is**
we **were**	we **are**
they **were**	they **are**

Present: Josie **is** at Alberto's party.

Past: She **was** not there last year.

Present: Josie and Alberto **are** good friends now.

Past: They **were** not good friends last year.

Try It

A. Rewrite each sentence. Use the past tense of the verb.

1. I am Josie's good friend. _I was Josie's good friend._

2. Josie and Alberto are good friends. _Josie and Alberto were good friends._

3. Alberto is not my friend. _Alberto was not my friend._

4. Josie is one of the kids invited to Alberto's party. _Josie was one of the kids invited to Alberto's party._

5. I am not on the guest list. _I was not on the guest list._

B. Complete each sentence. Write **was**, **were**, or **are**.

6. Last week, my feelings _____were_____ hurt.

7. Then Josie _____was_____ thoughtful of my feelings.

8. Her friends _____were_____ thoughtful, too.

9. They _____were_____ nice when they talked to Alberto.

10. He _____was_____ happy to invite me to his party.

11. I _____was_____ glad to be invited.

12. Now Alberto, Josie, and I _____are_____ all good friends.

Write It

C. Complete the sentences about a time you felt left out. Use **was** or **were** in each sentence.

13. I _____.

14. My friends _____.

15. We all _____.

16. It _____.

D. (17–20) Write at least four sentences about a time a friend of yours was left out. What did you do? Use **was** or **were** in each sentence.

_____

_____

_____

_____

_____

27 When Do You Use *Had*?

When You Tell About the Past

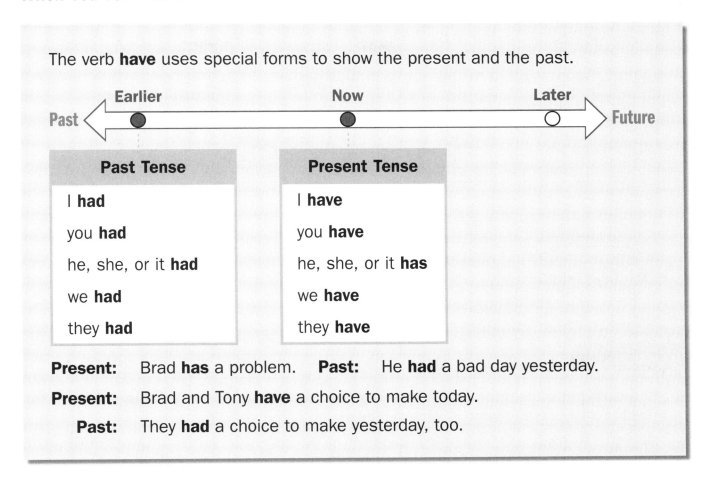

The verb **have** uses special forms to show the present and the past.

Earlier   **Now**   **Later**

Past ← Future

Past Tense	Present Tense
I **had**	I **have**
you **had**	you **have**
he, she, or it **had**	he, she, or it **has**
we **had**	we **have**
they **had**	they **have**

Present: Brad **has** a problem.   **Past:**   He **had** a bad day yesterday.

Present: Brad and Tony **have** a choice to make today.

Past: They **had** a choice to make yesterday, too.

Try It

A. Rewrite each sentence. Use the past tense of the verb.

1. Brad and Tony have a great friendship. _Brad and Tony had a great friendship._

2. They have a loud argument in the hallway. _They had a loud argument in the hallway._

3. On Tuesday, the principal has Tony in his office. _On Tuesday, the principal had Tony in his office._

4. Tony has a chance to protect Brad. _Tony had a chance to protect Brad._

B. Write **have** or **has** to complete each sentence. Then rewrite the sentence in the past tense.

5. Brad _____has_____ a strong sense of loyalty to his friend.

Brad had a strong sense of loyalty to his friend.

6. He _____has_____ a hard decision to make.

He had a hard decision to make.

7. His parents _____have_____ some advice for him.

His parents had some advice for him.

8. Brad _____has_____ good advice.

Brad had good advice.

9. Brad and Tony _____have_____ detention together on Tuesday.

Brad and Tony had detention together on Tuesday.

Write It

C. Complete the sentences about a time you and your friends got into trouble. Use the past tense of **have** in each sentence.

10. I _____

_____.

11. My friends _____

_____.

12. We _____

_____.

D. (13–15) Write three sentences about loyalty to friends. Use **have**, **has**, and **had**.

_____

_____

_____

_____

28 How Do You Show That an Action Is in Process?
Use *Am*, *Is*, or *Are* Plus the *-ing* Form of the Verb.

- The **present progressive** form of the verb ends in **-ing**.
- Use **am**, **is**, or **are** plus a **main verb** with **-ing** to show that an action is in the process of happening. The **helping verb** must agree with the subject.
  I **am helping** Ms. Torre.
  The group **is learning** how to save water.
  They **are learning** how much water these plants need.
  Ms. Torre **is teaching** us to use different plants to save water.

Try It

A. Complete each sentence. Write the correct present progressive verb form.

1. Ms. Torre _____ is designing _____ a garden that needs very little water.
   am designing / is designing

2. She _____ is showing _____ us how to use plants that grow well here.
   are showing / is showing

3. The neighbors _____ are planting _____ flowers that can survive without rain.
   is planting / are planting

4. I _____ am following _____ a plan for some tall grass plants.
   am following / are following

5. These plants _____ are costing _____ us very little money.
   is costing / are costing

B. Complete each sentence. Write the present progressive form of the verb in parentheses.

6. I _____ am discovering _____ plants that will conserve water. **(discover)**

7. Ms. Torre _____ is saving _____ the city money with these plants, too. **(save)**

8. She _____ is sharing _____ new techniques with the city planners. **(share)**

9. The plants _____ are growing _____ in a healthy way. **(grow)**

10. They _____ are filling _____ the city park with beauty. **(fill)**

C. You want to improve the environment. What is your plan to help save water and trees, or to recycle? Use present progressive verb forms.

11. What are you doing in your school or neighborhood to help the environment? I _____

_____.

12. How are people in your area trying to help the environment? _____

_____

13. Describe an animal or a plant that is in danger of becoming extinct. What are people doing to help change this situation? _____

_____

D. (14–16) Write three sentences about ways that people are improving the environment. Use present progressive verb forms.

_____

_____

_____

_____

Edit It

E. (17–20) Edit the community flyer. Fix the four mistakes with present progressive verb forms.

Logan Square Garden Club is learning about water!
are
You going to help us save water.
         ing
We are give classes on Saturday. We am teaching about good
                                       are
plants for our area.
       ing
You are help your town if you conserve.

Proofreader's Marks

Add text:
              are
You saving water.

Change text:
           ing
I am hope that you will
help.

See all Proofreader's Marks
on page xi.

29 How Do You Show That an Action Was in Process?

Use *Was* or *Were* Plus the *-ing* Form of the Verb.

- Sometimes you want to show that an action was happening over a period of time in the past. Use the past progressive form.

- To form the past progressive, use the helping verb **was** or **were** plus a **main verb** that ends in **-ing**. The **helping verb** must agree with the subject.

   Julio **was standing** outside the restaurant.
   Inside, the waiter **was serving** a customer.
   Other people **were sitting** patiently.
   They **were becoming** impatient, though.

Try It

A. Complete each sentence. Write the past progressive form of the verb in parentheses.

1. My family _____was trying_____ out the new restaurant. **(try)**

2. We _____were hoping_____ the food would taste really good. **(hope)**

3. Many customers _____were waiting_____ in line. **(wait)**

4. Two of the owner's friends _____were stopping_____ in at the restaurant. **(stop)**

5. The owner _____was seating_____ them right away. **(seat)**

B. Choose a verb from the box to complete each sentence. Use the past progressive form.

| begin | feel | ignore | leave |

6. My father _____was feeling_____ angry.

7. Some people _____were leaving_____ the restaurant.

8. One customer _____was beginning_____ to complain.

9. The owner _____was ignoring_____ his complaints.

C. Imagine that you were waiting in line at the restaurant. Answer the questions about your experience. Use the past progressive form of verbs in your answers.

10. What were you doing while you were waiting? _____

_____

11. How were you feeling when the owner's friends were seated first? _____

_____

12. Was the owner treating anyone unfairly? What was he doing? _____

_____

D. (13–16) Write four sentences about a time you were treated either fairly or unfairly at a store or a restaurant. Use the past progressive form of a verb in each sentence.

_____

_____

_____

_____

_____

Edit It

E. (17–20) Edit the restaurant review. Fix the four mistakes with past progressive verbs.

Danny's Fish Fry

My family ate at the fish restaurant last night. The experience was a huge disappointment. The food was good, but the service was not. The owner was giving special treatment to some customers. New customers were ~~get~~ getting angry. They were looking at their watches. These customers ~~was wish~~ were wishing they had eaten someplace else. Other customers ~~was~~ were waiting to be served their meals. It is important to treat loyal customers well, but it is important to treat new customers well, too!

Proofreader's Marks

Add text:
We were hoping for a good meal.

Change text:
The owner ~~were snub~~ was snubbing us.

See all Proofreader's Marks on page xi.

30 How Do You Show That an Action Already Happened?

Change the Verb.

Add **-ed** to most verbs to show that an action already happened.
Use special past tense forms for **irregular verbs**.

Present	Past	Example in the Past
am, is, are	was, were	Susan **was** a piano teacher.
say	said	My friend **said** she was a good teacher.
do, does	did	She **did** a great job teaching him to play.
have, has	had	My friend **had** fun studying with Susan.
wake	woke	He **woke** up every morning and practiced.
hear	heard	Sometimes I **heard** him from next door.
ring	rang	When my alarm clock **rang**, I was already awake.

Try It

A. Rewrite each sentence. Use the past tense of the verb.

1. My aunt Susan hears about a job at the music store. _My aunt Susan heard about a job at_ _the music store._

2. She is a great candidate for the job. _She was a great candidate for the job._

3. Aunt Susan has years of teaching experience. _Aunt Susan had years of teaching experience._

4. My friend rings up the store on the telephone. _My friend rang up the store on the telephone._

5. He says that she would be a great teacher. _He said that she would be a great teacher._

B. Complete each sentence with the past tense of a verb from the box. Use **be** two times.

be	do	have	hear	ring	say	wake

6. The telephone at my aunt Susan's house _____rang_____.

7. Aunt Susan _____heard_____ it from outside.

8. The manager at the music store _____had_____ bad news for her.

9. He _____said_____ someone else got the job.

10. That applicant _____was_____ a friend of the manager.

11. The call _____woke_____ Aunt Susan up to the realities of life.

12. Aunt Susan _____did_____ everything she could.

13. _____Were_____ things fair when a friend of the manager got the job?

Write It

C. Answer the questions to give your opinions about Aunt Susan's situation. Use the past tense of irregular verbs.

14. What loyalties did the store manager have? The store manager _____

_____.

15. Was what happened to Aunt Susan fair? _____

_____

16. What do you think Aunt Susan said to the manager? _____

_____

D. (17–20) Write four sentences about how loyalties helped you or kept you from getting something you wanted. Use the past tense of four irregular verbs.

_____

_____

_____

_____

31 How Do You Show That an Action Already Happened?

Change the Verb.

Add **-ed** to most verbs to show that an action already happened.
Use special past tense forms for **irregular verbs**.

Present	Past	Example in the Past
feel	felt	Carlos **felt** sad when Oscar ignored him on the basketball court.
go, goes	went	Carlos and Oscar **went** to school together.
get	got	Carlos **got** a strange feeling from Oscar whenever he saw him.
know	knew	He **knew** that Oscar wasn't being nice.
meet	met	Recently, Carlos **met** Eduardo.
tell	told	Eduardo **told** Carlos about a good movie.
see	saw	The boys **saw** the movie together.

Try It

A. Complete each sentence. Write the past tense form of the verb in parentheses.

1. Carlos _____knew_____ that something was wrong. **(know)**

2. Oscar _____saw_____ him and didn't say hello. **(see)**

3. Oscar _____went_____ off with some new friends. **(go)**

4. Carlos _____got_____ the message. **(get)**

5. He _____told_____ Eduardo that old friends were not always loyal friends. **(tell)**

B. (6–12) Complete the paragraph with past tense verbs. Possible responses:

Carlos _____knew_____ that Eduardo was a better friend than Oscar.
Even though he only _____met_____ Eduardo a few weeks ago, Carlos
_____felt_____ closer to him. Carlos and Eduardo _____saw_____ each other
a lot. They _____told_____ each other their problems and helped each other
out. They _____got_____ along better than Carlos and Oscar. Carlos and Oscar
_____went_____ their separate ways. Carlos learned that old friends were not
always best friends.

Write It

C. Answer the questions about a time when an old friend was not a good friend. Use the past tense of irregular verbs.

13. What did your friend tell you? My friend _____

_____.

14. How did you feel? I _____

_____.

15. What did you know? I _____

_____.

16. Where did you go? I _____

_____.

D. (17–20) Write four sentences about an old friend and a new friend. Use the past tense of at least four irregular verbs from the chart on page G61.

_____

_____

_____

_____

_____

32 How Do You Tell About the Future?

Use *Will* Before the Verb.

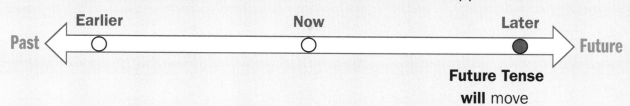

- The **future tense** of a verb shows that an action will happen later.

Past ← Earlier ○ — Now ○ — Later ● → Future

Future Tense
will move

- To form the future tense, use **will** before the main verb.
    Tim **will move** to a new town.

- You can also use **am**, **is**, or **are** plus **going to** before the main verb.
    He **is going to make** new friends.

Try It

A. Write the future tense of the verb in parentheses to complete each sentence. **More than one answer is possible.**   Possible responses:

1. Tim _____*will live*_____ close to his new school. **(live)**

2. His old friends _____*will visit*_____ him in his new home. **(visit)**

3. Tim _____*is going to go*_____ back to see them, too. **(go)**

4. Tim _____*will get*_____ to know new friends, too, though. **(get)**

5. He _____*will want*_____ to have friends in his new school. **(want)**

B. Write a future tense verb to complete each sentence.   Possible responses:

6. Tim _____*will stay*_____ loyal to his old friends.

7. He _____*is going to introduce*_____ them to his new friends.

8. Sometimes, all his friends _____*will go*_____ places together.

9. Other times, Tim _____*will hang out*_____ with his new friends.

10. Tim _____*will have*_____ fun being a loyal friend to everyone.

C. Imagine that you are going to move to a new town and go to a new school.
Answer the questions. Use future tense verbs.

11. How will you meet new friends? I _____ .

12. How will you stay loyal to old friends? I _____ .

13. Why will new friends want to know you? They _____

_____ .

14. How will old friends visit you? They _____ .

D. (15–18) Now write four sentences about something you will do with your
friends. Use a future tense verb in each sentence.

_____

_____

_____

_____

Edit It

E. (19–25) Edit the journal entry. Fix the seven mistakes with verbs. There is
more than one way to make each correction.   Possible responses:

May 16

Tomorrow, I will have a good time. I ~~got~~ [am going to get]
together with my friends. We will [go] on a long
hike together. Both my old friends and my
new friends [will] hike with me. We ~~climbed~~ [will climb] to the
top of a mountain. Then, we [are going to] eat a picnic
lunch. I ~~enjoyed~~ [will enjoy] the day because all my loyal
friends ~~had~~ [will have] fun together.

Proofreader's Marks

Add text:
I will [take] plenty of water
with me.

Change text:
Tomorrow, I ~~went~~ [will go] on a
hike.

See all Proofreader's Marks
on page xi.

© National Geographic Learning, a part of Cengage Learning, Inc.

33 Use Verb Tenses

Remember: You have to change the verb to show when an action happens. The action can happen in the **present**, **past**, or **future**.

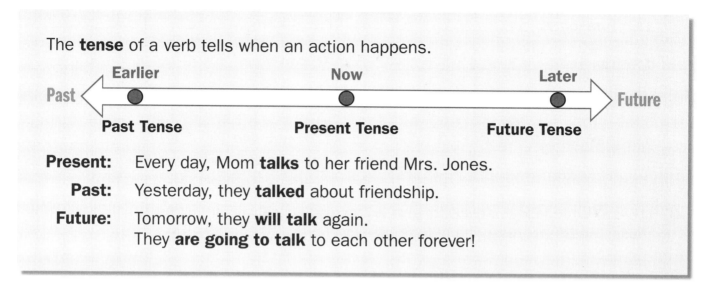

The **tense** of a verb tells when an action happens.

Earlier   Now   Later

Past ← Past Tense — Present Tense — Future Tense → Future

Present: Every day, Mom **talks** to her friend Mrs. Jones.

Past: Yesterday, they **talked** about friendship.

Future: Tomorrow, they **will talk** again.
They **are going to talk** to each other forever!

Try It

A. Complete each sentence. Write the correct tense of the verb in parentheses.

1. Mom _____met_____ Mrs. Jones years ago. **(past of *meet*)**

2. They _____went_____ to kindergarten together. **(past of *go*)**

3. Now Mrs. Jones _____has_____ a new home that is far away. **(present of *have*)**

4. She _____is_____ still Mom's loyal friend, though. **(present of *be*)**

5. Just yesterday, Mom _____was telling_____ me about the friendship. **(past progressive of *tell*)**

6–7. She _____said_____ that Mrs. Jones _____will visit_____ us later this year. **(past of *say*; future of *visit*)**

B. Complete each sentence. Write a verb in the tense in parentheses.   Possible responses:

8. Yesterday, I _____saw_____ my loyal friend Jenna. **(past)**

9. We _____were riding_____ our bicycles together. **(past progressive)**

10. I hope that Jenna and I _____will remain_____ loyal friends forever. **(future)**

C. Complete the sentences about a loyal friend. Use the verb tenses given in parentheses.

11. (present) I _____ a loyal friend named _____.

12. (past) We _____ a long time ago when _____.

13. (past progressive) Just yesterday, my friend and I _____.

14. (future) In the future, I hope that my friend and I _____

_____

D. (15–18) Write four sentences to give examples of loyalty. Use the past, present, past progressive, and future tenses.

_____

_____

_____

_____

_____

Grammar at Work

E. (19–25) Fix the <u>six</u> mistakes with verb tense. Fix <u>one</u> mistake with subject pronouns.

Dear Amanda,

    Yesterday, Marie ask ~~asked~~ about our long friendship. I share ~~shared~~ stories about our early years. They are ~~We were~~ in kindergarten then. Now, 40 years later, we were ~~are~~ still good friends. Last night, I took ~~looked~~ through our yearbook. We had ~~will have~~ a lot to talk about when you visit next month!

                      Love,

                      Shirley

Proofreader's Marks
Add text:
Loyal friends ^are important.
Change text:
Yesterday, I ~~write~~ wrote to my good friend. ^
See all Proofreader's Marks on page xi.

34 How Do Nouns Work in a Sentence?
They Can Be the Subject or the Object.

- A noun can be the **subject** of a sentence.
  My **grandmother** lives in Florida now.
       subject

- A noun can also be the **object** of an action verb. To find the object, turn the verb into a question such as: "Visit whom?" Your answer is the object.
  We visit my **grandmother** every year.
       verb   object

- Many English sentences follow this pattern: **subject → verb → object**.
  Grandmother loves **Florida**.
   subject   verb   object

  Sometimes she still misses her old **home**.
       subject   verb   object

Try It

A. Read each sentence. Write **subject** if the underlined noun is a subject. Write **object** if it is an object.

1. <u>Dad</u> phones my grandmother. _____subject_____

2. He invites <u>Grandmother Rachel</u> to visit. _____object_____

3. Grandmother Rachel makes <u>plans</u>. _____object_____

4. Dad sends <u>money</u> for a plane ticket. _____object_____

5. <u>Grandmother Rachel</u> arrives early. _____subject_____

B. Write a noun to complete each sentence. Then circle the subjects and underline the objects. Possible responses:

6. (Grandmother Rachel) cooks _____dinner_____.

7. (Mom and Dad) _____ love <u>turkey</u>!

8. (They) thank _____Grandmother Rachel_____ many times.

Write It

C. Answer the questions about a visit to a different country. Circle each subject and underline each object.

9. What country do you want to visit? _____

_____

10. What interests you about this country? _____

_____

D. (11–15) Imagine that someone from another country visits you. Tell what this person sees in your town. Write five sentences, using subjects and objects.

_____

_____

_____

_____

_____

Edit It

E. (16–20) Edit the paragraph. Add the five missing subjects or objects.   Possible responses:

                  letter   Brazil

I just got a ^from my cousin Paolo. He lives in. He visited
                         the food   He
me last summer. Paolo loved ^in New York. ^Also loved the
shows that we saw. ^Will visit Paolo in May.

Proofreader's Marks

Add text:
          cousin
My ^visited.

See all Proofreader's Marks on page xi.

35 Why Are There So Many Pronouns?

Some Work as Subjects, and Some Work as Objects.

- Use a **subject pronoun** as the subject of a sentence.

    My **mom** is running for mayor.
    She will be good for our city.

    Mom is running against **Mr. Greene**.
    He is the mayor now.

- Use an **object pronoun** as the object of the verb.

    The **election** is next month. I will watch **it** closely.

    My loyalties are with **Mom**. I support **her**.

Pronouns	
Subject	**Object**
I	me
you	you
he	him
she	her
it	it

Try It

A. Use pronouns from the chart to complete the sentences. Then underline the noun each pronoun stands for.

1. My mom will be a good mayor. _____ She _____ speaks well and likes people.

2. I respect my mom and her ideas. I will help _____ her _____ get votes.

3. The city needs to have a strong mayor. Mom can help _____ it _____ grow.

4. "Mrs. Gonzalez, please read this. Then _____ you _____ might vote for Mom," I said.

5. Mr. Lopez helps mom get votes. We appreciate _____ him _____ very much.

B. (6–12) Write pronouns from the chart to complete the paragraph.

In the last election, my older sister voted for Mr. Greene. _____ She _____
supported _____ him _____. Now her loyalty has changed. _____ It _____ is
with our mom. My sister was disappointed with Mr. Greene. _____ He _____ did
not keep his promises. "_____ I _____ think Mom will help other residents in
the city and _____ me _____," she said. "Mom will make this city a better place
to live. That's why I support _____ her _____."

C. Complete the sentences. Use a subject or object pronoun where necessary.

13. At school, _____ ran for _____. I supported _____ because _____

_____.

14. My friends voted for _____. They supported _____ because

_____

_____.

15. In the school election, _____ won. I think _____

_____.

D. (16–20) Some kids like one famous person a lot. Then they change their minds. They like a different famous person. Tell about a famous person you used to like and one you like now. Write five sentences, using subject and object pronouns.

_____

_____

_____

_____

_____

Edit It

E. (21–25) Edit the news article. Fix the five mistakes with pronouns.

> Yesterday, Mrs. Sonja Nelson won the election for mayor. ~~You~~ It
> was a huge victory. ~~Her~~ She won many, many votes. Mr. Roberts lost.
> ~~Him~~ He did not receive enough votes. Mrs. Nelson thanked every
> supporter. "Thank ~~him~~ you for your help," Mrs. Nelson said. "~~Me~~ I am
> so happy I won!" she said.

Proofreader's Marks

Change text: She

Mrs. Nelson won. ~~He~~ is
our next mayor. ^

See all Proofreader's Marks
on page xi.

36 Which Pronouns Refer to More Than One Person?

We, You, They, and *Us, You, Them*

- Use a **subject pronoun** as the subject.

  My **parents** are from Los Angeles.
  They have lived in Chicago for twenty years.
  subject

  My sister and I are from Chicago.
  We have always lived here.
  subject

Pronouns	
Subject	**Object**
we	us
you	you
they	them

- Use an **object pronoun** as the object of the verb.

  My parents are loyal to the Los Angeles sports **teams**.
  My parents watch **them** on TV.
  object

  We are loyal to the Chicago teams. Mom and Dad take **us** to home games.
  object

Try It

A. Write pronouns from the chart to complete the sentences. Then underline the noun each pronoun stands for.

1. <u>Mom and Dad</u> are loyal to the Los Angeles teams. _____They_____ have not changed their loyalty in twenty years.

2. I argue with <u>Mom and Dad</u>. I want _____them_____ to like the Chicago teams.

3. <u>My sister and I</u> make a plan. _____We_____ get season tickets for our parents.

4. My parents are surprised by my <u>sister and me</u>. Dad thanks _____us_____.

5. My parents enjoy the home <u>games</u>. Mom likes _____them_____ so much that she becomes a fan.

6. After twenty years, my <u>parents</u> finally change their loyalty. _____They_____ still like Los Angeles, but Chicago is better!

B. Edit each sentence. Fix the plural pronouns.

7. Our friends ask ~~we~~ ^{us} to go to a hockey game.

8. ^{We} ~~Us~~ don't like hockey.

9. We tell ~~they~~ ^{them} that basketball is better.

10. Our friends tell ~~we~~ ^{us} to go, anyway.

11. After the game, ~~us~~ ^{we} thank our friends.

12. ^{They} ~~Them~~ definitely changed our minds about hockey!

Write It

C. Complete the sentences about sports loyalties. Use at least two plural subject pronouns and two plural object pronouns.

13. My friends like _____.

14. My family and I like _____

   _____.

15. Sports are important. I _____.

16. My classmates and I _____. The school takes _____

   _____.

D. (17–20) Tell how friends or family members have changed sports loyalties over time. Write four sentences, using a plural pronoun in each sentence.

_____

_____

_____

_____

_____

_____

37 What's an "Antecedent"?

It's the Word a Pronoun Refers to.

- A **pronoun** usually refers back to a noun. This noun is called the **antecedent**.

  A space station stays in space. **It** orbits way above Earth.
  antecedent   pronoun

- A pronoun must **agree** with its antecedent. This means that the pronoun has to go with the noun it refers to.

  Some **astronauts** go to space stations. **They** live there for a while.

  Mimi and I learn about space. **We** want to go there someday.

Try It

A. Rewrite the sentences. Replace the underlined antecedents with pronouns that agree.

1. Patti and I wonder how the astronauts get new food. _____We wonder how the astronauts get_____ new food.

2. Workers load supplies on a shuttle. _____They load supplies on a shuttle._____

3. The shuttle brings the crew more food. _____It brings the crew more food._____

B. (4–7) Complete each sentence with a pronoun from the box. Match it to the antecedent.

he	it	she	they

Mimi's dad knows about the space station. _____He_____ tells Mimi how the station floats in space. _____She_____ learns that a shuttle brings supplies to the station. _____It_____ has to land at a special place. The crew waits for the shuttle to dock. Then _____they_____ cheer!

C. Answer the questions about life on Earth and in space. Use antecedents and pronouns in your responses.

8. What is your home like? _____

_____

9. Where do you get your food and other supplies? _____

_____

10. Could you stay in a space station? Why or why not? _____

_____

D. (11–15) Write five sentences that tell more about life on Earth and in space. Use pronouns and antecedents.

_____

_____

_____

_____

Edit It

E. (16–19) Edit the article. Fix the four mistakes with pronouns.

People in ancient times wondered about space. A man named Galileo watched the sky through a telescope. ~~She~~ He discovered that our planet was just one part of the universe. ~~Them~~ It contained more than just Earth. Others watched how things moved in the sky. ~~We~~ They used the sun and moon to tell time. My friends and I still wonder about space. ~~He~~ We want to learn more about it.

Proofreader's Marks

Change text:

Tim and I watch the stars. ~~They~~ We do it all the time.

See all Proofreader's Marks on page xi.

38 How Do You Know Which Pronoun to Use?

Figure Out the Noun That It Refers to.

- Use a **subject pronoun** in the subject of a sentence. Use an **object pronoun** after the verb or after a preposition.

  Marco uses **a computer**. **He** uses **it** to research space.

  The **friends** are curious about the **planets**. **They** talk about traveling to **them** .

- All **pronouns** must agree with the **noun** they refer to. This noun is called the antecedent.
  1. If the noun names a male, use **he** or **him** .
  2. If the noun names a female, use **she** or **her** .
  3. If the noun names one thing, use **it** .
  4. If the noun names more than one thing, use **they** or **them** .

Try It

A. Complete each sentence about the planets. Write the correct pronoun.

1. Marco and Gina think about the future. _____ They _____ imagine visiting
   They/Him
   a planet.

2. I ask _____ them _____ which planet is best to visit.
   her/them

3. Gina likes Saturn. _____ She _____ thinks Saturn's rings are interesting.
   He/She

4. Marco and I choose Mars. _____ We _____ want to know why Mars
   We/They
   is called the Red Planet.

5. My group and I discuss how to get to the planets. Maybe a shuttle can take
   _____ us _____ there!
   us/we

B. (6–11) Edit the paragraph. Fix the six mistakes with pronouns.

> My partner and ~~her~~ [I] have an idea. ~~Them~~ [We] imagine having a hotel in space. Abe names ~~them~~ [it] Deep Space 8. ~~Him~~ [He] thinks about the hotel rooms. Guests could stay in rooms without gravity. That way ~~she~~ [they] can enjoy floating all around. The meals would be tied down, though. That is so hungry guests won't have to grab ~~they~~ [them] off the ceiling!

Write It

C. Answer the questions about travel to different places. Use pronouns and antecedents.

12. What places do you visit? Why? _____

_____

13. How do you get where you are going? _____

_____

14. Do you travel alone or with someone else? _____

_____

15. Where do you stay when you travel? _____

_____

16. What does it feel like when you go somewhere new? _____

_____

D. (17–20) Write four more sentences about what it is like to travel. Use pronouns correctly.

_____

_____

_____

_____

_____

39 Do You Ever Talk About Yourself?

Then Learn to Use the Words *I* and *Me*.

Subject Pronoun: I

- Use the pronoun **I** in the **subject** of a sentence.

   I like science.

- In a compound subject, name yourself last.

   Correct: Dad and I like science.

   Correct: He and I talk about science topics.

   Incorrect: Me and dad enjoy science articles.

Object Pronoun: me

- Use the pronoun **me** as the **object**.

   Dad tells **me** about the moon landing.

- In a compound object, name yourself last.

   Correct: My sister asks **Dad and me** about the moon.

   Correct: She asks **him and me**.

   Incorrect: She asks me and him.

Try It

A. Write **I** or **me** to complete each sentence.

1. Pictures from space amaze _____ me _____.

2. My friends and _____ I _____ saw a man walking on the moon.

3. The picture made _____ me _____ wonder about the future.

4. Will _____ I _____ ever walk on the moon?

5. Hopefully, Jon and _____ I _____ can take that walk someday.

B. (6–13) Write **I** or **me** to complete the paragraph.

_____ I _____ love the night sky. The stars make _____ me _____ smile. The moon interests _____ me _____. Katy and _____ I _____ look together. She and _____ I _____ wonder if we'll ever go there. One night, Tim comes to see _____ me _____. Katy tells him and _____ me _____ to hurry. Tim and _____ I _____ get to see a beautiful full moon!

C. Answer the questions. Use **I** or **me** in each answer.

14. What do you like to watch in the sky? _____

_____

15. Have you ever seen a full moon? What is it like? _____

_____

16. What do you imagine as you look at the stars or the moon? _____

_____

D. (17–20) Write four sentences about the night sky and what it makes you think about. Use **I** or **me** in each sentence.

_____

_____

_____

_____

Edit It

E. (21–25) Edit the journal entry below. Fix the five mistakes with pronouns.

October 15

My brother and I went to the space museum
today. The train picked up my brother and I^me
at the station. It dropped me and my brother^(my brother and me)
off a block away from the museum. Me^I bought
the tickets. The displays pleased I.^me My brother
and I are fans now. We will tell everyone to
go. I and my brother^(My brother and I) can't wait to go again.

Proofreader's Marks

Change text:
Craig and I
Me and Craig are fans.

See all Proofreader's Marks
on page xi.

40 Can a Compound Subject Include a Pronoun?

Yes, and the Pronoun Comes Last.

A **compound subject** can include nouns and pronouns joined by **and** or **or**.

1. My **teammates** **and** **I** are in the competition this year.
2. **Parents** **and** **students** think the competition is tough.
3. The **team** **and** **I** are excited.
4. The **coach** **or** the **captain** helps us.
5. **Tracy**, **Janine**, **or** **I** am first to score a point.

How do you know where to place the pronoun?

- Nouns always come before pronouns.
- The pronoun **I** always comes last.

Try It

A. Complete each sentence. Write the correct compound subject.

1. _____ think we have a small team.

Our coach and I

Our coach and I / I and our coach

2. Sandra and Ms. Smith work on speed. _____

Ms. Smith and she

Ms. Smith and she / She and Ms. Smith

think that speed is our best skill.

3. _____ gather extra equipment.

The two teachers and we

The two teachers and we / We and the two teachers

4. _____ know there are few resources for us.

Chris, the captain, and I

Chris, the captain, and I / The captain, I, and Chris

5. _____ save a little money each week.

Sarah, Sandra, and I

Sarah, Sandra, and I / I, Sarah, and Sandra

6. Ms. Smith, _____ think having heart is more

the captain, and I

the captain, and I / I, and the captain

important than resources.

B. Rewrite each sentence. Fix the compound subjects. Make sure the verbs agree.

7. My mom, I, sister, and brother patch up the uniforms.

My mom, sister, brother, and I patch up the uniforms.

8. Our neighbors, we, and friends think we have a lot of potential.

Our neighbors, friends, and we think we have a lot of potential.

9. But they or the opposing school often think we won't win.

But the opposing school or they often think we won't win.

10. She, I, or he helps with new plays.

She, he, or I help with new plays.

11. We and the top two players have several strategies.

The top two players and we have several strategies.

12. They, I, and Chris like to surprise the other team.

Chris, they, and I like to surprise the other team.

Write It

C. Answer the questions about a team or an organization that exceeded expectations. Use compound subjects.

13. How does an underdog team win? The players aren't expected to win. _____
_____ play with less pressure.

14. How do members of the team overcome challenges? _____
_____

15. Who thought the team would fail? _____

D. (16–20) Write five sentences that tell more about the team or organization that exceeded expectations. Use compound subjects.

_____

_____

_____

_____

_____

41 What Is a Past Participle?

It is One of the Main Parts of a Verb.

- A verb has four principal, or main, parts. The parts are used to show when things happen. The **past participle of a verb** is used for the passive voice and with forms of **have**.

Present	Present Participle	Past	Past Participle
be	being	was	been
do	doing	did	done
heat	heating	heated	heated

- The past participle of a regular verb ends with **-ed**
  Our class has **started** on time.
  A new project is **described** by the teacher.

- The past participle of an irregular verb has a special form.
  We have **been** curious about the assignment.
  A diagram of the solar system was **chosen** by my group.

Try It

A. Complete each sentence. Use the past participle of the verb.

1. My partner and I have _____ drawn _____ a diagram of the solar system.
   draw/drawn

2. It has _____ been _____ enjoyable to do together.
   being/been

3. A huge yellow sun is _____ placed _____ in the center by Jan.
   place/placed

4. The planets are _____ sketched _____ all around it.
   sketch/sketched

5. Orbits are _____ shown _____ by circular lines.
   showing/shown

6. Finally, our diagram is _____ done _____!
   doing/done

B. (7–10) Complete the paragraph. Use the past participles of the verbs in the box.

display	sign	take	tell

    My dad has _____taken_____ me to the space museum. A model of a space shuttle is _____displayed_____ there. We have _____signed_____ up for a tour. Dad and I are _____told_____ all about the shuttle by the tour guide.

Write It

C. Imagine you have traveled into space on a spaceship. Answer the questions about your experience. Use past participles of verbs in your answers.

11. What has your spaceship or ride been like? _____

_____

12. What have you seen outside the window? _____

_____

13. What have you eaten while on board? How was it prepared? _____

_____

14. How has the experience made you feel? _____

_____

Edit It

D. (15–18) Edit the article. Fix the four mistakes with verbs.

>   I have learn^(learned) that the sun is a giant ball of gases. The activity in the sun has producing^(produced) a lot of energy and heat. The sun is surround^(surrounded) by the planets. The planets are think^(thought) to be far enough away so they won't get burned.

Proofreader's Marks

Change text:

Scientists have studying^(studied) the sun.

See all Proofreader's Marks on page xi.

42 How Do You Show the Present in the Passive Voice?

Use the Present Tense Form of *Be* with the Past Participle.

- Use the passive voice to emphasize the receiver of the action or the action itself.

  A bright moon **is seen** by people on Earth.

  Emphasizes what is seen, not who does the viewing.

  The moon's light **is created** by the sun.

  Emphasizes what is created, not what does the creating.

- Use **am**, **is**, or **are** with the **past participle** of the main verb to tell about something that happens now or often.

  The sun's light **is reflected** by the moon.

Try It

A. Complete each sentence in the passive voice. Add the correct present tense of *be* to the past participle of the verb.

1. When my homework _____ is _____ **done**, I go outside.

2. I _____ am _____ **given** a chance by nature to see something beautiful.

3. The night sky _____ is _____ **lit** up by a full moon.

4. Interesting objects and shapes _____ are _____ **created** by the twinkling stars.

B. (5–8) Complete the paragraph. Use the passive voice. Add the present tense of *be* and the past participle of the verb.

Every day, my little sisters _____ are told _____ a story. Today's story
                                            tell

_____ is presented _____ by my brother. He _____ is asked _____ what
     present   **ask**

the story is about. They _____ are entertained _____ by a story called "The Fox in
                                  entertain

the Moon."

Write It

C. Answer the questions about the night sky. Use the present in the passive voice in your answers.

9. Are people fascinated by the night sky? _____

_____

10. Is the dark sky lit up by a full moon? _____

_____

11. Are interesting shapes outlined by the twinkling stars? _____

_____

Edit It

D. (12–15) Edit the paragraph. Fix the four mistakes with verbs.

> Now, I ~~was~~ am given information about the moon
> by my teacher. She explains how telescopes
> ~~is~~ are used by scientists. Craters on the moon's
> surface ~~am~~ are studied by the scientists. A crater
> ~~are~~ is made by something crashing into the
> moon's surface.

Proofreader's Marks
Change text:
Moon rocks ~~is~~ are studied by geologists.
See all Proofreader's Marks on page xi.

43 How Do You Show the Past in the Passive Voice?

Use the Past Tense Form of *Be* with the Past Participle.

- Use the **passive voice** to emphasize the receiver of the action or the action itself.

    A research project **was assigned** by the teacher.

    Emphasizes what was assigned, not who assigned it.

    A different space topic **was chosen** by each group.

    Emphasizes what the topic was, not who chose it.

- To tell about a past action in the passive voice, use **was** or **were** with the **past participle** of the verb.

    Stars **were researched** by Terry's group.

Try It

A. Complete each sentence in the passive voice. Add the correct past tense of *be* to the past participle of the verb.

1. The moon _____was_____ **researched** by our group.

2. The moon _____was_____ **observed** by everyone last week.

3. Each night, its shape _____was_____ **drawn** by each member.

4. The moon's different phases _____were_____ **confirmed** by all of us.

5. The results _____were_____ **shared** with the class by our group leader.

B. (6–9) Complete the paragraph. Use the passive voice. Add the past tense of *be* and the past participle of the verb.

In the 1960s, short missions into space _____were planned_____ by
                                             plan

scientists. Several astronauts _____were sent_____ into space by NASA. Alan
                                   send

Shepard _____was chosen_____ to ride on *Freedom 7* by the team.
           choose

John Glenn, Jr., _____was selected_____ by the group to go on *Friendship 7* and
                    select

orbit the Earth.

C. What were you asked, chosen for, or assigned to do yesterday or the day
before? Complete the sentences. Use the past in the passive voice.

10. I _____ to _____ by _____

_____ .

11. My partner and I _____ to _____ by _____

_____ .

12. My group _____ to _____ by _____

_____ .

Edit It

D. (13–16) Edit the article. Fix the four mistakes with verbs.

                                    was
In 1969, the world ~~is~~ fascinated by the
                    ^
landing of two astronauts on the moon. Neil
                              were
Armstrong and Edwin Aldrin ~~was~~ sent there
                      were ^
by NASA. Soil and rocks ~~was~~ gathered by
                          ^
the astronauts to bring back to Earth.   An
                      was
American flag ~~were~~ put in the ground by
                ^
the men.

Proofreader's Marks

Change text:

The first moon walk
          was
~~was~~ seen by people
  ^
everywhere.

See all Proofreader's Marks
on page xi.

44 Use Subject and Object Pronouns

Remember: Use a subject pronoun as the subject of a sentence. Use an object pronoun as the object of the verb.

Subject Pronouns	I	you	he	she	it	we	you	they
Object Pronouns	me	you	him	her	it	us	you	them

My friends and **I** love to eat ice cream in the summer. **We** go to the same ice cream stand every year. **It** has the best ice cream. Will **you** join **us** today? Tony's parents are driving. **We** can ask **them** for a ride. **They** will take **us**.

Try It

A. Rewrite the sentences. Use pronouns for the underlined words.

1. When Tony and Alex get to the ice cream stand, <u>Tony and Alex</u> are surprised. _When Tony_
   and Alex get to the ice cream stand, they are surprised.

2. <u>The ice cream stand</u> has new owners. _It has new owners._
   _____

3. Tony says, "I am surprised, but <u>Alex and I</u> should try the new ice cream." _Tony says, "I am_
   surprised, but we should try the new ice cream."

B. Complete each sentence about what happens at the ice cream stand.
Write the correct pronoun.

4. Alex misses the old stand, but the new flavors excite _____him_____.
   he/him

5. Tony has been a loyal customer, but _____he_____ wants to try the new
   he/him
   place.

6. The next day, Alex's sister also tries the new ice cream. _____She_____ thinks
   She/Her
   it is delicious.

C. Answer the questions about where you like to eat. Use subject and object pronouns in your answers.

7. What restaurant are you a loyal customer of? I am a loyal customer of _____

_____.

8. What food does the restaurant serve? The restaurant serves _____

_____.

9. Who takes you to eat there? _____

10. Why might you change your loyalty? _____

D. (11–14) Imagine that you could open your own ice cream stand or burger place. Write four sentences about how you would attract loyal customers. Use subject and object pronouns.

_____

_____

_____

_____

Grammar at Work

E. (15–20) Fix the four mistakes with plural pronouns. Fix two mistakes with verb tenses.

My friends and I love Green World Burgers. ~~Us~~ We are very loyal customers. The cooks at Green World Burgers are amazing. ~~Them~~ They use foods from all over the world. Yesterday, I ~~have~~ had a burger with spices from South America. My friend came with me. He ~~order~~ ordered a burger with cheese from Mexico. My brothers should try the burgers. ~~He~~ They will love ~~it~~ them!

Proofreader's Marks

Change text:
~~Her~~ She is a loyal customer.

See all Proofreader's Marks on page xi.

45 Use the Active and Passive Voice

Remember: In the **active voice**, the subject <u>performs</u> the action expressed by the **verb**. In the **passive voice**, the subject <u>receives</u> the action. The performer of the action often shows up in a phrase after the verb.

Active Voice: Ben **knows** that moving is difficult.

                            He **moved** from Haiti to Florida.

Passive Voice: He **is asked** by his new friends to describe Haiti.

                            They **were told** by Ben what Haiti was like.

Try It

A. Read each sentence. Decide if the sentence is in the active or passive voice. Then rewrite the sentence in a different voice.

1. Ben was given advice by his dad. _____

_____

2. He tells Ben not to worry. _____

_____

3. Everyone experiences new situations. _____

_____

4. New situations are made less scary by friends and family. _____

_____

B. (5–8) Complete the paragraph. Use the correct verb forms for the passive voice.

My new friends helped me adjust to the city. Last Saturday, I __was taken__ by
                                                  take

them to the park. On Sunday, they __were given__ permission to take me to the
                                 give

movies. Today, I __am asked__ to walk with them to school. My whole family __is pleased__
                  ask   **please**

by their friendliness.

C. Use the verbs to write sentences. Write one sentence using the active voice. Then write a sentence using the passive voice.

9. ask _____

_____

10. tell_____

_____

11. give _____

_____

D. (12–14) Write three sentences about advice someone has given you. What was the situation? Who gave you the advice? Use the passive voice.

_____

_____

_____

Grammar at Work

E. (15–20) Edit the description written in the active voice. Fix the <u>six</u> mistakes in the verbs.

I was nervous about my first day in a new school. I ~~am~~ walked into the classroom. Everyone smiled. Then the teacher ~~is~~ introduced ~~by~~ me. Everyone wanted to know more about my home country. They asked A lot of questions ~~were asked~~. After that, I was stopped being so nervous.

Proofreader's Marks

Change text:

They <u>were</u> watched me enter the classroom

See all Proofreader's Marks on page xi.

46 What Are Adjectives?

They Are Describing Words.

- You can describe people, places, or things with **adjectives**.
  They answer the question: What is it like?

- Use adjectives to describe:
  1. how something looks: **green, crowded, dusty, empty, elegant, tall**
  2. how something sounds: **dull, screechy, loud, quiet**
  3. how something feels, tastes, or smells: **rough, bumpy, sweet, fragrant**
  4. a person's mood: **anxious, cheery, friendly, frustrated**

- Adjectives help the reader picture what you describe.
  The **crowded** streets are filled with **loud** traffic.
  The **dusty** road leads to a **sunny** park.

Try It

A. Complete each sentence with an adjective from the box.   Possible responses:

| lively | modern | peaceful | simple | sleepy | spicy | towering | vibrant |

1. Mr. Lucas likes to walk down the streets of the _____sleepy_____ town.

2. Ms. Seri admires the _____modern_____ buildings in the city.

3. Mr. Lucas prefers the _____towering_____ trees that line Main Street.

4. She eats _____spicy_____ food from the sidewalk vendors.

5. He likes the _____simple_____ menu at the corner diner.

6. She goes to street festivals to listen to _____lively_____ music.

7. Mr. Lucas listens to the _____peaceful_____ songs of the birds in the park.

8. Ms. Seri prefers the _____vibrant_____ energy of the big city.

B. Now, think of your own adjectives to describe how life is different in a big city and a small town. Write the new sentences on the lines.   Possible responses:

9. Mr. Lucas has a smile for everyone he meets on his walk.

Mr. Lucas has a friendly smile for everyone he meets on his walk.

10. Ms. Seri takes the subway to visit the museum.

Ms. Seri takes the crowded subway to visit the museum.

11. The building has exhibits.

The huge building has interesting exhibits.

12. Mr. Lucas meets his friend for lunch in the park.

Mr. Lucas meets his friend for lunch in the shady park.

Write It

C. Answer the questions about the differences between life in a small town and a city. Use adjectives.

13. What do you find in cities? Cities have _____

_____.

14. Describe the sounds or sights of a small town. A small town has _____

_____.

15. What is the biggest difference between a city and a small town? A city has _____

_____ , and a small town has _____.

D. (16–20) Write five sentences that describe a big city or a small town. Use adjectives in your sentences.

_____

_____

_____

_____

_____

_____

47 How Do You Use a Predicate Adjective?

After a Form of the Verb *Be*

- Most of the time, **adjectives** come before **nouns**.
  Juan keeps his shoes on the **lower shelf**. He has **red sneakers**.

- But if your verb is a form of **be**, you can put the adjective after the verb. The forms of **be** are **am**, **is**, **are**, **was**, and **were**.
  Juan is **happy** when he runs. His **mind** is **empty**.

- If you use two predicate adjectives, join them with **and**, **but**, or **or**.
  Ivan is **friendly** and **generous**. His **hobbies** are **simple** but **expensive**.
  He is either **broke** or **busy**.

Try It

A. Complete each sentence with an adjective from the box.

foolish	excited	sensible	shocked

1. Ivan is _____excited_____ about getting new running shoes.

2. Juan is _____shocked_____ by the prices at the store.

3. Juan is _____sensible_____ about choosing new shoes.

4. Ivan's choice of shoes is sometimes _____foolish_____.

B. Complete each sentence. Use predicate adjectives. Possible responses:

5. At the athletic store, the shoes are _____trendy_____ but _____expensive_____.

6. At the discount store, the shoes are _____dull_____ or _____cheap_____.

7. Juan will choose shoes that are _____practical_____.

8. Ivan prefers shoes that are _____bright_____ and _____colorful_____.

C. Answer the questions about clothes. Use predicate adjectives.

9. How do you choose your clothes? _____

10. Do you have a friend who likes clothes a lot? Describe him or her. **My friend** _____

_____.

11. Describe a friend who doesn't care about clothes. **My friend** _____

_____.

12. Describe one item that you really like to wear. **I have** _____.

It is _____.

D. (13–16) Write four sentences about how you choose your clothes.
Use predicate adjectives.

_____

_____

_____

_____

_____

Edit It

E. (17–20) Edit the journal entry. Fix the four missing predicate adjectives.   Possible responses:

August 17

Today I went to the athletic store with Ivan.

He has a lot of shoes. He likes shoes that are ^stylish.

The prices at the athletic store were ^high. Then

we went to the discount store. The shoes there

were ^cheap but nice. I need a pair of running shoes.

I am ^particular about my shoes.

Proofreader's Marks

Add text:
This is ^expensive.

See all Proofreader's Marks
on page xi.

48 When Do You Use an Indefinite Adjective?

When You Can't Be Specific

- If you are not sure of the exact number or amount of something, use an **indefinite adjective**.

  I haven't spent **much** time with that group. **Some** people in that group are nice. **Many** people in that group do **a lot of** activities that my parents don't like.

- How do you know which adjective to use?

These adjectives go before a noun you can count, like **friends**:		These adjectives go before a noun you can't count, like **courage**:	
many	**a lot of**	**much**	**a lot of**
a few	**several**	**a little**	**not much**
some	**no**	**some**	**no**

Try It

A. Complete each sentence. Use indefinite adjectives from the chart. Possible responses:

1. I need _____a lot of, much_____ courage when I talk to my parents about my friends.

2. They like most of my friends, but they think _____a few, some_____ kids are not good for me.

3. They don't want me to spend _____a lot of, much_____ time with these friends.

B. Write the correct indefinite adjective to complete each sentence.

4. _____Several_____ friends do positive and healthy activities.
   Several / A little

5. _____A few_____ friends are not good role models.
   A few / Much

6. _____Several_____ friends are foolish sometimes.
   Several / Much

7. I know there are _____many_____ reasons to talk to my parents about my friends.
   many / much

C. Answer the questions about a time when you needed to tell your parents something difficult. Use indefinite adjectives.

8. What did you need to tell your parents? I told them that I _____.

9. What was difficult about talking to your parents? _____

10. What was a benefit of your talk with your parents? _____

_____

11. Why is it sometimes difficult to talk to parents? _____

_____

D. (12–15) Write four sentences about the benefits and difficulties of talking to parents. Use indefinite adjectives.

_____

_____

_____

_____

Edit It

E. (16–20) Edit the letter. Fix five indefinite adjectives.   Possible responses:

Dear Mom and Dad,

Thanks for spending some time talking about my friendships
with me. At first, I agreed with only ~~no~~ points that you made.
                                  a few   many
Now, I understand you want me to have ~~much~~ good friendships.
                          much   several
I should not spend ~~several~~ time with people who are not making
                            several
healthy decisions. We have had ~~a little~~ good conversations this
                    a lot of / much
past year. I have ~~many~~ appreciation for your advice.

                                        Love,

                                        Denise

Proofreader's Marks

Change text:
                several
I have ~~much~~ good
friends.

See all Proofreader's Marks
on page xi.

49 Can You Use an Adjective to Make a Comparison?

Yes, But You Have to Change the Adjective.

- Use a **comparative adjective** to compare two people, places, or things.
  Jared's present is **large**, but my present is **larger**.
  The necklace is **more beautiful** than the bracelet.

- There are two ways to turn an adjective into a comparative adjective:

1. If the adjective has one syllable, add **-er**. If it has two syllables and ends in **y**, change the **y** to i before you add **-er**.	smart small pretty smarter smaller prettier
2. If the adjective is three or more syllables, use **more** before the adjective.	delicate responsible more delicate more responsible

- If an adjective has two syllables, sometimes you can use either form, but it is safer to use **more**.

  lively   **anxious**
  livelier or **more lively**   **more anxious**

Try It

A. Complete each sentence with a comparative adjective.

1. That present will make Inga happy, but this one will make her _____ happier _____.

2. This gift is beautiful, but the other gift is _____ more beautiful _____.

3. I am excited about her birthday, but Inga is _____ more excited _____ about it.

4. I found it hard to decide on a gift, and you found it even _____ harder _____.

5. It was scary for me to choose a gift, but it was was even _____ scarier _____ for Jared to choose.

B. Write the comparative form of the adjective in parentheses.

6. The necklace is _____more expensive_____ than the earrings. **(expensive)**

7. The chain on the gold necklace is _____wider_____ than the chain on the silver necklace. **(wide)**

8. This charm is _____smaller_____ than that charm. **(small)**

9. Your present is _____more special_____ than what you gave her last year. **(special)**

10. Inga is _____more gracious_____ when she receives gifts than I am. **(gracious)**

11. Which of these two necklaces looks _____prettier_____? **(pretty)**

12. The note you wrote in the card is _____longer_____ than the note I wrote. **(long)**

Write It

C. Answer the questions about a time when you bought a gift for a special friend or family member. Use comparative adjectives.

13. What gift did you buy? I bought a _____.

14. What made your gift special? _____
_____

15. What makes your friend or family member special? _____
_____

16. Was the person happy with your gift? Explain. _____
_____

D. (17–20) Write four sentences that compare two items that you might like to buy for someone special. What makes you choose one item over the other? Use comparative adjectives.

_____

_____

_____

_____

_____

50 Can an Adjective Compare More Than Two Things?

Yes, But You Have to Use a Different Form.

- A **superlative adjective** compares three or more people, places, or things. To turn an adjective into a superlative adjective:

1. Add **-est** to a one-syllable adjective or a two-syllable adjective ending in y. Add **the**.	It was **the roughest** and **dirtiest** trail I ever tried to ride.
2. Use **most** before an adjective with three or more syllables. Add **the**.	It was **the most challenging** trail I ever tried to ride.

- Adjectives have different forms. Use the form that fits your purpose.

To Describe 1 Thing	rough	challenging
To Compare 2 Things	rougher	more challenging
To Compare 3 or More Things	roughest	most challenging

- Never use **more** and **-er** together. Never use **most** and **-est** together.

  It was the ~~most~~ roughest trail I ever tried.

Try It

A. Complete each sentence with the correct adjective.

1. My uncle took his bike on the _____ steepest _____ trail in the park.
   steeper / steepest

2. The first part of the trail was _____ more dangerous _____ than the last.
   more dangerous / most dangerous

3. He was not the _____ slowest _____ person in his group.
   slower / slowest

4. His friend Sam was _____ faster _____ than he was on the flat parts.
   faster / fastest

5. The _____ hardest _____ part of the ride was the climb up the hill.
   harder / hardest

B. Complete each sentence. Use the correct superlative form of an adjective from the box.

| challenging | cool | dirty | easy | experienced | rocky | thrilling |

6. The group leader was the _____ most experienced _____ rider of all the participants.

7. The _____ easiest _____ way down the mountain was on the paved road.

8. The turns were the _____ most challenging _____ part of the course.

9. My uncle said the steep slopes were the _____ most thrilling _____ of all.

10. After he rode through the puddles, his bike was the _____ dirtiest _____ in the group.

11. My uncle just missed the _____ rockiest _____ part of all when he went off the trail.

12. He said this trail is the _____ coolest _____ trail he has been on.

Write It

C. Answer the questions about an intense athletic activity. Use superlative adjectives.

13. What is the most intense athletic activity? I think _____ is the

_____.

14. What are the greatest challenges of this activity? _____

_____

15. What makes this a popular sport or activity? _____

_____

D. (16–20) Write five sentences comparing two intense athletic activities. Use superlative adjectives.

_____

_____

_____

_____

_____

51 Which Adjectives Are Irregular?

Good, Bad, Many, Much, and Little

- These adjectives have special forms.

To Describe 1 Thing	good	bad	many	much	little
To Compare 2 Things	better	worse	more	more	less
To Compare 3 or More Things	best	worst	most	most	least

- This sentence compares two people:
    My friend Kyra is a **better** basketball player than Sarah.

- This sentence compares three or more people:
    My friend Kyra is the **best** player in the neighborhood.

Try It

A. Complete each sentence. Write the correct irregular comparative adjective.

1. Kyra is the _____ most _____ talented player on the team.
    more / most

2. Kyra feels like the _____ worst _____ player of all.
    worse / worst

3. Kyra has _____ more _____ defensive skills than Michelle.
    more / most

4. She is _____ better _____ than Luanne at free throws.
    good / better

B. Complete each sentence. Write the correct form of good, bad, many, much, or little. Possible responses:

5. Kyra feels _____ bad _____ about the first set of tryouts.

6. I tell her the second tryout will be _____ better _____ than the first.

7. She has the _____ best _____ offensive skills of all of the athletes.

8. Kyra gets the _____ least _____ number of fouls of all the players.

C. Imagine that you have a friend who is worried about a team tryout. Answer the questions. Use irregular comparative adjectives.

9. What do you say to encourage your friend? I tell him/her that _____.

10. How could your friend improve his or her skills? _____

11. What do you tell your friend if he or she doesn't make the team? _____

_____

12. Why is it good to keep trying? _____

_____

D. (13–16) Write four sentences that compare the skills and talents of three people on a school team. Use irregular comparative adjectives.

_____

_____

_____

_____

_____

Edit It

E. (17–20) Edit the letter. Fix the four irregular comparative adjectives.

Dear Kyra,

    You are so good at basketball. You really are the *best* player on the team. You should feel strong, but you seem nervous. I think you have ~~least~~ *less* confidence than Sarah. You are the *most* talented player of all. I hope you feel ~~good~~ *better* about making the team than you did yesterday.

               Good luck,

               Emily

Proofreader's Marks

Add text:
       worst
She is the player on the team. ^

Change text: *better*
You are ~~gooder~~ than you think. ^

See all Proofreader's Marks on page xi.

52 Why Do You Need Adverbs?

To Tell *How*, *When*, or *Where*

- Use an **adverb** to describe a verb. Adverbs often end in **-ly**.
  We packed **carefully** for the family trip.
  My father said we would leave **immediately** after breakfast.
  Rain poured **down** as we packed the car.

- Use an **adverb** to make an adjective or another adverb stronger.
  I was **extremely** excited about the trip.
  adjective
  I ate **very** quickly that morning.
  another adverb

- Adverbs add details and bring life to your writing.
  Suddenly, a bolt of lightning flashed across the sky.
  The rain fell **heavily**.

Try It

A. Complete each sentence. Use adverbs to add details. Possible responses:

1. The other cars swerved _____dangerously_____ on the slippery road.

2. My father held _____firmly_____ onto the steering wheel.

3. The car in front of us moved _____quickly_____ out of the way.

4. My father pressed his foot _____down_____ on the brakes.

5. He drove _____safely_____ away from the cars in front of us.

6. We stopped _____briefly_____ to calm down.

7. I understood _____instantly_____ that we had avoided an accident.

B. Add details to the story. Choose from the adverbs in the box.

> exactly   extremely   lightly   patiently   very

8. One car slowed down and nearly stopped before it _____lightly_____ hit another car's bumper.

9. I was _____extremely_____ frightened as the events unfolded.

10. My father acted _____very_____ quickly in that situation.

11. I was happy that he knew _____exactly_____ what to do.

12. A woman asked _____patiently_____ if we were okay.

Write It

C. Your friend reacts well during a moment of crisis. Imagine you are with him or her. Answer the questions. Use adverbs to add details.

13. What is the best way to react during a moment of crisis? I think _____
   _____.

14. What can you do to help your friend in this situation? I can help by _____
   _____.

15. What is an unhelpful way to react during a crisis? _____
   _____

16. What did you learn about yourself or your friend from this uncertain situation? _____
   _____

D. (17–20) Write four sentences to describe a time when you reacted well in a moment of crisis or an uncertain situation. What did you learn about yourself?

_____

_____

_____

_____

53 Can You Use an Adverb to Make a Comparison?

Yes, But You Need to Change the Adverb.

- Adverbs have different forms. Use the form that fits your purpose.

To Describe 1 Action	hard	quickly	well	badly
To Compare 2 Actions	harder	more quickly	better	worse
To Compare 3 or More Actions	hardest	most quickly	best	worst

- How many things are being compared in these sentences?
    I wrote **better** than my friend did.
    I decided to work **hardest** of all my friends to excel at writing.

Try It

A. Write the correct adverb to describe the action in each sentence.

1. I checked my drafts _____<u>more carefully</u>_____ than the other students did.
   more carefully / most carefully

2. I worked _____<u>harder</u>_____ than my friends did.
   harder / more hard

3. One teacher helped me _____<u>more patiently</u>_____ than the others did.
   more patiently / most patiently

4. Mr. Hingis advised me to plan this assignment _____<u>better</u>_____ than the last assignment.
   better / best

5. I really wanted to write _____<u>more creatively</u>_____ than I did last year.
   creatively / more creatively

B. Write the correct form of the adverb in parentheses to complete each sentence.

6. I did ____<u>worse</u>____ at grammar than at story ideas. **(badly)**

7. I did ____<u>best</u>____ of all as an imaginative writer. **(well)**

8. Now, I work ____<u>more slowly</u>____ than I did before. **(slow)**

9. I write ____<u>more clearly</u>____ since I took Mr. Hingis's class. **(clearly)**

C. Answer the questions about a friend of yours. Use adverbs that compare.

10. What do you do better than your friend? I _____.

11. What skill or talent does your friend do better than you? My friend is _____

_____.

12. What does it take to be best at something? _____

_____

13. Describe a time when you discovered that hard work is important. _____

_____

D. (14–16) Write three sentences about a way you would like to improve.
Use adverbs that compare.

_____

_____

_____

Edit It

E. (17–20) Edit the journal entry. Fix the four adverbs that compare.

September 22

My Goals for the New School Year

English: I do well on short assignments. I need
    better
to do this year than last year on long assignments.
    ^   more
Math: I should work carefully on my homework
              ^
than I did last year.
              fastest
Science: I work the faster in the labs. I
          worst   ^
clean up the better of all. I need to improve
          ^
this.

Proofreader's Marks

Add text:
                most
You helped me of all.
              ^

Change text:
        more
I work most patiently
than I did last year.

See all Proofreader's Marks
on page xi.

54 What Happens When You Add *Not* to a Sentence?

You Make the Sentence Negative.

- The word <u>not</u> is an adverb. Add it to a sentence to make it negative.
  If the verb is an **action verb**, change the sentence like this:
  My mom **wants** me to help Mr. Bobera.
  My mom **does** <u>not</u> **want** me to watch television.

- If the verb is a form of **be**, just place <u>not</u> after the verb:
  Mr. Bobera **is** our elderly neighbor. He **is** <u>not</u> very active.

- When you shorten a verb plus <u>not</u>, replace the **o** in <u>not</u> with
  an apostrophe (').

  1. Mom **does not** want Mr. Bobera to lift heavy boxes.

  Mom **doesn't** want Mr. Bobera to lift heavy boxes.

  2. I **can not** let him do the work alone.

  I **can't** let him do the work alone.

Try It

A. Rewrite each sentence to make it negative. Use the adverb **not**.

1. Mr. Bobera is lazy. ___Mr. Bobera is not (isn't) lazy.___

2. He asks for help. ___He does not (doesn't) ask for help.___

3. At first, I like the work in his yard and house. ___At first, I do not (don't) like the work in his yard and house.___

B. Complete each sentence. Use the adverb **not**.

4. Mr. Bobera ___is not (isn't)___ a bore.

5. He ___can not (can't)___ do many things, but he knows a lot.

6. He ___does not (doesn't)___ have a strong voice, but he tells good stories.

7. I ___did not (didn't)___ earn money when I helped, but I gained a good friend.

C. Think about things you like and dislike (activities, sports, chores, foods).
Answer the questions. Use the adverb **not** in some of your sentences.

8. Name one thing you like and another thing you do not like. I like _____, but I
   _____.

9. Is there something you do not like but that you know is good for you? Explain. _____
   _____

10. What have you gained from doing something you did not like at first? _____
    _____

D. (11–15) Write five sentences that compare something you like with
something you do not like. Use the adverb **not** in some of your sentences.

_____

_____

_____

_____

_____

Edit It

E. (16–20) Edit the journal entry. Use the adverb *not* to make five sentences negative.

April 4

I didn't know why Mom asked me to help

Mr. Bobera on a Saturday. I ^don't think working on

Saturdays is fun. At first, I did ^didn't want to go.

Then, I saw he can ^can't do much on his own. He

wanted to pay me, but I did ^not want it. He is

now my good friend. He is ^not just a neighbor.

Proofreader's Marks

Add text:
He is ^not a boring person.

Change text:
Mr. Bobera can ^can't lift
heavy things.

See all Proofreader's Marks
on page xi.

55 Use Adjectives Correctly

Remember: You can use adjectives to describe or compare people, places, or things.

- How do you know which adjective to use?

To Describe 1 Thing	loud	difficult	good	much
To Compare 2 Things	louder	more difficult	better	more
To Compare 3 or More Things	loudest	most difficult	best	most

Try It

A. Complete each sentence with the correct adjective.

1. The recent hurricane was the _____ most damaging _____ storm in the town's
   more damaging / most damaging
   history.

2. After the storm, people had _____ some _____ doubt that the
   a few / some
   neighborhood would ever be livable again.

3. _____ Many _____ students wanted to help the people whose homes
   Many / Much
   were damaged.

4. Will the new houses make this a _____ better _____ neighborhood than it
   best / better
   was before?

B. (5–8) Complete the paragraph by writing adjectives in the correct form. Possible responses:

The old houses needed improvements. It was _____ a lot of _____ work.
Everyone helped out. We made _____ many _____ decisions together during
the project. Some people were _____ better _____ than others at different
tasks. I liked the sense of teamwork. It was the _____ most important _____ experience
of my whole life.

Write It

C. Your friends and you volunteer to help a family in need. Answer these questions. Use adjectives correctly to describe or compare.

9. What is the most important reason to help others? I think that _____

_____.

10. How does your work help make life better for the family in need? _____

_____

11. What do you learn from the experience? _____

D. (12–15) Write four sentences that describe a service project young people can join at home or school. Use adjectives correctly.

_____

_____

_____

_____

Grammar at Work

E. (16–20) Edit the journal entry. Fix the **three** mistakes with adjectives. Fix **two** mistakes with pronouns.   Possible responses:

July 20

I had a lot of enthusiasm about this service

project. The work was ~~most hard~~ than the
            harder
            I

work ~~me~~ did last summer. There was hardly
            few

any time to rest—only a ~~little~~ minutes each

day. But knowing I had helped a family in
            most satisfying

need was the ~~satisfyingest~~ part of the
                            me

whole experience for ~~I.~~

Proofreader's Marks

Change text:
                a lot of
We like doing ~~many~~
work.

See all Proofreader's Marks
on page xi.

56 Use Adverbs Correctly

Remember: You can use adverbs to describe and compare actions. An adverb can also make another adverb or adjective stronger.

Describe	Compare	Make Stronger
I sat **quietly** as I waited for the results.	I reacted **more calmly** than my friend did.	The school election results were **completely** new to me.
The students cheered **enthusiastically**.	I thought **best** when I was relaxed.	The assembly hall was **very** noisy.

Try It

A. Write adverbs to add details to the sentences. Possible responses:

1. I stood up _____slowly_____ when the principal said my name.

2. I reacted _____more quietly_____ than the other candidates.

3. The cheers for me were _____extremely_____ loud.

4. I _____suddenly_____ realized that I was elected class president.

5. I was _____very_____ grateful to all of the people who voted for me.

6. Afterward, a student said I spoke the_____best_____ of all the candidates.

B. Write the correct adverb to complete each sentence.

7. My election team worked _____harder_____ than the other candidate's team.
$\qquad$ **hard / harder**

8. I focused _____more_____ intently on the issues than the other candidate did.
$\qquad$ **more / most**

9. The support I got from my classmates made me _____incredibly_____ proud.
$\qquad$ **incredible / incredibly**

10. I realized that I succeed _____best_____ of all when I really believe in something.
$\qquad$ **better / best**

C. Answer these questions about why personal achievements are important.
Use adverbs correctly to describe or compare actions.

11. Compare two students you know who compete with each other in a sport or school activity. _____

_____

12. How can an achievement make a big change in your life? _____

_____

13. When have you felt that an achievement was going to change your life for the better?

_____

_____

D. (14–17) Write four sentences that describe your friends and compare their talents, skills, or personalities. Use adverbs in your sentences.

_____

_____

_____

_____

Grammar at Work

E. (18–20) Edit the newsletter. Fix the <u>two</u> mistakes with adverbs. Fix <u>one</u> mistake with pronouns.   Possible responses:

Haven School Newsletter

The students voted individually in private booths last Friday.
They ~~careful~~ carefully considered all the candidates. Out of all the choices,
Annie Broderick ~~more~~ most impressed the student body. The teachers
are very proud of ~~she~~ her and the other candidates for their hard
work. Congratulations, Annie!

Proofreader's Marks
Change text: *best*   She campaigned ~~better~~   of all.
See all Proofreader's Marks on page xi.

57 How Are Phrases and Clauses Different?

A Clause Has a Subject and a Predicate.

- A **phrase** is a group of words that function together. One sentence often has several phrases.

  Many **people** / at the restaurant / **feel** / strongly / about no cell phones.

  noun phrase   adjective phrase   verb   adverb   adverb phrase

  This sentence is complete because it has a **subject** and a **verb**.
  A phrase never has both, so it does not express a complete thought.

- A **clause** contains a **subject** and a **verb**. These clauses can stand alone as sentences.

  Some **people want** rules about the use of cell phones.
  Others want a looser policy.

Try It

A. Decide which parts of each sentence are phrases. Write the phrases after the sentence. Separate them with commas.

1. Some people talk loudly on cell phones in restaurants. _____ Some people, on cell phones, in _____ restaurants _____

2. Other people hear these noisy conversations during their meal. _____ Other people, these noisy _____ conversations, during their meal

3. One restaurant owner solves this annoying problem. _____ One restaurant owner, this annoying problem _____

4. He hangs a polite sign on the front door of the restaurant. _____ a polite sign, on the front door, of the _____ restaurant

5. Most people turn off their phones in this restaurant with pleasure. _____ Most people, turn _____ off, their phones, in this restaurant, with pleasure

B. Rewrite each sentence. Include the phrase in parentheses in the correct place in the new sentence. Possible responses:

6. Some students bring cell phones. **(to school)** Some students bring cell phones to school.

7. Most schools have about cell phones. **(clear rules)** Most schools have clear rules about cell phones.

8. In some schools, students may talk in the building at certain times. **(of the day)**
In some schools, students may talk in the building at certain times of the day.

9. In other schools, students must their phones at all times. **(turn off)**
In other schools, students must turn off their phones at all times.

10. At our school, students may use inside the building during lunch period. **(cell phones)**
At our school, students may use cell phones inside the building during lunch period.

Write It

C. What is your opinion on the right to use cell phones at school? Answer the questions. Use at least one phrase in each answer.

11. Do you think students should use cell phones at school? I think _____

12. What rule about cell phones do you think is right? _____

13. How do cell phones affect school life? _____

D. (14–15) What is an important right for students in your school? Does anyone misuse that right? How does the misuse affect other students' rights? Write two complete sentences. Use at least one phrase in each sentence.

_____

_____

_____

58 What's a Compound Sentence?
Two Clauses Joined into One Sentence

The words **and**, **but**, and **or** are conjunctions. They join the two clauses in a **compound sentence**. A comma (**,**) comes before the conjunction.

- Use **and** to join similar ideas.

  Sari is new to our school.
  One day I see her in the hallway.

  **Sari is new to our school,
  and one day I see her in the hallway.**

- Use **but** to join different ideas.

  I start to go up to her.
  I stop.

  **I start to go up to her,
  but I stop.**

- Use **or** to show a choice.

  Some students stare at Sari.
  They whisper to each other.

  **Some students stare at Sari,
  or they whisper to each other.**

- Use a semicolon (**;**) to join clauses in a compound sentence when the conjunctions **and, but,** or **or** are not used.

  I know that their actions are unkind.
  I'm not sure what to do.

  **I know that their actions are unkind;
  I'm not sure what to do.**

Try It

A. **(1–3) Use and, but, or, or a semicolon to combine each pair of sentences.** Possible responses:

Some students at school may be new. **, but** They don't deserve to be teased. It's important to make new students feel comfortable. **, and** You can do this by being kind. You can show them around the school. **, or** You can invite them to join in activities.

B. **These compound sentences are missing and, but, or, or a semicolon. Fix the mistakes.**
Possible responses:

4. Mia has a problem _____ **, but** _____ she doesn't know how to solve it.

5. Haley meets with Mia _____ **;** _____ she gives Mia some advice.

Proofreader's Marks

Add text: **, but**

We are good friends.
Sometimes we disagree.

Do not capitalize:

Be kind to Everyone.

See all Proofreader's Marks on page xi.

C. Write compound sentences to tell about each situation.

6. Give a friend advice about ways to improve his or her grades. Use **or**. _____
_____.

7. Tell what you would do for a new student at your school. Use **and** or a **semicolon**. _____
_____.

8. Tell what you might do and won't do in an unfamiliar place. Use **but**. _____
_____.

D. (9–11) Students have responsibilities at school and at home. Write three compound sentences about some responsibilities you have. Use **and**, **but**, **or**, or a **semicolon**.

_____

_____

_____

_____

_____

Edit It

E. (12–15) Edit the school newspaper article. Fix the four mistakes with compound sentences. Possible responses:

Ms. Clark's Student Wins Essay Contest

Sam Nguyen is a new student in Ms. Clark's class; he won the essay contest. Sam was not sure about entering the contest , but ~~and~~ Ms. Clark talked him into it. Sam could write about his own experiences , or he could focus on historical events. He decided to write about his life , and that was a good idea. We have copies of Sam's essay in the office; you are invited to take a copy home with you.

Proofreader's Marks
Add text: hard   He worked ^ on his essay.
Add a comma: His writing is interesting, ^ and so is yours.
Do not capitalize: The Essay contest is over.
See all Proofreader's Marks on page xi.

59 What's a Run-on Sentence?

A Sentence That Goes On and On

- To fix a run-on sentence, break it into shorter sentences.

  Run-on: We have a dress code and many of us think the code is old-fashioned and we want the principal to change her mind about it.

  Better: We have a dress code. Many of us think the code is old-fashioned. We want the principal to change her mind about it.

- Sometimes you can rearrange words to express the same idea.

  Run-on: We gathered support **and** we made plans **and** we hoped the principal would agree with us.

  Better: We gathered support and made plans. We hoped the principal would agree with us.

- You can also add a comma and a conjunction or separate the clauses with a semicolon (;).

  Run-on: Our class has good ideas and plans we will give them a try.

  Better: Our class has good ideas and plans; we will give them a try.

Try It

A. Edit these run-on sentences to break them into shorter sentences.
Possible responses:

1. In 1995, our school administrators met and they put a dress code in place and students have obeyed it since then.

2. At first the dress code was successful and students were happy to go along with it because the rules made sense to them.

3. Times have changed and so have styles so the dress code no longer works for today's clothing.

4. Students have rights and they want to be able to choose what they wear and so the school needs to change the dress code.

Proofreader's Marks

Add a comma:

  I like to dress well and so do you.

Delete:

  The dress code is really so old fashioned.

Do not capitalize:

  I dress Responsibly.

Capitalize:

  we all dress carefully.

See all Proofreader's Marks on page xi.

B. Rewrite each run-on sentence. Break it into shorter sentences, rearrange the words, or use a semicolon to create a compound sentence.   Possible responses:

5. The principal looked at our plans and he read our suggestions and we hoped he would overturn the dress code.

   The principal looked at our plans and read our suggestions. We hoped he would overturn the dress code.

   _____

   _____

6. The principal called a meeting and we were very excited but we did not like what we heard when we got to his office.

   The principal called a meeting. We were very excited, but we did not like what we heard when we got to his office.

   _____

   _____

Write It

C. Complete each sentence about dress codes. Then reread your sentences to check for and fix run-ons.

7. Schools use dress codes to _____.

8. Some students _____

   _____.

9. One option is to _____.

10. Another idea is to _____.

D. (11–15) How do you feel about dress codes? Does your school have one? Write five sentences. Then reread your sentences to check for and fix run-ons.

_____

_____

_____

_____

_____

_____

_____

60 What's a Complex Sentence?

A Sentence with Two Kinds of Clauses

- A clause has a **subject** and a **verb**. An **independent clause** can stand alone as a sentence.

  Service groups help people around the world.

  independent clause

- A **dependent clause** also has a subject and a verb. It cannot stand alone because it begins with a **conjunction**.

  when disaster strikes

  dependent clause

- You can use the conjunction to "hook" the dependent clause to an independent clause. The new sentence is complete, and it is called a **complex sentence**.

  Service groups help people around the world **when disaster strikes**.

  independent clause   dependent clause

Try It

A. Draw a line from each independent clause to a dependent clause. **There is more than one correct answer.** Possible responses:

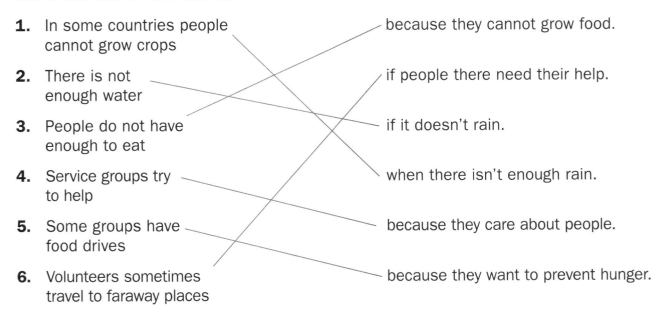

1. In some countries people cannot grow crops

2. There is not enough water

3. People do not have enough to eat

4. Service groups try to help

5. Some groups have food drives

6. Volunteers sometimes travel to faraway places

because they cannot grow food.

if people there need their help.

if it doesn't rain.

when there isn't enough rain.

because they care about people.

because they want to prevent hunger.

B. Write an independent clause to make each dependent clause into a complete sentence.

7. _____ I volunteer at the local food bank _____ because I want to help people.

8. _____ Some people won't have the food they need _____ if groups like ours don't help out.

9. _____ I stock the shelves _____ when we receive new supplies.

10. _____ I help collect money _____ if we need more funds.

11. _____ I always feel good _____ after I finish my work.

12. _____ People in need get help _____ because groups like ours care.

Write It

C. Make each independent clause into a complex sentence. Add a dependent clause.

13. People volunteer in service groups _____

_____.

14. It is important to volunteer _____

_____.

15. Some people don't have enough to eat _____

_____.

16. I help out _____.

D. (17–20) Do you think people have a duty to volunteer in their communities? Write four complex sentences to explain your opinion.

_____

_____

_____

_____

_____

61 Can a Clause Act Like an Adverb?

Yes, and It Often Tells When or Why.

- A **complex sentence** has one independent clause and one dependent clause.

  People volunteer because they want to help others.

  _____independent clause_____   _____dependent clause_____

- When the **dependent clause** acts like an adverb, it begins with a **subordinating conjunction**. The conjunction shows how the two clauses are related.

Tells When:	**After I get out of school,** I volunteer at a pet shelter.
Tells Why:	I volunteer **because it makes me feel good.**
Tells What May Happen:	**If everyone volunteered,** we could change the world.

- **Conjunctions include:** after, because, if, before, when, whenever, while, until, since, unless, although, where

Try It

A. Create a complex sentence. Add a clause that begins with a subordinating conjunction.   Possible responses:

1. Everyone should volunteer _because all communities have needs_ _____

   _____.

2. _When people volunteer_ _____, important work gets done.

3. Volunteering has increased in our town _although we still need more help_____.

4. Opportunities exist for many people _if they want to help others_____.

5. _Before you volunteer_ _____, make sure the position is right

   for you.

6. People at the volunteer center will place you _where you can do the most good_____.

B. **Fix these complex sentences. Add subordinating conjunctions.**

Possible responses:

7. Volunteers have a responsibility to show up ∧ they are expected. *when*

8. ∧ Volunteers arrive at an assignment, they should *Before*
   know what to do.

9. Good readers are needed at daycare centers ∧ children like *since*
   to hear stories.

10. Careful workers are placed at the library ∧ there is a lot of paperwork. *because*

11. Some volunteers always work ∧ there are many other people. *where*

12. Volunteers are honored with a party ∧ they work for six months. *after*

13. People show their appreciation ∧ volunteers make a real difference in people's lives. *because*

Proofreader's Marks

Do not capitalize:
   I like to work at the /Library.

Add text: busy
   The food bank was. ∧

See all Proofreader's Marks
on page xi.

Write It

C. **Answer each question about volunteering. Use complex sentences.**

14. Why do you think people should volunteer? _____

   _____

15. Where would you like to volunteer? _____

   _____

16. When do you have time to volunteer? _____

   _____

D. **(17–20) How do volunteers improve a community? Write four complex sentences
to tell what you think about volunteering.**

   _____

   _____

   _____

   _____

   _____

62 Can a Clause Act Like an Adjective?

Yes, and It Often Begins with *Who*, *That*, or *Which*.

- A **complex sentence** has one independent clause and one dependent clause.

  <u>I have school books</u> <u>that help me learn important skills.</u>
  independent clause   dependent clause

- Some **dependent clauses** act like adjectives and tell more about nouns. They begin with a **relative pronoun**.
  1. Use **who** to tell about people.   2. Use **that** for things or people.
  3. Use **which** for things.

- Place an **adjective clause** right after the noun it describes.

  Some children **who go to school** don't have school books.

  I joined a club **that collects school supplies for children**.

Try It

A. Write adjective clauses to make complex sentences. Possible responses:

1. There are many people _who donate school supplies to children in need_____.

2. I am in a club _that collects school supplies for children_____.

3. I shop at a store _that donates paper and pencils_____.

4. Some people _who live in my community_____ collect books and supplies to send.

B. (5–8) Write adjective clauses to make complex sentences about a school that has an adopt-a-school program. Possible responses:

My school has an adopt-a-school program. It donates supplies to a school

__that needs school supplies_____. Many children __who go to the other school____

can't afford to buy supplies. My school asks businesses __that are in our community____

to donate supplies to the program. My school also asks the students

__who go to school here_____ to donate school supplies, like backpacks.

        Unit 6 Conflict and Resolution **G123**

C. Write complex sentences about how the people or things named in parentheses could provide school books or supplies. Use an adjective clause in each sentence.

9. (service clubs) _____

_____

10. (student volunteer) _____

_____

11. (local business or store) _____

_____

D. (12–15) Why is it important for students to have books and supplies? What can you do to help? Write four complex sentences with adjective clauses.

_____

_____

_____

_____

Edit It

E. (16–20) Edit the journal entry. Add five relative pronouns.

June 29

My mom had a friend who couldn't afford school supplies when she was young. Now, she is an adult. She has started a program ^that donates supplies to children in need. She works for a store ^that helps her. The person ^who manages the store is a big help. The store has a big bucket ^that shoppers can fill with donated supplies, ^which are sent to relief organizations.

Proofreader's Marks

Add text:

I know a student ^who needs supplies.

See all Proofreader's Marks on page xi.

63 When Can Sentence Parts Be Combined?

When Two Sentences Share Related Subjects or Predicates.

- Find sentences that have the same or similar subjects. Use **and** or **or** to create a **compound subject**. Remember to use a plural verb if you use **and**. Match the verb to the last noun if you use **or**.

  Family is important to me. Friends are also important.

  Family and friends are important to me.
  <u>compound subject</u>

  A brother can help you solve a problem. Maybe your sister can help instead.

  A brother or a sister can help you solve a problem.
  <u>compound subject</u>

- Look for verbs that tell about the same subject. Use the coordinating conjunction **and** or **or** to create a **compound predicate.**

  At dinnertime, we talk about our activities. Sometimes we plan new ones.

  At dinnertime, we **talk about our activities or plan new ones.**
  <u>compound predicate</u>

Try It

A. Combine each pair of sentences. Use a compound subject or a compound predicate. Write the new sentence.

1. Last year, a hurricane knocked over trees in our neighborhood. The rain from it flooded the streets. _Last year, a hurricane knocked over trees and flooded the streets._

_____.

2. The water soaked the ground. It seeped into houses. _The water soaked the ground and seeped_ _into houses._

_____.

3. Our neighbor's basement flooded. It was filled with mud. _Our neighbor's basement flooded and_ _filled with mud._

_____.

4. Michael vacuumed out the water. I helped him. _Michael and I vacuumed out the water._

_____.

5. Mom will come over to sweep out the mud. Dad says he'll come with her. _Mom or Dad will_ _sweep out the mud._

_____.

C. Complete each sentence with a compound subject or a compound predicate.

6. _____ and _____ are in my group.

7. I would _____ or _____ to help people in trouble.

8. _____ or _____ is the friend I'd ask for advice.

9. At school, we _____ and _____.

D. (10–13) Write four sentences to describe a recent event you witnessed or saw in the news. Use compound subjects and compound predicates in your sentences.

_____

_____

_____

_____

Edit It

E. (14–18) Edit the article. Combine sentences using a compound subject or a compound predicate.

>   and earthquakes
> Hurricanes are natural disasters.
> ~~Earthquakes are destructive, too.~~ Volunteer
>   and concerned citizens
> groups often go to the site of the disaster
> to offer their help. ~~Sometimes concerned~~
>   or fly
> ~~citizens go.~~ They drive there. ~~They might~~
>   , and
> ~~fly there.~~ Helpers give people food. ~~They~~
>   and governments
> clean their homes. Residents are thankful for
> the aid. ~~So are the governments.~~

Proofreader's Marks

Add text:
               very
Hurricanes are ^
dangerous.

Delete:
We saw ~~saw~~ a lot of
damage.

See all Proofreader's Marks
on page xi.

64 Can Details in Sentences Be Combined?

Yes. Move Words or Phrases and Create Adjective Clauses

- If one sentence adds just a little more information about something, try to **move the words or phrases** into the main sentence.

  My mom misses Marie.
  Marie is her childhood friend.

  Combined Sentence:
  My mom misses her childhood friend Marie.

- Turn one sentence into an **adjective clause** that begins with **that**, **which**, or **who**.

  Marie and her family have survived a war.
  They live far away.

  Combined Sentence:
  Marie and her family, **who** live far away, have survived a war.

Try It

A. Combine each pair of sentences. Move words or phrases, or turn one sentence into an adjective clause. Write the new sentence.

1. Mom writes a letter to Marie. The letter is long. <u>Mom writes a long letter to Marie.</u>

_____.

2. Mom asks about the conflict in Marie's country. It started two years ago. <u>Mom asks about the</u> <u>conflict in Marie's country that started two years ago.</u>

_____.

3. She asks about Marie's city. The city was heavily damaged. <u>She asks about Marie's city, which was</u> <u>heavily damaged.</u>

_____.

4. Mom wants to know if Marie's brother is safe. He fought in the war. <u>Mom wants to know if</u> <u>Marie's brother, who fought in the war, is safe.</u>

_____.

5. Finally, Mom drives to the post office. She goes to mail the letter. <u>Finally, Mom drives to the post</u> <u>office to mail the letter.</u>

_____.

C. Choose words or phrases, or adjective clauses from the box to complete the sentences.

that began in 2002	everywhere	who lived
on TV	that the war created	

6. Mom saw a news report _____on TV_____ about Marie's country.

7. The war ___that began in 2002___ was over.

8. People _____who lived_____ in Marie's city cheered.

9. People celebrated _____everywhere_____.

10. Now the people had to repair the damage ___that the war created___.

D. (11–14) Imagine you saw a report about the end of a war. Write four sentences. Check your sentences and combine some of them.

_____

_____

_____

Edit It

E. (15–20) Edit the letter. Move words or phrases, or combine sentences.

Dear Erin,

The war is finally over! ~~It divided us.~~ My
(that divided us)
brother has returned home. ~~He was gone~~
(who was gone for months)
~~for months.~~ Workers have already started
to repair the buildings. ~~They were heavily~~
(heavily damaged)
~~damaged.~~ The food shelves are full again.
(empty)
~~The shelves were empty for so long.~~
People go outside whenever they can now.
(who used to be afraid)
~~They used to be afraid.~~ I hope that you and
your family are well. ~~They are wonderful.~~
(wonderful)

Marie

Proofreader's Marks

Add text:
terribly
Wars are ^ destructive.

Delete:
They ~~are~~ destroy lives.

See all Proofreader's Marks on page xi.

65 How Can Whole Sentences Be Combined?

Join Related Ideas with Conjunctions.

- Look for related ideas in neighboring sentences. If the ideas are equally important, join the complete sentences with **and, but,** or **or** to make a **compound sentence.**

  The Bill of Rights protects our citizens. _{, and} It makes sure everyone is treated fairly. I know a little bit about those rights. _{, but} I want to know more.

- If one idea is more important than the other, turn the less important idea into a clause beginning with a conjunction such as **if, because,** or **when.** Then add it to the more important idea to make a **complex sentence.**

  _{Because} One of our rights is to speak freely. We can share our ideas without getting into trouble. We can say what the government should do. _{if} We ~~might~~ think the government is wrong.

Try It

A. (1–4) Combine the sentences. Use conjunctions to make two compound sentences and two complex sentences.

Our country's founders had a difficult job. _{, but} They did it well. They added rights to the Constitution to protect everyone. _{because} They believed in equality. We must learn about these rights. _{, or} We risk losing them. U.S. citizens are guaranteed certain rights. _{wherever} They live in America.

Proofreader's Marks

Add text:
_{have}
We ^ rights

Delete:
We ~~are~~ are lucky.

See all Proofreader's Marks on page xi.

B. Use the correct conjunctions to complete the combined sentences. Be sure to add any necessary punctuation.

5. We have the right to free speech _____, and_____ we can worship the way we want.

6. We can meet peacefully with others _____whenever_____ we want to.

7. _____If_____ you get into trouble, you have the right to hire a lawyer.

8. Citizens can criticize the government _____, or_____ they can ask for changes.

Write It

C. (9–12) Citizens have rights and responsibilities. Write two compound sentences and two complex sentences about some rights and responsibilities you have.

_____

_____

_____

_____

_____

_____

_____

D. (13–16) Write two compound sentences and two complex sentences to tell what you think about the Bill of Rights. Consider what it might be like without the Bill of Rights, or if citizens in other countries had similar rights.

_____

_____

_____

_____

_____

_____

_____

_____

_____

Name _____

66 Use Compound and Complex Sentences

Remember: You can combine two short sentences to make a **compound sentence** or a **complex sentence**.

- For a **compound sentence**, use a **coordinating conjunction** or **semicolon** to join ideas. Use **and** to join like ideas, **but** to join different ideas, or **or** to show a choice.

    Cars use the road, **and** bicycles do, too.
    Some cities have special bike lanes; cars aren't allowed in them.

- For a **complex sentence**, use a **subordinating conjunction** such as **because**, **even though**, or **if** to connect a less important idea to a more important idea.

    Pedestrians could get hurt **if** drivers and cyclists didn't follow the rules.

Try It

A. Use a conjunction to combine each pair of sentences into a compound or complex sentence. Possible responses:

1. In my state, pedestrians in crosswalks have the right of way. Cars have to stop.

Even though
2. Pedestrians have the right of way. They still need to pay attention.

B. Edit these run-on sentences. When possible, use compound sentences. Possible responses:

3. Dad was driving, and he didn't stop for a pedestrian in the crosswalk and he got a ticket and he has to pay a fine.

4. Rita rides her bike to school and she doesn't always ride in the bike lane, and once she got a ticket for riding the wrong way on a one-way street.

Proofreader's Marks

Add text: have
Bike riders to follow rules.

Add a comma:
Rules should be obeyed and it is our responsibility to follow them.

Delete:
Cars have to stop stop at crossroads.

Capitalize:
please follow the rules.

See all Proofreader's Marks on page xi.

Write It

C. Write compound or complex sentences to answer the questions. Use the correct conjunctions.

5. Why is it important to know the rules of the road? _____

_____

6. What rules of the road do you think are most important? _____

_____

7. What should happen when people don't respect other people's rights to use the road?

_____

D. (8–12) Do you think it is better to walk, ride the bus, or ride a bike to school? Write five sentences to explain your opinion. Use compound and complex sentences. Then reread your sentences to check for and fix any run-ons.

_____

_____

_____

_____

Grammar at Work

E. (13–15) Fix the <u>one</u> run-on sentence. Create <u>one</u> compound sentence. Fix <u>one</u> mistake with an adjective that compares. Possible responses:

September 10

Today, I was late for school, and I was in a rush, and I rode my bike through a stop sign. A police officer saw me, stopped me, and gave me a ticket. I broke the rules of the road, and I got punished. I learned a good lesson about obeying the rules. It is important to stay safe on the road.

Proofreader's Marks

Add text:
I ride my bike to school.

Add a comma:
Drivers must drive safely, or they will be stopped.

Delete:
Rules of the road are are important.

Capitalize:
please follow the rules of the road.

© National Geographic Learning, a part of Cengage Learning, Inc.

Name _____

67 Combine Sentences

Remember: You can combine sentence parts, details, and entire sentences to make writing interesting and easier to read.

- You can combine subjects and predicates.

  Maureen loves to travel. **Her friend** does, too.

  Maureen and her friend love to travel.

- You can **move details** from one sentence into another or turn one sentence into an **adjective clause** using who, that, or which.

  People learn about other countries. They travel. Travelers enjoy the sights. They are interesting.

  People **who travel** learn about other countries. Travelers enjoy the **interesting** sights.

- You can join neighboring sentences or sentences with related ideas.

  Maureen spends hours at ancient buildings. She loves history.

  Maureen spends hours at ancient buildings because she loves history.

Try It

A. Combine these sentences in different ways.   Possible responses:

1. My brother is a volunteer in a service group. It sends volunteers all around the world.
   My brother is a volunteer in a service group that sends volunteers all around the world.

2. He travels to villages. The villages are poor and underprivileged.
   He travels to villages that are poor and underprivileged.

3. People don't always have the rights or freedoms we do. People living in some of those villages don't. People who live in the villages don't always have the rights and freedoms we do.

4. My brother travels. He sees how other people live. When my brother travels, he sees how other people live.

5. I like to read about different times and places. Mom does, too. Mom and I like to read about different times and places.

6. I would travel to every continent. I wish I could. If I could, I would travel to every continent.

Write It

C. Answer the questions. Check your answers to see which sentences you can combine.

7. How can reading help you learn about different cultures around the world? _____

_____

8. Where might you find out about people with customs that are different from yours? _____

_____

9. How can you promote understanding among people around the world? _____

_____

D. (10–13) Where would you like to travel to? Why? Write four sentences about a trip you would like to take. Try to use *and* and *or*, and *because* and *that* to join ideas in your sentences.

_____

_____

_____

_____

Edit It

E. (14–16) Combine sentences with related ideas. Fix one error in comparing with adverbs.

Possible responses:

Proofreader's Marks

Add text:

It is interesting to read about people. ^who lived long ago

See all Proofreader's Marks on page xi.

May 29

Today, I read a book about colonial America. I
read it ~~fast~~ faster than the last book I read. I
learned about the colonists. ~~The first ones~~ who sailed here from England
~~sailed here from England.~~ This was an
interesting and exciting time. I learned about
the hard times. that the colonists experienced ~~The colonists experienced a~~
~~lot of them.~~ Living was tough at first, because They
weren't used to the new land. The colonists
lived in small villages. They learned much
about surviving from the Native Americans.

© National Geographic Learning, a part of Cengage Learning, Inc.

68 Can a Verb Act Like an Adjective?

Yes, When It Is a Participle.

- Verbs have **four principal parts**. For example:

Present	Present Participle	Past	Past Participle
laugh	laughing	laughed	laughed
do	doing	did	done

- Sometimes a **participle** is part of a verb phrase. Sometimes, however, it acts as an adjective to describe a noun or pronoun.

  The girl was **laughing**. The **laughing** girl loved the funny story.

  Laughing, she put down the book.

  Done, the girl gave the book to her friend.

- Insert a comma **(,)** after a participle that begins a sentence.

Try It

A. Combine the sentences. Move the underlined participles to tell about a noun or a pronoun in the other sentence. Possible responses:

1. I rewrite a story about some pigs. The pigs are determined.

   I rewrite a story about some determined pigs.

2. They are upset about their homes. Their homes are destroyed.

   They are upset about their destroyed homes.

3. Their homes are blown down by a wolf. The wolf is scheming.

   Their homes are blown down by a scheming wolf.

4. The pigs have to decide what to do. They are worried.

   Worried, the pigs have to decide what to do.

5. They think a judge can help. A judge is understanding.

   They think an understanding judge can help.

B. Use the participle to combine the sentences. Possible responses:

6. In my story, the pigs talk to a judge. The pigs are complaining.

In my story, the complaining pigs see a judge.

7. The case goes to court. The case is complicated.

The complicated case goes to court.

8. The jury says the wolf should stop. A jury is chosen.

The chosen jury says the wolf should stop.

9. The wolf is not happy. The wolf is grumbling.

The grumbling wolf is not happy.

Write It

C. Write four sentences. Use the participle from the box to describe a noun or pronoun.

10. rushed _____

_____.

11. giggling _____

_____.

12. satisfied _____

_____.

13. frowning _____

_____.

D. (14–15) Write two sentences about your favorite story. Tell why you like it. Use a participle to describe a noun or pronoun in each sentence.

_____

_____

_____

_____

69 What Are Participial Phrases?
Phrases That Start with a Participle

- A **phrase** is a group of related words that does not have a subject and a predicate. A **participial phrase** begins with a present **participle** or past **participle**. It describes a noun or pronoun.

  Determined to keep peace, Dad asks us to share.
  participial phrase

  But there are problems with Ferial **borrowing my things.**
  participial phrase

- Sometimes you can combine sentences by using a participial phrase. Place the participial phrase near the word that it describes. If the phrase begins a sentence, follow it with a comma (,).

  I have some new shirts. They **hang in my closet.**
  I have some new shirts **hanging in my closet.**

  Ferial and I can share the shirts. We **wear the same size.**
  Wearing the same size, Ferial and I can share the shirts.

Try It

A. **Use a participial phrase to combine the sentences. Write the new sentence.** Possible responses:

1. I see Ferial at school. She is wearing one of my shirts.

I see Ferial at school wearing one of my shirts.

2. The shirt is ruined. It is tearing at the sleeves.

Tearing at the sleeves, the shirt is ruined.

3. Its color has disappeared. It is covered with dirt.

Covered with dirt, its color has disappeared.

4. I can't wear the shirt now. I am disappointed by its condition.

Disappointed by its condition, I can't wear the shirt now.

5. I reconsider sharing things with Ferial. I see what can happen!

I reconsider sharing things with Ferial seeing what can happen!

B. Change the verb to a present or past participle to complete the sentence. Possible responses:

6. complain   ___Complaining___ about my ruined shirt, I talk to Dad.

7. determine   Dad, ___determined___ to calm me down, says we should try again.

8. worry   ___Worried___ about the problem, he talks to Ferial.

9. promise   ___Promising___ to be more careful, Ferial apologizes to me.

10. consider   ___Considering___ her apology, I decide to try one more time.

11. respect   I feel a lot better now when I see Feria ___respecting___ my things.

Write It

C. Use participial phrases to write your own sentences. Use four of the verbs from Part B. above to create participial phrases for your sentences.

12. _____.

13. _____.

14. _____.

15. _____.

D. (16–20) What advice would you give to someone about borrowing things? Write five sentences to answer this question. Use a participial phrase in each sentence.

_____

_____

_____

_____

_____

70 What Is a "Dangling Participle"?

It's a Participle That Describes the Wrong Word.

- Always place a **participial phrase** by the word it describes. Sometimes you can just move the phrase to fix the problem.

  Not OK: I learned about fairness **listening to Mom.**

  OK: **Listening to Mom,** I learned about fairness.

- Sometimes you need to rephrase the sentence and include a word for the participle to describe.

  Not OK: **Asking for ideas,** each opinion is spoken.

  OK: **Asking for ideas,** Mom waits to hear each opinion.

Try It

A. Rewrite each sentence to fix the dangling participle. Possible responses:

1. People become angry and upset treated unfairly.

Treated unfairly, people become angry and upset.

2. Each person can explain what's wrong given a chance.

Given a chance, each person can explain what's wrong.

3. People can solve legal issues going to court.

Going to court, people can solve legal issues.

4. A judge makes some decisions listening from the bench.

Listening from the bench, a judge makes some decisions.

5. A jury determines a guilty or innocent party considering both sides.

Considering both sides, a jury determines a guilty or innocent party.

6. People in small villages finding a magistrate can request justice.

Finding a magistrate, people in small villages can request justice.

C. Answer the questions about people who help judge what's fair. Use a participial phrase in each answer.

7. Who helps solve an argument at home? _____

_____

8. Who helps solve an argument at school? _____

_____

D. (9–12) What do people argue or complain about? Write four sentences. Use a participial phrase in each sentence. Check for and fix any dangling participles.

_____

_____

_____

_____

_____

_____

Edit It

E. (13–15) Edit the journal entry. Fix the three mistakes with dangling participles. Possible responses:

August 30

Yesterday, some tree branches fell into our
Belonging to the neighbors,
yard. The tree was not our responsibility
belonging to the neighbors. However, the

neighbors said they wouldn't clean up the
Checking the local property laws,
branches. Dad discovered that the neighbors

checking the local property laws were
Apologizing for the misunderstanding,
responsible. The neighbors hauled away the

branches apologizing for the misunderstanding.

Proofreader's Marks
Add text:
had
A tree fallen.
^
Do not capitalize:
Confused, We looked up the law.
See all Proofreader's Marks on page xi.

71 How Can You Improve Your Writing?

Combine Sentences.

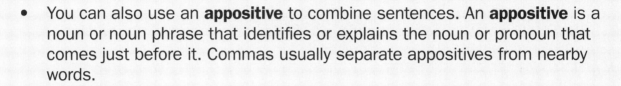

- You can use a **participial phrase** to combine sentences.

  The students were overloaded with homework. They couldn't finish it.

  Overloaded with homework, the students couldn't finish it.

- You can also use an **appositive** to combine sentences. An **appositive** is a noun or noun phrase that identifies or explains the noun or pronoun that comes just before it. Commas usually separate appositives from nearby words.

  Ms. Roberts gives a lot of homework. She is my English teacher.

  Ms. Roberts, **my English teacher**, gives a lot of homework.

Try It

A. Use a participial phrase to combine the sentences. Write each new sentence.

Possible responses:

1. Our group complained about the homework. We felt it was unfair.

Feeling that it was unfair, our group complained about the homework.

2. We wrote some homework "laws." We acted like the colonists.

Acting like the colonists, we wrote some homework "laws."

3. We listed some ideas. We brainstormed together.

Brainstorming together, we listed some ideas.

4. We gave the rules to Ms. Roberts. We worried about her reaction.

Worried about her reaction, we gave the rules to Ms. Roberts.

5. Ms. Roberts read the rules. She agreed with some of them.

Reading the rules, Ms. Roberts agreed with some of them.

6. Ms. Roberts agreed to less homework on weekends. She understood our feelings.

Understanding our feelings, Ms. Roberts agreed to less homework on weekends.

B. **Use an appositive to combine the sentences. Write each new sentence.**

7. Our teacher describes the Constitutional Convention. His name is Mr. Neil.

Our teacher, Mr. Neil, describes the Constitutional Convention.

8. It was held in Philadelphia. Philadelphia is a city in Pennsylvania.

It was held in Philadelphia, a city in Pennsylvania.

9. The delegates met to establish a government. They were asked to share ideas.

The delegates, asked to share ideas, met to establish a government.

10. Ben Franklin attended the meeting. He was a statesman and an inventor.

Ben Franklin, a statesman and an inventor, attended the meeting.

11. George Washington was also there. He was our nation's first president.

George Washington, our nation's first president, was also there.

12. Both men signed the Constitution. There were famous for their patriotism.

Both men, famous for their patriotism, signed the Constitution.

Write It

C. **Use each participial phrase or appositive in a sentence of your own.**

13. Finishing my homework, _____.

14. Searching for a research topic, _____.

15. _____, my favorite subject, _____.

16. _____, one of my closest friends, _____.

D. **(17–20) How do you feel about colonial history? Write four sentences. Use participial phrases in the first two sentences. Use appositives in the last two sentences.**

_____

_____

_____

_____

_____

72 Can Absolutes Help Your Writing?

Absolutely!

- An **absolute** is almost a complete sentence, but is missing a form of the word **be**. It has a subject and a participle. An absolute relates to the entire sentence after it.

  The script sitting on my desk, I get ready for the mock convention.

  absolute

  The actors practicing their parts, the cast prepares for the performance.

  absolute

- Sometimes you can use an absolute to combine sentences and make your writing more interesting. These sentences were combined to form the sentences above.

  I get ready for the mock convention. **The script is sitting on my desk.**

  The cast prepares for the performance. **The actors are practicing their parts**.

Try It

A. **Use an absolute with a present participle to combine each pair of sentences.**
Possible responses:

1. Sarah finishes the scenery. The podium is going on the stage.

The podium going on the stage, Sarah finishes the scenery.

2. The actors dress in their costumes. The wigs are fitting perfectly.

The wigs fitting perfectly, the actors dress in their costumes.

3. The play will begin soon. The actors are clearing their voices.

The actors clearing their voices, the play will begin soon.

B. **Use an absolute with a past participle to combine each pair of sentences.**
Possible responses:

4. The curtain starts to rise. The audience is filled with anticipation.

The audience filled with anticipation, the curtain starts to rise.

5. The mock convention starts. The cast is positioned on the stage.

The cast positioned on the stage, the mock convention starts.

C. Read the absolute. Then complete each sentence.

6. The audience listening carefully, _____

_____.

7. The document written, _____

_____.

8. The actors taking a bow, _____

_____.

D. (9–12) How would you describe the scene at the Constitutional Convention? Write four sentences. Use an absolute in each sentence.

_____

_____

_____

_____

_____

Edit It

E. (13–15) Edit the description. Fix the three mistakes with absolutes.

The convention is called to order. The seats are filling up, the delegates wait for the speaker. A man is stepping up to the podium, the audience stops their conversations. Everyone's attention is focused on the speaker. The statesman's speech is being presented, the delegates applaud.

Proofreader's Marks

Delete:

The speaker is beginning, everyone stops talking.

See all Proofreader's Marks on page xi.

73 What's a Compound-Complex Sentence?

It's Complicated.

> • A **compound-complex sentence** has two or more independent clauses and one or more dependent clauses.
>
> • You can combine short sentences into one compound-complex sentence. Long sentences add variety to your writing. They also show the relationship between ideas.
>
>   You have customs. I have different customs. They are important to me.
>
>   <u>You have customs</u>, but <u>I have different customs</u> <u>that are important to me.</u>
>   independent clause   independent clause   dependent clause

Try It

A. Combine the sentences into a compound-complex sentence.   Possible responses:

1. You travel. You meet many different people. They may have different beliefs.

    When you travel, you meet many different people, and they may have different beliefs.

2. Some people have customs. They are very different from yours. That makes travel fun.

    Some people have customs that are very different from yours, but that makes travel fun.

3. We live in America. We see many different customs. We should always respect the customs of others.   Because we live in America, we see many different customs, so we should always respect the customs of others.

B. (4–7) Write a dependent clause to change each compound sentence into a compound-complex sentence.   Possible responses:

People ____ who live in some countries ____ don't have freedom of speech, but people in America do. I can say what I believe, and you can have beliefs ____ that are different from mine ____.

____ Although I might disagree with you ____, you can have your beliefs, and I can have mine. ____ Because we have this right ____, our country is special, and I'm glad to live in it.

C. Write compound-complex sentences about customs that are important to you.

8. One important custom that _____ is _____, and _____

_____.

9. It is important because _____, but _____

_____.

10. When _____, I _____, or _____

_____.

D. (11–15) Write five compound-complex sentences about different customs or beliefs that people you know have.

_____

_____

_____

_____

_____

_____

Edit It

E. (16–20) Edit the letter. Fix the five mistakes with compound-complex sentences.

Dear Aunt Mary,

Today, we read about the United Nations, and I learned
                that
about some rights are granted to all people. These rights are
        because   ∧   and   that
important they protect us, they give us freedoms. A right
          ∧   ∧   ∧
guarantees free speech is important. Maybe one day everyone
                                                    who
                                                    ∧
lives in the world will have equal rights, but I don't think that
everyone has equal rights today.

Love,

Dan

Proofreader's Marks

Add text:
                    and
You have rights, I have
because   ∧
rights we live in this
      ∧
country.

See all Proofreader's Marks
on page xi.

74 Can A Verb Act Like a Noun?

Yes, When It Is a Gerund.

- A **gerund** acts like a noun in a sentence. It is often the **subject** of a sentence.
  Campaigning is a way to make your ideas known.
     subject

- When a **gerund** or **gerund phrase** is used as a subject, the verb is always singular.
  Campaigning takes a lot of people or just a few.
     gerund   verb

  Taking action is how people can change things.
     gerund phrase verb

- Use **gerunds** to replace words and make writing concise.
         Advertising
  ~~We can advertise~~ our feelings about a longer lunch period. ~~If we advertise, we~~
       s
  show that we are serious about the issue.

Try It

A. Change the underlined word in the first sentence into a gerund. Use the gerund to complete the second sentence.

1. The school doesn't <u>allow</u> enough time for lunch. ___Allowing___ five more minutes gives us enough time.

2. We have to <u>eat</u> too fast. ___Eating___ too quickly is bad for you.

3. Then we need to <u>clean</u> up. ___Cleaning___ up our trash takes a few minutes.

4. We want to <u>meet</u> with the principal. ___Meeting___ with the principal gives us a chance to share our ideas.

5. We <u>make</u> a list of reasons. ___Making___ a list of reasons helps us prepare for the meeting.

B. (6–9) Complete each sentence by adding a subject. Use gerunds from the box.

Chatting with friends	Taking a lunch break	Studying	Having more time to eat

_____Studying_____ takes concentration. __Taking a lunch break__ gives us time to rest.

__Chatting with friends__ helps us relax. __Having more time to eat__ refreshes our minds.

C. Complete the sentences. Use gerunds to tell how to learn about people's opinions. Possible answers:

10. _Speaking_ helps get your ideas across to a live audience.

11. _Writing letters_ is a way to share ideas in print.

12. _Listening to debates_ helps you understand different sides of an issue.

13. _Campaigning_ allows you to talk to people where they live.

Write It

D. Change the underlined word to a gerund. Rewrite the sentence using the gerund as the subject.

14. You can make things happen. All you need to do is <u>take</u> action.

Taking action makes things happen.

15. <u>Give</u> reasons for your opinions. The reasons help people understand your beliefs.

Giving reasons for your opinions helps people understand your beliefs.

Edit It

E. (16–18) Combine six sentences to make three sentences. Use gerunds as subjects.

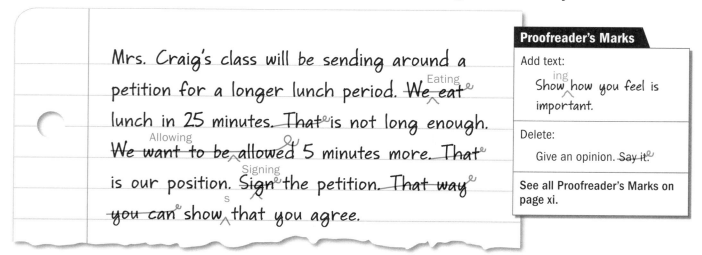

Mrs. Craig's class will be sending around a petition for a longer lunch period. We eat lunch in 25 minutes. That is not long enough. We want to be allowed 5 minutes more. That is our position. Sign the petition. That way you can show that you agree.

Proofreader's Marks

Add text:
Show how you feel is important. (ing)

Delete:
Give an opinion. Say it.

See all Proofreader's Marks on page xi.

75 Can a Gerund Be an Object?

Yes, It Can Be an Object of a Verb or a Preposition.

- Sometimes a **gerund** can be the **object of a verb.** The **gerund** answers a *What* question.

  David starts **recycling**. (What does David start?)
       verb   object

  He hates **seeing trash everywhere.** (What does he hate?)
       verb   object

- Other times, a **gerund** can be the **object of a preposition.**

  David knows a lot about **recycling**.
       preposition   object

  He gives the neighbors ideas for **reusing paper and plastic.**
       preposition   object

- Use **gerunds** to make writing concise.

  David believes we can keep the Earth unpolluted. ~~One way to do this is to~~ by ^ recycling ~~recycle~~ ^ our trash.

Try It

A. Use a gerund as an object of a verb or a preposition to complete each sentence.

1. David starts _____teaching_____ his neighbors how to recycle.

2. He finds old boxes for _____keeping_____ recyclables in.

3. David begins _____labeling_____ the boxes.

4. The boxes are used for _____saving_____ glass bottles, paper, and cans.

5. David demonstrates _____separating_____ the trash into the boxes.

6. The neighbors are good about _____listening_____ to his instructions.

B. Choose a gerund from the box to complete each sentence.

organizing the recyclables	helping the environment
carrying the full bins to the curb	recycling

7. Most communities support ___recycling___ .

8. They provide special bins for ___organizing the recyclables___ .

9. Residents don't mind ___carrying the full bins to the curb___ .

10. They feel good about ___helping the environment___ .

Write It

C. Use gerunds to finish these sentences using your own ideas.

11. My family supports _____ .

12. We are good at _____ .

13. We use old plastic bags for _____ .

14. We believe _____ .

Edit It

D. (15–18) Edit the list. Use gerunds as objects to combine eight sentences into four sentences.

Instructions for Keeping Our Earth Clean
- Keep ~~things you can recycle.~~ recycling. You can~~try~~ reusing to ~~keep~~ old cans. ~~Or, save~~ plastic bags ~~to reuse.~~
- If you go outside, carry bags. ~~Sometimes~~ for ~~you might have some trash.~~ Pick it picking up and ~~put trash in the bags.~~
- Help others be aware. ~~You can show~~ by showing them where to put their trash.

Proofreader's Marks

Change text:
Help the environment. ~~You can reuse things.~~ by reusing things.

See all Proofreader's Marks on page xi.

76 What Can an Infinitive Do?

Like a Noun, It Can Receive the Action of a Verb.

- The word **to** plus a main verb forms an **infinitive**. An infinitive can act as a noun by itself or it can start a phrase.

  Ricardo and Miriam like **to volunteer**.
  infinitive

  They want **to be good citizens**.
  infinitive phrase

- Like a noun, an **infinitive** can be the **object of a verb**. It can answer the question "*What?*"

  The students like **to help**.
  object

  They offer **to go to the homeless shelter** in their community.
  object

- Use **infinitives** to combine sentences and remove unnecessary words.

  The students ~~heard about some hungry families. They~~ decided ^to^ ~~they could~~ collect food for the families in the shelter.

Try It

A. Change the verb in ( ) to an infinitive. Use the infinitive to complete the sentence.

1. (call)   Ricardo decides _____to call_____ the shelter first.

2. (know)   He needs _____to know_____ what the families need.

3. (list)   The students begin _____to list_____ the foods.

4. (make)   They ask each grocery store _____to make_____ a donation.

5. (contribute) All the stores want _____to contribute_____.

6. (deliver)   Ricardo's parents offer _____to deliver_____ the food to the shelter.

B. (7–11) Use infinitives to complete the paragraph.

Our family always gets <u>to eat</u> a nice meal on Thanksgiving. But some people can't afford <u>to buy</u> food for the meal. So, every Thanksgiving my dad likes <u>to donate</u> food at the shelter. He wants <u>to serve</u> the people a hot meal. Next year, I want <u>to go</u> with him.

Write It

C. Use each infinitive in a sentence of your own. Tell what you want to do to help others in your community.

12. to give _____

13. to volunteer _____

14. to make _____

15. to contribute _____

Edit It

D. (16–20) Edit the article. Turn the ten sentences into five sentences. Use infinitives to combine the sentences and make them concise.

Many groups like ^to organize food drives. ~~They organize ways for getting food.~~ Some say ~~you can~~ give canned food ~~from home. They ask that you leave it~~^to leave on your doorstep. A postal carrier arranges to ~~come by. The carrier can~~ pick it up. Sometimes, a group or club you belong to wants ~~food.~~ ^to ~~They~~ collect food. Other times, a grocery store likes donations, ^to request ~~They request food~~ for special times of the year.

Proofreader's Marks

Change text:
We want ^to eat a nice meal.
~~We are ready for a meal.~~

See all Proofreader's Marks on page xi.

Name _____

77 Combine Sentences

Remember: You can improve your writing by combining sentences.

- You can use participial phrases, appositives, and absolutes to combine sentences. Commas are often used to set off these phrases.

    My parents won't let me go to the concert. They worry about my safety.
    Worried about my safety, my parents won't let me go to the concert.
    participial phrase

    Dawn is going. She is my best friend.
    Dawn, **my best friend**, is going.
    appositive

    I must persuade my parents quickly. The concert comes soon.
    The concert coming soon, I must persuade my parents quickly.
    absolute

Try It

A. Use a participial phrase to combine each pair of sentences. Write the new sentence. Don't forget the comma after a participial phrase at the start of a sentence.   Possible responses:

1. My favorite band is on tour. It will play here next week. <u>Playing here next week, my</u>
   <u>favorite band is on tour.</u>

2. My parents say I can't go. They are worried about the crowds. <u>Worried about the crowds, my</u>
   <u>parents say I can't go.</u>

3. I asked them to think about it again. I promised to be very careful. <u>Promising to be very careful, I</u>
   <u>asked them to think about it again.</u>

4. I discussed the problem with Dawn. I figured out a solution. <u>Discussing the problem with</u>
   <u>Dawn, I figured out a solution.</u>

5. My cousin is old enough to take us to the concert. He is a college student. <u>_____</u>
   <u>Being a college student, my cousin is old enough to take us to the concert.</u>

B. Use an appositive or absolute to combine each pair of sentences. Write the new sentence. Possible responses:

6. I will go with my cousin. My parents accept my idea.

My parents accepting my idea, I will go with my cousin.

7. Dawn is very excited. She is a big fan of the band.

Dawn, a big fan of the band, is very excited.

Write It

C. Use each participial phrase or appositive in a sentence of your own.

8. Pleased with their decision, _____

_____.

9. _____ , my other friends,

_____.

D. (10–11) What can you do when you think your parents are being unfair? Write two sentences. Use a participial phrase, an appositive, or an absolute in each sentence.

_____

_____

Edit It

E. (12–15) Add a participial phrase, appositive, or absolute to describe each of the <u>three</u> underlined words. Then fix <u>one</u> run-on sentence. Possible responses:

April 24

, Wind Rose,

I'm so glad I went to the concert! <u>The band</u>

Lasting three hours,

was fantastic. <u>The show</u> was longer than

decorated with the band's logo

we expected. We all got <u>t-shirts</u>. After the

show, we stopped for a snack and my cousin

bought us ice cream○and Dawn and I thanked

him for taking us to the concert.

Proofreader's Marks

Delete:

My heart ~~is~~ racing, I am still excited.

See all Proofreader's Marks on page xi.

78 Use Gerunds and Infinitives

Remember: Gerunds and infinitives act like nouns. They can be used to make writing more interesting and concise.

- A **gerund** ends with **-ing**. It can be used as a subject, object of a verb, or object of a preposition. A gerund used as a subject takes a singular verb.

  Compromising is a good strategy for solving problems.
  subject

  A good compromiser keeps **suggesting** ideas for solutions.
  object of the verb

  Ideas are presented for **reaching** a solution everyone agrees with.
  object of the preposition

- An **infinitive** is formed with the word **to** plus the main verb. An infinitive can be the object of a verb.

  At home, families want **to keep** the rules fair for everyone.

  In our nation, the government promises **to treat** each citizen fairly.

Try It

A. Change the verb in ( ) to a gerund. Use the gerund to complete the sentence.

1. (Build) _____Building_____ a new park is on the agenda for the city council.

2. (create) Part of the proposal includes ___creating___ a path around the lake.

3. (walk) Right now the path is designed only for ___walking___.

4. (Give) ____Giving____ just walkers a new path seems unfair.

5. (make) We propose ___making___ the path wider so cyclists can use it, too.

6. (Keep) ____Keeping____ everyone happy is better for the community.

B. Change the verb to an infinitive to complete the sentences.

7. We decided _____ to write _____ a letter to the city council.
write

8. In it, we argued _____ to redesign _____ the path around the lake.
redesign

9. We wanted the council _____ to consider _____ bike riders.
consider

10. Many families in our community like _____ to ride _____ bikes in parks.
ride

Write It

C. Complete the sentences with your own ideas. Use a gerund or an infinitive.

11. I like _____.

12. You can share ideas by _____.

D. (13–14) Write two sentences to describe what you or others can do to change things that seem unfair. Use gerunds and infinitives.

_____

_____

Edit It

E. (15–18) Fix the three mistakes with gerunds or infinitives. Combine the underlined sentences into one sentence to make the writing concise.

Making
~~Make~~ a speech gets your opinions across to
to
others. You want ^ vary the volume of your
voice, so people stay interested. Emphasize
using
your opinion by ~~use~~ a clear, steady voice.
After a good persuasive speech, people want
to take action.
~~things to change. They think about taking~~
~~action after hearing it.~~

Proofreader's Marks

Change text:

Speak in front of a
to practice
mirror. ~~That's good for~~
~~practice~~

See all Proofreader's Marks
on page xi.

79 When Do You Use the Present Perfect Tense?

When an Action Happened, but You're Not Sure When, or When a Past Action May Still Be Happening

- Use a **past tense** verb if you know when an action happened in the past.

  The trucks **delivered** some food yesterday.

- Use a **present perfect tense** verb if you're not sure when an action happened, or if an action began in the past and may still be happening.

  The boy **has waited** a long time for the truck.

  The villagers **have needed** grains and fresh water for a while.

- To form the **present perfect tense**, add **has** or **have** to the **past participle** of the verb. For regular verbs, the past participle ends in **-ed**.

  The boy always **has offered** to help unload the truck.

Try It

A. Complete each sentence. Write the present perfect form of the verb in parentheses.

1. Since June, the village _____has needed_____ food. **(need)**

2. The people _____have asked_____ for rice and beans. **(ask)**

3. Those foods _____have provided_____ them with good nutrition. **(provide)**

4. Each family _____has used_____ rice for a variety of meals. **(use)**

5. Often they _____have mixed_____ the beans in with the rice. **(mix)**

B. Complete each sentence. Use the past or present perfect form of the verb in parentheses, whichever is correct.

6. Staples like rice and beans _____have helped_____ people survive. **(help)**

7. Villagers often _____have stored_____ the dry foods for later. **(store)**

8. The people _____used_____ all of the stored food two days ago. **(use)**

9. Yesterday, a truck _____arrived_____ with more. **(arrive)**

C. (10–15) Complete each sentence with a verb in the present perfect tense. Choose words from the box.

supply	provide	satisfy	depend	help	search

Basic, or staple, foods _____have helped_____ people survive. These foods _____have supplied_____ the fats, protein, and carbohydrates people need. Rice, maize, and potatoes _____have provided_____ carbohydrates. In some places, olive or coconut oil _____has satisfied_____ the need for fats. Wherever possible, a villager _____has searched_____ for a good place to fish. Many families _____have depended_____ on fish for their protein.

Write It

D. Answer the questions. Use the present perfect tense.

16. Why have some families needed help with food? _____

_____

17. How have foods reached hungry families? _____

_____

18. What has fish provided for people's diets? _____

_____

19. What foods has your family prepared? _____

_____

20. What foods have you cooked? _____

_____

E. (21–25) Write five sentences about how volunteers have helped the hungry.

_____

_____

_____

_____

_____

80 Do All Past Participles End in *-ed*?

No, Irregular Verbs Have Special Forms.

- Past participles of irregular verbs have a completely new spelling.

	Verb	Past Tense	Past Participle
Forms of *Be*	am, is	was	been
	are	were	been
	give	gave	given
	go	went	gone
	see	saw	seen

- Use **has** or **have** plus the past participle to form the **present perfect tense**. We **have seen** the results of a hurricane in Haiti. Dad **has gone** there to help.

Try It

A. Complete each sentence. Write the present perfect form of the verb in parentheses.

1. Dad _____has been_____ upset about his relatives. **(be)**

2. The hurricane _____has done_____ a lot of damage. **(do)**

3. Many of the people _____have gone_____ without food for a while. **(go)**

4. Dad _____has seen_____ many damaged homes. **(see)**

B. Rewrite each sentence in the present perfect tense.

5. Dad saw his aunt. Dad has seen his aunt. _____

6. She was safe at home. She has been safe at home. _____

7. They gave each other a hug. They have given each other a hug. _____

C. (8–13) Complete the sentences. Use the present perfect tense of the verb in the box. One verb will be used twice.

be	take	see	do	go

There are a lot of reasons people _____have gone_____ hungry. Perhaps you

_____have seen_____ the results of a natural disaster like a hurricane. Or maybe

you _____have done_____ some research about droughts. That's when the ground

_____has been_____ much too dry for crops to grow. Also, war _____has taken_____ away

people's homes. Moving to new places, it _____has been_____ difficult for people to know

where to find food.

Write It

D. Follow each instruction. Use the present perfect tense in your sentences.

14. Tell where you or a relative has gone. _____

_____

15. Tell what you have seen that makes you feel good. _____

_____

16. Tell what your last year has been like. _____

_____

Edit It

E. (17–20) Edit the letter. Fix the four mistakes with present perfect tense verbs.

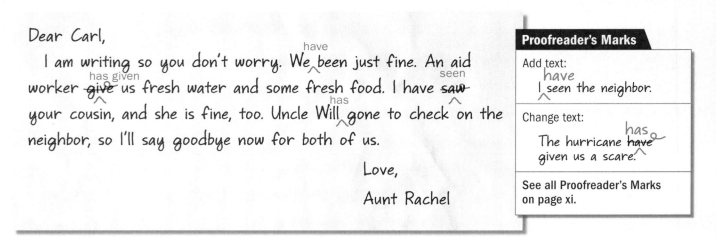

Dear Carl,

    I am writing so you don't worry. We ^have^ been just fine. An aid worker ~~give~~ ^has given^ us fresh water and some fresh food. I have ~~saw~~ ^seen^ your cousin, and she is fine, too. Uncle Will ^has^ gone to check on the neighbor, so I'll say goodbye now for both of us.

Love,

Aunt Rachel

Proofreader's Marks

Add text:
I ^have^ seen the neighbor.

Change text:
The hurricane h~~ave~~ ^has^ given us a scare.

See all Proofreader's Marks on page xi.

81 How Do You Form the Present Perfect Tense?

Use *Have* or *Has* Plus the Past Participle of a Verb.

- The past participle of a **regular verb** ends in **-ed**.
  For five years, my dad **has work<u>ed</u>** for a relief agency. **(work + -ed)**
  They **have provid<u>ed</u>** food for thousands of children. **(provide [-e] + -ed)**

- The past participle of an **irregular verb** has a completely new spelling.

Verb	Past Participle
be	been
do	done
see	seen

Verb	Past Participle
send	sent
show	shown
take	taken

Try It

A. Complete each sentence. Write the present perfect tense of the verb in parentheses.

1. Conflicts in some countries _____ *have been* _____ problems especially for children. **(be)**

2. Dad _____ *has seen* _____ what happens to children who are refugees. **(see)**

3. They _____ *have suffered* _____ by not having enough food to eat. **(suffer)**

4. Many families _____ *have been* _____ unable to find food. **(be)**

5. His group _____ *has tried* _____ to get food to them. **(try)**

B. Rewrite each sentence in the present perfect tense.

6. Dad shows that he cares. *Dad has shown that he cares.* _____

7. Dad asks others to help. *Dad has asked others to help.* _____

8. They take steps to feed the children. *They have taken steps to feed the children.* _____

C. Imagine that the sentences are about your dad. Complete each sentence about how you and your family have felt about what he does. Use the present perfect tense.

9. My dad _____

_____.

10. I _____

_____.

11. My whole family _____

_____.

D. (12–15) Think of a person you have respected. Why have you respected that person? Write four sentences. Use the present perfect tense.

_____

_____

_____

_____

_____

E. (16–20) Edit the journal entry. Fix the five mistakes in present perfect verb forms.

October 19

         been

It has ~~be~~ a busy week. Our agency has

received

~~receive~~ reports about refugees in the Sudan.

         have

Many of the children ~~has~~ been without food

         sent

for a while. We have ~~sended~~ a shipment of

         done

rice and fresh water. I hope we have ~~did~~

enough.

Proofreader's Marks

Add text:

have

I ∧ been reading about the

∧ problem.

Change text:

seen

Dad has ~~saw~~ all the

reports.

See all Proofreader's Marks on page xi.

82 How Do You Show Which Past Action Happened First?

Use the Past Perfect Tense.

- Use the **past tense** of a verb to tell about an action that was completed in the past.
  My older brother **taught** me how to cook.

- If you want to show that one past action happened before another, use the **past perfect tense** for the action that happened first.
  He **had shown** me what to do before he **left** for college.

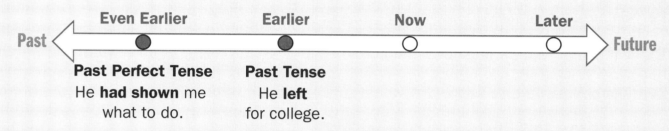

| Even Earlier | Earlier | Now | Later |

Past Perfect Tense
He **had shown** me
what to do.

Past Tense
He **left**
for college.

- To form the **past perfect tense**, use **had** plus the **past participle** of the main verb.
  I **missed** him after he **had been** at college for a while.

Try It

A. Complete each sentence with the past perfect form of the verb in parentheses.

1. Before Jim _____had started_____ to pack, we made some soup. **(start)**

2. We _____had gathered_____ all the ingredients earlier, so we were prepared. **(gather)**

3. After we _____had poured_____ broth into a pan, we put it on the stove. **(pour)**

4. Before the broth boiled, I _____had chopped_____ the vegetables. **(chop)**

5. We added the vegetables after the broth _____had boiled_____. **(boil)**

6. Before the vegetables were done, Jim _____had sprinkled_____ in some special spices. **(sprinkle)**

7. We talked about giving some of the soup away because we _____had made_____ so much! **(made)**

B. Complete each sentence. Write the past tense or past perfect tense of the verb in parentheses.

8. I asked Mom what to do with all the extra soup Jim and I _____had made_____. **(make)**

9. She had heard from a neighbor that a local shelter _____needed_____ some food. **(need)**

10. So after I _____had found_____ the name of the shelter, we called them. **(find)**

11. A volunteer said to bring the soup because they _____had used_____ up a lot of their food. **(use)**

12. Before an hour passed, Mom and I _____had packed_____ the car. **(pack)**

13. We had arrived at the shelter before the soup _____turned_____ cold. **(turn)**

14. The people were so happy that we _____had brought_____ them a hot meal. **(bring)**

Write It

C. Complete each sentence about something else the writer and his brother did together before Jim went to college. Use past and past perfect tense verbs.

15. Before he _____, my brother and I _____

_____.

16. I _____ until he _____

_____.

17. After he _____, I _____

_____.

D. (18–20) Write three sentences about a relationship that you have with a family member. Tell about something you did together in the past. Use the past perfect tense in each sentence.

_____

_____

_____

_____

_____

83 How Do You Know Which Tense to Use?

Think About When the Action Happened.

- When you tell about the past, you may need to relate actions in time. First use the **past tense** to tell what happened.

  Maura **moved** in September.

- Then use the **past perfect tense** to tell what happened before Maura moved.

  Maura **moved** to Glendale, but she **had lived** in Springfield for many years.

- Sometimes a past action may still be going on. That's when you use the **present perfect tense**.

  Maura **has** worked as a waitress for a while.

  She **has** missed the work since she **moved**.

Try It

A. Complete each sentence. Write the correct tense of the verb.

1. Maura _____has lived_____ in Glendale since September.
   lived / has lived

2. She _____grew_____ up in Springfield.
   grew / has grown

3. By the time she moved, Maura _____had worked_____ at a restaurant for a year.
   has worked / had worked

4. Yesterday, she _____applied_____ for a new job in Glendale.
   applied / has applied

B. Complete each sentence. Write the past, present perfect, or past perfect tense of the verb in parentheses.

5. Last week, Maura _____went_____ for an interview at a café. **(go)**

6. She _____had discovered_____ that the café was just around the corner from her home. **(discover)**

7. She always _____has believed_____ that people who go to small restaurants are friendlier.
   (believe)

8. Before she left the interview, Maura _____had been_____ hired. **(be)**

Write It

C. Complete each sentence about a restaurant you or someone you know has gone to. Use the correct tense of verbs to show past actions.

9. Last week, I/we _____

_____.

10. Before we ordered, we _____

_____.

11. Since then, we _____

_____.

D. (12–15) Have you heard the expression "Worries go down better with soup"? Write four sentences about how it has related to you. Use the past tense, the present perfect tense, and the past perfect tense at least one time each.

_____

_____

_____

_____

Edit It

E. (16–20) Edit the letter. Fix the five mistakes in verb tenses.

Dear Isabella,

    I'm sorry, I ~~have~~ missed your call yesterday. By the time you called, I ~~went~~ [had gone] on an interview. A little café down the street had ~~want~~ [wanted] a waitress for a long time. And I ~~have gotten~~ [got] the job! I can't wait for you to come out for a visit. The people here [have] been so friendly. But no one will replace you as my best friend! Write soon.

                    Love,

                    Maura

Proofreader's Marks

Change text:
Maura ~~write~~ [wrote] to her friend last night.

See all Proofreader's Marks on page xi.

84 When Do You Use the Future Perfect Tense?

When You Want to Relate a Future Action to a Future Time

- Sometimes an action that hasn't yet happened depends on another future event. That's when you use the **future perfect tense**.

   Soon **we will leave for the restaurant**. By then, **we will have made** reservations.
   Before we go, **I will have confirmed** the number of people.

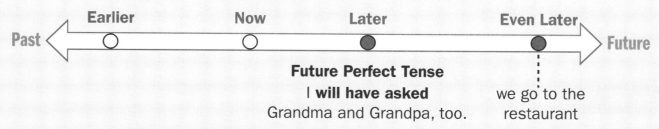

- To form the **future perfect tense**, use **will have** plus the **past participle** of the main verb.

   Before we get in the car, we **will have grabbed** the directions.
   Before we get to the restaurant, we **will have driven** for fifteen minutes.

Try It

A. Complete each sentence. Write the future perfect tense of the verb in parentheses.

1. By six o'clock, we _____will have arrived_____ at the new restaurant. **(arrive)**

2. Someone _____will have shown_____ us where to sit. **(show)**

3. The waiters _____will have given_____ us menus. **(give)**

4. We _____will have decided_____ what we want to eat. **(decide)**

5. Grandma _____will have asked_____ if the bread was fresh. **(ask)**

6. Grandpa _____will have ordered_____ steak. **(order)**

7. Mom and Dad _____will have told_____ us to order vegetables. **(tell)**

8. Finally, we _____will have eaten_____ a delicious meal! **(eat)**

B. Complete each sentence with a future perfect tense verb. Possible responses:

9. By the end of the month, the restaurant _____will have trained_____ all its staff.

10. The waiters _____will have learned_____ what's on the menu.

11. They _____will have practiced_____ how to take orders for food.

12. The chef _____will have planned_____ what meals to cook.

13. He and the manager _____will have ordered_____ the food.

14. The dishwashers _____will have gathered_____ the cleaning supplies.

Write It

C. Suppose your family will eat lunch or dinner at a favorite restaurant. Complete the sentences about what you or your family members will do or experience. Use the future perfect tense.

15. Before we get in the car, _____

_____.

16. By the time we arrive, _____

_____.

17. In the restaurant, _____

_____.

D. (18–20) What is your favorite place? What do you do there? Write three sentences about the place. Use the future perfect tense.

_____

_____

_____

_____

_____

_____

85 How Do You Show Real-Life Possibilities?

Use Conditionals.

- A conditional sentence has two parts. One part begins with **if** or **when** and states a condition. The other part uses a **present tense verb** or **will** plus a main verb to describe the result.

  When the trap is good, Uncle Muskrat **catches** fish.

  If he catches enough fish, he **will feed** the village.

- Some conditionals tell about situations and results that are always true.

  He **will ask** about his nephews **if he doesn't see** them.

- Other conditionals describe situations and results that happen all the time in real life.

  If dinner is ready, **the family will gather** to eat.

Try It

A. Complete the conditional sentence. Use *if,* a present tense verb, or *will* plus a main verb.

Possible responses:

1. _____If_____ the villagers are hungry, everyone tries to help.

2. The brothers _____will go_____ hunting if the villagers have no meat.

3. If they see animal tracks, the hunters _____follow_____ them.

4. People will gather plants for food _____if_____ the hunters return empty-handed.

5. If the fire starts to go out, someone _____will add_____ wood.

B. Create a conditional sentence by changing one of the sentences into an if-clause.

6. The weather is good. We go camping. _____ If the weather is good, we go camping. _____

7. We take our fishing gear. There is a lake nearby. _____ We take our fishing gear if there is a lake nearby. _____

8. It is a good sign. The fish leap out of the water. _____ It is a good sign if the fish leap out of the water. _____

9. We are patient. We will catch several fish. _____ If we are patient, we will catch several fish. _____

10. We catch enough trout. Mom cooks them over an open fire. _____ If we catch enough trout, _____ Mom cooks them over an open fire. _____

Write It

C. Complete each sentence. Use an if-clause to state a condition or a clause with the correct verbs to describe the result. Use your own ideas. Possible responses:

11. If we act out "The Girl and the Chenoo," we _____ will need to assign parts. _____

12. _____ If we want wigwams, _____ we will draw them on butcher paper.

13. We will use a cooking pot from home _____ if Mom lets us. _____

14. _____ If we send out invitations, _____ others will come to the performance.

Edit It

D. (15–18) Edit the invitation. Fix the four mistakes in conditionals.

If
∧You come to Room 55 on Tuesday at 3 p.m., you will see something special. If you read "The Girl and Chenoo," you
will
∧enjoy our performance. You will get a good seat if you will
                                            When
arrive early. ∧The play ends, we will expect a rousing applause!

86 What Are Unreal Conditionals Like?

Unreal Conditionals Tell About Imaginary or Impossible Events.

- One kind of unreal conditional expresses an event that is unlikely to happen in the present or future. Another kind describes events that are "contrary-to-fact," or impossible.

    Unlikely, But Possible:

    If Haley knew the answer, she would tell us.

    (Haley probably doesn't know the answer, so it's unlikely she can tell us.)

    Not Possible:

    If Mike won, he would get a trophy.

    (He doesn't win, so it's not possible for him to get a trophy.)

- An unreal conditional has a **past tense verb** in the **if**-clause and **would** (**could** or **might**) plus a main verb in the clause that describes the result.

    If I **studied**, I **might pass** the test.

- For singular subjects in an unreal conditional, always use **were**, <u>not</u> was.

    If I **were** you, I **would not do** that.

Try It

A. Read the sentence. Write *real* if the conditional expresses a real-life possibility. Write *unreal* if it expresses an unlikely or impossible result.

1. If I write a story, I will share it with you. _____ real _____

2. If I saw a monster, I would be afraid. _____ unreal _____

3. If I catch a big fish, I will tell everyone. _____ real _____

4. If I saw Mia, I could tell her. _____ unreal _____

5. If my brother were here, he might help me. _____ unreal _____

B. Complete the sentence. Choose the correct verbs to form an unreal conditional.

6. If we _____ *had* _____ a feast, I would invite all my relatives.
   have/had

7. If Dad caught a wild turkey, he _____ *would bring* _____ it home.
   will bring/would bring

8. If my sisters _____ *gathered* _____ vegetables, they might steam them.
   gather/gathered

9. If Mom found berries, she _____ *could put* _____ them in a pie.
   puts/could put

10. If everyone _____ *came* _____ , we would be happy.
    comes/came

Write It

C. Complete the sentence. Use your own ideas to tell the unlikely or impossible result of the condition. Possible responses:

11. If the boys brought home meat, the family _____ *would be happy* _____ .

12. If the villagers had wood, they _____ *could make a fire* _____ .

13. If they fixed a fire, they _____ *could cook the meat* _____ .

14. If she made stew, the family _____ *would have a nice meal* _____ .

Edit It

D. (15–18) Edit the paragraph. Fix the four mistakes in conditionals.

>   *would*
> If it rained, the village ∧ flood. The fire would go out *if* it was in
>   *might not go* ∧
> the open. If the villagers built a fire in a wigwam, it ~~goes~~ out.
>   *could*
> If the fire got too high though, the birch bark ∧ ~~catches~~ on fire.

Proofreader's Marks
Add text:
If
∧The fire went out, we could have a problem.
Delete:
If I were there, I could ~~helped~~.
See all Proofreader's Marks on page xi.

87 How Can We Tell About Our Wishes?

Tell How Things Should Be Different or What You Want to Happen.

- A wish presents an imaginary or possible way to make a situation different in the present or the future.

  I wish I knew how to write like that. (Imaginary: I don't know how to write like that.)

  I wish I could go to the play. (Possible: Maybe I can go to the play if things work out.)

- Like some unreal conditionals, wishes in the present are "contrary-to-fact." They present ideas that are untrue but desired. Use **I wish** and the **past tense** to express wishes about the present.

  I wish I **lived** in a small village. (The truth is I don't live in a small village.)

  I wish I **were** a good singer. (I'm not a good singer.)

- Use the words **I wish** plus **could** or **would** plus a main verb to express possibilities or needs for the future.

  I wish Grandma **could be** here. (a possibility)

  I wish Joe **would stop** bothering me. (a need for the future)

Try It

A. Complete the sentence. Use the correct form of the verb in ( ).

1. I wish I _____were_____ a good writer. **(be)**

2. I wish I _____could tell_____ a story about legendary monsters. **(tell)**

3. I wish I _____had_____ a computer. **(have)**

4. My friend wishes she _____could help_____ me. **(help)**

5. She wishes we _____would publish_____ the story in the school paper. **(publish)**

B. Choose the correct verbs to complete each wish.

6. Our group wishes we _____*could meet*_____ Mr. Bruchac.

meet/could meet

7. We wish we _____*had*_____ more of his stories.

have/had

8. I wish I _____*could ask*_____ him about Chenoo.

ask/could ask

9. Fran wishes she _____*could learn*_____ more about the Abenaki people.

learns/could learn

10. We wish Mr. Bruchac _____*would visit*_____ our class.

visit/would visit

Write It

C. **(11–14) What things do you wish would change now? What wishes do you have for the future? Write two wishes for the present and two wishes for the future.**

_____

_____

_____

_____

_____

_____

_____

D. **(15–18) Think about your home and school. What kinds of wishes do your family members or friends have? Write four sentences to tell about their wishes.**

_____

_____

_____

_____

_____

_____

_____

Name _____

88 Write with the Perfect Tenses

Remember: Use the present perfect, past perfect, and future perfect tenses to show how actions are related in time. Study the chart.

Tense	When Do You Use It?	Examples
Present Perfect	For actions that began in the past and are still going on	Aunt Lil **has been** my role model for years.
	For actions that happened at an unknown past time	I **have visited** her a lot.
Past Perfect	For actions completed before another past action	By the time she got her apartment, Aunt Lil **had lived** with us for two years.
Future Perfect	For actions that will happen before a future time	By the end of the month, she **will have bought** a house.

Try It

A. Complete each sentence. Write the correct perfect tense of the verb in parentheses.

1. I _____have known_____ Aunt Lil my whole life. **(know)**

2. She always _____has served_____ as a role model to me. **(serve)**

3. By the time she was 30, she _____had finished_____ medical school. **(finish)**

4. Next month, she _____will have been_____ a doctor for 30 years. **(be)**

B. (5–8) Complete each sentence with a verb in a perfect tense. Use **work**, **spend**, and **accomplish**. You may need to use a verb more than once.

Aunt Lil _____has worked_____ hard her whole life. By the time she was 22, she _____had worked_____ her way through college. By the time she became a doctor, she _____had spent_____ years working at a hospital. By the time I am her age, I hope I _____will have accomplished_____ as much as she has.

C. Answer the questions. Use the present perfect, the past perfect, and the future perfect tenses.

9. What have you worked hard at? _____

_____.

10. What had you done before you turned 12? _____

_____

11. By the time you grow up, what will you have accomplished? _____

_____

D. (12–16) Who is your role model? Why has that person been a role model to you? Write five sentences. Use the present perfect, the past perfect, and the future perfect tenses.

_____

_____

_____

_____

_____

Grammar at Work

E. (17–20) Edit the letter. Fix the three mistakes with perfect tense verbs. Fix one mistake with a possessive word.   Possible responses:

Dear Aunt Lil,

    I have completed my first session of science camp. ~~Yours~~ Your
encouragement ~~have~~ has helped me tremendously. By the time I
finish camp, I will have learned so much. You have always been there to
support me. I hope that one day I will get to be a doctor just
like you.

                          Love,

                          Juanita

Proofreader's Marks

Add text:
        have
I had a great time.

Change text:
        has
Aunt Lil ~~have~~ been a
great role model.

See all Proofreader's Marks on page xi.

89 Write with Conditionals

Remember: A conditional sentence tells how one action depends upon another.

- In a conditional sentence, a dependent clause beginning with **if** or **when** states a condition and an independent clause states the result.

  <u>**If** the shelter is open,</u> <u>I will read to the children.</u>

      dependent clause   independent clause

- To express real-life possibilities in the present or future, use the **present tense** in both clauses. Or use the present tense in the **if**-clause and **will** plus the main verb in the independent clause.

  If I ask Mom, she **will drive** me there.

     present   will + main verb

- To express imaginary or unreal possibilities in the present or future, use a **past tense verb** in the **if**-clause and **would** (**could** or **might**) plus a main verb in the independent clause.

  If I **had** my favorite story, I **would bring** it with me.

     past   would + main verb

Try It

A. Add words to complete the conditional sentences. Possible responses:

1. If I had time, I _____would go_____ to the shelter every day.

2. _____If_____ you go there, you will see many children.

3. If the children _____are_____ hungry, the shelter feeds them.

4. If the children want to hear stories, I _____will read_____ to them.

5. If they liked your story, they _____might clap_____ .

B. Change each unreal conditional into a real conditional. Write the <u>real</u> conditional.

                                                Possible responses:

6. If I practiced reading aloud, I would sound better.

    If I practice reading aloud, I will sound better.

7. I could be more like the character if I changed my voice.

I will be more like the character if I change my voice.

8. If the volume increased too much, I might scare the children.

If the volume increases too much, I scare the children.

C. Change each real conditional into an unreal conditional. Write the <u>unreal</u> conditional.

Possible responses:

9. If I show the story's pictures, the kids study them carefully.

If I showed the story's pictures, the kids would study them carefully.

10. When I reach the end, the kids will sigh loudly.

When I reached the end, the kids would sigh loudly.

11. They will beg me to stay if I walk toward the door.

They would beg me to stay if I walked toward the door.

Write It

D. Complete the sentences with your own ideas. Use conditionals.

12. If I volunteer, _____.

13. If I read a story, _____.

14. If I had time, _____.

Edit It

E. (15–18) Edit the letter. Fix the <u>three</u> mistakes with conditionals. Fix the <u>one</u> mistake with a command.

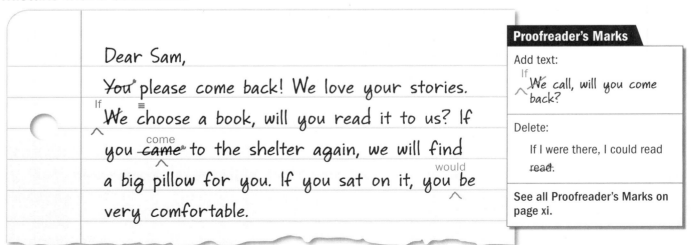

Dear Sam,

~~You~~ please come back! We love your stories.
                    If
We choose a book, will you read it to us? If
        come
you ~~came~~ to the shelter again, we will find
                                        would
a big pillow for you. If you sat on it, you be
very comfortable.

Proofreader's Marks

Add text:
       If
We call, will you come
back?

Delete:
If I were there, I could read
~~read~~.

See all Proofreader's Marks on
page xi.